THE HISTORY OF MOLISE AND ABRUZZO ITALY

A JOURNEY FROM THE ANCIENT SAMNITES TO MY MOTHER!

Giuseppe Ferrone

ISBN: 978-0-646-82476-5

First published in Australia in 2020 by Giuseppe Ferrone

© Giuseppe Ferrone 2020

The History of Molise and Abruzzo Italy.

Cover design by Ross MacLennan of www.bookcoversaustralia.com

Typesetting: allinonebookdesign.com.au

Author can be contacted at giuseppeferrone@outlook.com

A catalogue record for this book is available from the National Library of Australia

Ferrone, Giuseppe, 1959-,

CONTENTS

Part One – The History

Part Two – Carmelina's Story

This book is dedicated to my mother Carmelina,

whose amazing life journey

is the heart and soul of this story.

About the Author

GIUSEPPE FERRONE is a High School history teacher, with degrees in history, business and education. He lives in Perth, Western Australia. He is passionate about the important lessons we can learn from the past and critical thinking skills students of history can learn and apply throughout their lives.

The author welcomes your feedback by email at giuseppeferrone@ outlook.com

PART ONE

THE HISTORY

WHY THIS BOOK?

⌁

OM JONES WAS BELTING OUT 'DELILAH' ON THE RECORD PLAYER. It was a cloudy Sunday morning in the autumn of May1972 when I awoke with a feeling of trepidation and dread. I should have known! This song, and Dean Martin's *That's Amore* were the two songs that my mother and father liked the most. And whose voice could I hear singing along with the Welsh crooner? It was my mother of course. She loved to sing in those days. It wasn't unusual for me to wake up to the sound of her melodic voice. But today was different.

1. *Tom Jones*

Today was the day my parents Filippo and Carmelina along with my youngest brother Luciano were about to embark on a long sea voyage to Italy. They would be away for six months, leaving their three older sons, including myself, to be looked after by my uncle Antonio and my grandparents, Assunta and Raffaele. I was thirteen years old and in my first year of high school.

My voice was deepening. My once clear olive skin was now being invaded by those dreaded pimples. The time between haircuts was getting longer as I allowed my wavy black hair to grow down to my shoulders.

In the summer of 1971-72 I discovered what would become a lifelong love of the British rock band, Status Quo. I had only bought their

(2) *Dog of Two Head*

album, *Dog of Two Head*, the previous week; the first vinyl record album I ever bought. Also over the summer I developed a crush on the girl who lived across the road, the lovely brown-eyed, Rosemary. She was in my form class but I may as well have been invisible. It was only two years later at a social in the high school gym that I finally found out she thought I was cute.

As if that wasn't enough to occupy my delicate mind, I was now the head altar boy at my local catholic church, the Redemptorist Monastery. This came with great responsibilities. I had led the procession of priests and other altar boys at the Good Friday midnight mass, in April. I was responsible for making sure all of the other altar boys attended their scheduled mass, suitably attired in the "red and white," ready well before the start of the procession down the church aisle. I remember thinking this was too much responsibility for a teenage boy going through the dreaded werewolf hormonal changes.

I had also developed a passion for astronomy, which remains with me to this day. My fascination with the planets, stars and galaxies was ignited by the Apollo 11 moon landing. I will never forget watching Neil Armstrong set foot on the moon while sitting with over four hundred other students, on the polished wooden floorboards of the main hall at Highgate primary school in Western Australia, watching a small black and white television beaming in the flickering satellite images live, on that historic morning of the 21st July 1969.

Fast forward to the summer of 1971, when I had saved enough money to buy a small telescope and observe the heavens directly. I

(3) *Apollo 11 astronauts*

still remember how awe-struck I was when I first saw the craters of the Moon, the landing site of Neil Armstrong and Buzz Aldrin's historic moonwalk at the Sea of Tranquility, the rings of Saturn, the great storm of Jupiter and the Andromeda galaxy, amongst other spectacles. At age thirteen, I had joined the Astronomical Society of Western Australia, becoming its youngest member. On the first Tuesday of every month, I would take two buses to attend the society meetings in the Physics building at the University of Western Australia, which would start at 7pm sharp.

But all of this paled into insignificance when I awoke that Sunday morning because I was not going to be seeing my parents for six months. How did it come to this? It was going to be my parents' first trip back to Italy since my father arrived in Australia in 1956 and my mother in 1958. Carmelina had thrown her heart and soul into creating a new family life in Perth Australia, with four sons and her husband Filippo. Two of my brothers, Antonio and Francesco were only sixteen months apart in age. They were particularly demanding on her. As well as her family duties, Carmelina worked part time cleaning offices in the evening with my father. She would prepare our meals before they departed for work at 5pm, returning home at around 8.30pm, five nights a week. I had the responsibility of looking after my three younger brothers, making sure they were well fed and occupied without distraction.

I remember one evening my parents had arrived home to find the wallpapered walls of our kitchen covered in multi-coloured crayon drawings of "stick men." I tried in vain to stop my two middle brothers, but to no avail. The deed was done. I had to choose between our brotherly bond or my loyalty to my parents. I decided on the former on that occasion, so to this day my parents don't know who did the graffiti. I guess they will now find out. "*Giuseppe, you are my little man,*" my mother would say as she kissed me on the cheek each afternoon, before leaving to clean the offices of a prosperous brick and tile manufacturing company called Bristile. I knew what that meant. She was depending on me to keep our family safe and secure while they worked so hard to establish a foundation in this country by paying off their home mortgage as quickly as possible. I went through my entire childhood unsure of whether I was Australian, Italian or some cultural hybrid.

I couldn't speak a word of English until I started primary school. My parents had settled in an area full of Italians and other southern Europeans when they arrived in Perth from the Molise region of central Italy. Italian was my first language. I still remember how terrified I felt on my first day of school in 1965 when my mother left me with the stoic Irish nuns at St Brigid's catholic school, while this one particularly friendly nun tried to reassure and comfort me, speaking in what to me was a foreign tongue. I just remember wailing big drops of tears and screaming out for my mum to come back, as she left me alone at school. Then in my later years at Highgate primary school, I have recollections of constantly getting into fights because the Aussie kids were either teasing and bullying my brothers and I, making fun of our broken English, or they wanted to take our authentic Italian mixed cold meat and cheese continental rolls and eat them for lunch instead of their boring vegemite or peanut butter sandwiches. I definitely felt I was Italian on those occasions!

My mother had a nervous breakdown when I was twelve. It was all too much for her. She needed a break. Her doctor agreed that a long trip to Italy, away from her enormous daily grind of hard work was the perfect remedy. She longed to immerse herself again in the mountains, lush green pastures and pine forests of the Molise region and was particularly looking forward to seeing her many friends and relatives in the 950 years old medieval town of Montagano, where she was born.

The Molise region of Italy has always been a powerful magnet to my parents. Since their first trip back in 1972, they have returned many more times. As I write this book in 2020, my father is 85 and my mother 80, their health remains good and they always yearn to go back to the fertile soil and clean air of Montagano in Molise. Twenty-five

(4) *Montagano – The birth village of my parents, in Molise Italy.*

years ago, they bought a home in the centre of the village next door to where my mother was born, so they have their own place to stay, every time they visit.

It feels like travelling back in time whenever I visit Montagano. Our place has a wonderful large upstairs bedroom with polished wooden floorboards, shutters and a wrought iron enclosed balcony. I have fond memories of waking up to the singing of birds, the "mooing" of cows in the fields and the chiming of the church bells every thirty minutes as the bright rays of sunshine radiate through the shutters. Early in the morning I would get out of bed, draw the shutters open and step out onto the balcony where I was immediately struck by the cool fresh mountain breeze.

Looking out from the balcony there is a spectacular panoramic view of the lush green farming land that surrounds our historical village. Further in the distance are the Apennine mountains, greenish brown in colour and a scattering of many small medieval villages perched all over them. Then there is a lovely view of the pine forest nearby which is a favorite destination for walks, picnics and the wood fired pizzas served by the trattoria in the forest. The aroma of freshly baked bread and roasted coffee coming from the nearby bakery and café would overwhelm my senses just as I was waking up. It's a wonderful experience being in the heart of Molise. Nobody is in a hurry. The village literally has not changed in its long history. Time slows right down.

My original intention for writing this book was going to be a family history as seen through the eyes of my mother, Carmelina. But then I realized, to fully appreciate her family roots and the enriching customs, traditions and lifestyle in which she was brought up, I needed to immerse myself more deeply in the rich and diverse history and culture of the Molise region first. This part of Italy remains relatively unknown, even to Italians. Very few tourists visit there. As a result, it is one of the most natural and un-spoilt regions in Italy. This book is divided into two parts. The first section is a history of Molise and its surrounding central Italian regions, including Abruzzo and the historical centres of power in cities like Naples and Benevento which heavily influenced this region. The second section of the book traces my mother Carmelina's life from her childhood in the Molise village of Montagano during the Second World War, to her arrival and early years in Australia in the late

1950s and 1960s to start a new life. As I recount the history in the first section, I have made frequent references to my family. My family on my mother's side have been living in the mountains of Molise for many generations. I know that my father's family originated from Naples and only moved to Molise in the early nineteenth century when the region was under the control of Napoleonic France.

I

INTRODUCTION

⌒✕

S URPRISINGLY FEW PEOPLE HAVE HEARD OF MOLISE. YET THIS IS ONE OF the most beautiful and historically engaging areas of Italy. Emerging from the highway leading into the region as you drive from Rome, you get the impression you are entering a forgotten world. In many ways you are. Molise (pronounced "moll-easy") lies immediately south of the Abruzzo region, along the Apennine mountain range, deep in the heart of central Italy about halfway down the "calf" of its "boot."

Hilltop towns and villages crowned by castles and forgotten by time dot the region, with steep stone cobbled roads winding up through terraces of stone built medieval houses, many of which are perched high up on rock faces atop mountains. This is how Molise gets its nickname "Region of Little Cities." Molise borders Abruzzo to the north, Lazio to the north west, Campania to the south west, Puglia to the south and the Adriatic Sea to the north east. It is the second smallest and least densely populated region of Italy. It was in 1963 when Abruzzo and Molise were separated into two autonomous regions.

Molise is the least populated region of Italy in sheer numbers too. Between 1861 and 1951 the population increased from 345,138 to 406,823. This is not a significant population increase for a 90-year period because Molise experienced a great wave of emigration to other regions of Italy and to other countries, during this same time. The people of Molise and adjoining Abruzzo experienced difficult economic conditions during this period and regular work was difficult to come by. Agriculture was the main activity with little investment by the government in industry and commerce. As a result, many people migrated to the northern industrial cities of Italy such as Milan and Turin, to affluent European countries like Switzerland, Belgium, France and Germany; and to countries with rapidly growing economies that were in need of more labour, like Australia, Argentina, Brazil, Canada and the United States, which all welcomed Italian unskilled workers.

Between 1951 and 1971 there was a further declining demographic trend in the Molise region with the total population dropping to a low point of 319,807 in 1971. It was during this period that the great post Second World War wave of emigration occurred mainly because economic conditions in Molise had deteriorated even further; with the traditional family peasant lifestyle and the economic independence that came with it, beginning to breakdown. During this period, Canada, United States, Switzerland, United Kingdom, Australia, Germany, France, Belgium, Venezuela and Argentina became the most popular destinations for Molise and Abruzzo emigrants.

In 1951, and for most of the following decade, the people of Molise not only had to deal with the aftermath of the Second World War, and the ruinous impact it had on the lives of so many Italians, but also they had to come to terms with

(5) *Molise women picking grapes for winemaking.*

being typecast by other Italians as "ruralissimo," a land of profoundly rural backward peasant people. This unfortunately mirrored the feudal farming and social system, fragments of which still existed in Molise at the time, and reflected the manner in which this region had been neglected as an economic backwater by successive national Italian governments in the late nineteenth and first half of the twentieth centuries, including the fascist regime of Mussolini. The serene tranquil lifestyle of the people of Molise, with its close knit families and hardworking people in the fields, living in unchanged medieval towns and villages, was literally another world cut off from the rest of Italy during this time. Domestic and international tourism into Molise was virtually nonexistent.

During the wave of emigration occurring between 1951 and 1971 the overall picture in Molise was desolate, with few opportunities for economic advancement available to those families choosing to remain. Nevertheless, in the two decades after 1971 there seemed to be signs of a demographic revival with the population reaching 330,991 by 1991. But looking at it now, this was a passing phenomenon mainly caused by some emigrants deciding to return back to their homeland after accumulating some savings or experiencing homesickness, because between 1991 and 2011 the population decreased again to an all-time low of 313,660 people in 2011.

The drop in the Molise population becomes starkly clear when we consider that during the decade 2001-2011 the overall Italian population increased by 4.3%, whereas the overall Molise population decreased by 2.2%. Between 1951 and 2011 the overall population of Molise decreased by 22.9%! Many of the smaller mountainous villages literally became abandoned and serious social imbalances were created throughout the region because of the falling population. For example, many smaller villages, including Montagano, the village of my parent's birth, were forced to close their schools, meaning that children had to travel what was often long distances to attend schools in other larger villages and towns.

The Molise regional government has projected that the population will remain static over the next decade at around 314,000 inhabitants, and will ultimately drop to a forecast level of 257,000 by 2060. They cite an ageing population, low birth rate, continual movement of younger people seeking educational and employment opportunities into more industrialized regions in Italy, continuing overseas emigration mainly for family reasons and declining economic activity as the principal reasons for the further falls in population numbers.

If present population trends continue, a large number of munici-palities in Molise will be subject to "demographic crumbling" meaning they will no longer have a sufficient population to continue as viable communities. There are already 23 villages with a population of less than 500 inhabitants, and a further 45 with a range of between 501 and 1,000 inhabitants. So exactly half of the municipalities of Molise (68 out of a total of 136) are threatened as viable future communities because their populations are below 1,000.

The big opportunity that can turnaround this declining population trend is tourism. Incredibly, the national and regional governments have not really done enough to promote Molise as an attractive tourist destination until recent years. Molise is a naturally beautiful region of mountains, lakes, forests, stunningly beautiful fields, archaeological sites and medieval villages, that ironically, because it has not been visited by hordes of tourists, makes it a pristine and attractive area to experience an "authentic Italy."

Molise is one of Italy's most discrete and geographically unique regions. It is mountainous with a wealth of incredibly interesting attractions scattered throughout the region, often in the most unexpected places or hidden in nearly inaccessible mountain villages. All of this, makes it a paradise for travellers wishing to explore the heart and soul of Italy. It is a sanctuary of peace and natural beauty, a land of unspoiled nature, stunningly diverse landscapes, amazing history and traditions, delicious local wine and food, and a hospitable, humble, noble and independent people.

Travelling in Molise is like going on a treasure hunt. The myriad of relatively unknown and unexplored secret spots and little gems in the most unexpected places is what distinguishes Molise from other parts of Italy. There are so many things to discover, but I will highlight just a few, to give you a taste of what I mean. There is a marvelous medieval crypt with frescoes dating from the fourteenth century Siena tradition, in a small modest village, Sant Angelo in Grotte. Or an ancient Roman mausoleum dedicated to a VIP of the first century CE, in the middle of a sheep trail, next to a working farm in the town of Altilia.

You can visit an impressive Samnite theatre built in the second century BCE outside a village with less than 850 inhabitants, Pietrabbondante. Another example is the abbey of San Vincenzo al Volturno, dating from the seventh century CE that was completely dismantled and carried across the river to be reconstructed on the other bank of the river, seemingly in the middle of nowhere, in an open field.

The network of major roads in Molise is scarce, with only one motorway along the coast, and two highways flowing inward, one coming west from Rome and the other coming east from the Adriatic coastal city of Termoli. Instead, the region is well interconnected with a maze of smaller back roads and asphalted rural roads. As 79% of the region is mountainous though, a lot of these roads end up winding around mountains, offering spectacular scenic views. Molise is definitely best explored by car.

Apart from the two provincial capital cities, Isernia and Campobasso and the beautiful seaside town of Termoli, most of Molise's population live in remote mountain villages. Out of the 136 municipalities (or communes) in the region, 111 are medieval mountain villages. Many settlements in Molise were not built in the valleys or on the mountain slopes, but on the very top of mountains and hills, creating a very unique and stunningly beautiful landscape. It is relatively uncommon to see isolated single residences; instead most of the houses are grouped in small clusters or hamlets, leaving the rest of the territory as relatively uninhabited open fields.

Molise and Abruzzo have numerous castles dating back to the Lombard and Norman periods of control of this region. Some of the most spectacular are the Castle of Venafro, the Monforte Castle of Campobasso, the Castle of Tufara, the Castle of Pescolanciano, the Castle of Roccamondolfi, the Gambatesa Castle and the Svevo Castle of Termoli, just to name a few.

There are few regions where you can still immerse yourself in the worlds of the traditional fisherman and shepherd farmer; the trabucchi along the coast and the tratturi inland. They are like snapshots frozen in time, originating in ancient times. The great Italian writer Gabriele D'Annunzio in *Il Trionfo della Morte*, ('The Triumph of the Dead')

Top left (6): *Venafro Castle in Molise*. Bottom left (7): *Monforte Castle in Campobasso, Molise*. Above right (8): *Gambatesa Castle*.

(9, 10) *Trabucchi ancient fishing devices originated during the time of the Samnites.*

described the trabucchi as "strange fishing machines that look like giant spiders, made of boards and beams, respectively." The trabucchi are ancient fishing devices typically seen in the lower Adriatic from the coast of Abruzzo and Molise reaching further south to Puglia. However, the types found in Molise are usually smaller and are built on a platform above the sea, instead of being anchored on rocks as they are in Puglia. Trabucchi are used to intercept schools of fish as they move along the shore. They were a way to guarantee a decent catch of fish even when the fishing boats could not sail due to bad weather.

The tratturi on the other hand, are the natural trails followed by pastoral shepherd farmers during the seasonal rotation of mainly sheep herding between the summer and winter pastures. Traditionally, Molise was the region through which the flocks of sheep coming from the northern cool mountain pastures in Abruzzo, would pass, on their way to the southern warmer Puglia tablelands in autumn; and vice versa in spring, in order to cope with seasonal fluctuations in heat, water and fodder availability. The farmers practicing this "transhumance" form of herding had their own customs, cuisine and handicraft that all related to this particular way of life. A way of life that can be traced back to the ancient Samnite tribes that lived in the mountains centuries before the settlement of ancient Rome was established in 753 BCE.

Visitors to Molise will see this heritage in the cuisine, folklore, traditions and the economy. Twelve tratturi cross the Molise region, covering

(11) *Fonderia Marinelli bell foundry.*

a distance of about 1,500 kilometres from the north to south and from the Adriatic coast to the foot of the Matese mountain range which forms part of the Apennine mountains. Some are still used by shepherd farmers to this day. These routes of transhumance form a rich network of green roads for hikers and bicycle riders who wish to explore unaltered natural environments, archaeological sites, monuments and medieval towns, while immersing themselves in this rich territory.

It was the ancient Samnites who first organized and controlled this network of roads formed by these sheep trails, so it will not come as a surprise that many of the most fascinating Samnite settlements and later Roman colonies lie precisely on the original tratturi trails.

Being a region with many traditions that have been passed on by families from generation to generation, it is not surprising that Molise can still pride itself on a wide variety of ancient traditional crafts. It is home to the oldest continuously family owned and run manufacturing business in the world, the Fonderia Marinelli bell foundry, which was founded over 1,000 years ago. Molise is also renowned for its tradition of handmade folding knives; its own unique bagpipes, used by the shepherds of Scapoli; pottery of Guardiaregia; and the very refined art of Isernia.

Festivals are a big part of Molise and Abruzzo tradition and culture. The rivers of fire "Ndocciata" is an ancient festival celebrated in the town of Agnone. The Ndocciata consists of an impressive torchlight parade

(12, 13) *The Uomo Cervo Deer Man festival, held annually in Castelnuovo al Volturno.*

of a large number of hand fan-shaped wooden "ndocce" or torches, carried by men dressed in traditional colorful costumes. This festival is celebrated on December 8th, the day of the Immaculate Conception of the Madonna, and also on Christmas Eve. Then there is the Larino Carrese festival which dates back to 842 CE, when the inhabitants of Larino took possession of the relics of Saint Pardus, kept in Lucera in the region of Foggia, which is the reason why this festival is dedicated to that saint. What is wonderful about Molise and Abruzzo is that each community has its own uniquely peculiar and historical festival. The Jelsi Wheat festival, celebrated on July 26th is peculiar. It is celebrated with a procession of the "traglie," antique carts without wheels carried by the strongest men in the village. Also noteworthy is the Uomo Cervo Deer Man festival celebrated in the village of Castelnuovo al Volturno. It is a pantomimic performance that combines magical religious rituals and hunting scenes, with a deer, ram and a hunter. The origin and meaning of this ancient festival can be traced back to our ancestral Samnites.

3

SAMNITE WARS
WITH ROME

⌒⌒⌒

HE MOLISE AND ABRUZZO REGION IS ALSO ARGUABLY, THE BIRTHPLACE
of Italy. It was the heartland of the Samnites, a brave, proud and
feisty collection of warrior tribes who united in the first century BCE
under the single banner of the "Italic League" and were a constant
aggressive thorn in the side of the Romans for centuries. So we see
the word "Italic" which then became "Italian" appear for the first time
in reference to the Samnites. My ancestors! When the city of Rome
was founded by Romulus in 753 BCE, the Samnites were already
established in the Apennine mountains of central Italy. Other Italian
tribal groups not far from the city of Rome included the Sabines,
Etruscans, Campanians and Latins.

All Samnite families used the land for the farming of crops and animals.
Unlike the Romans, slavery did not exist in the Samnite culture. They traded
and interacted freely with surrounding tribal and ethnic groups in the Italian

peninsula, including the Romans, until the wars started over the control of territory. Most people associate gladiators with the Romans, but it was in fact the Samnites who first conducted gladiatorial contests in order to prepare their soldiers for battle. The Romans then introduced gladiators into their society in the second century BCE as a form of entertainment in specially built amphitheaters and arenas, using mainly slaves.

We know very little about the Samnites prior to the fourth century BCE. What we do know is that as their population grew, these fierce warriors came out of the mountains to regularly raid fertile neighboring fields including in Campania and Latium, further to the west and north.

It was becoming clear to the Roman Republic that the single biggest obstacle to its conquest of the Italian peninsula were the Samnites. In the 380s BCE the Romans had fought a series of battles with the Gauls after they had come from northern Italy, invaded and briefly occupied the city of Rome in 387, causing much destruction. Also feeling threatened, the Samnites joined the Romans in ultimately successfully driving the Gauls out of the city of Rome and pushing them back to their lands in the far north of Italy.

The threat from the Gauls was not over though. In 360, 359 and 349, they conducted more raids into central Italy including venturing into Roman controlled Latium. Each time the Romans, with the assistance of the Samnites, were militarily successful in forcing them out and back to the far north. The Romans had learnt a valuable lesson from their encounters with the Gauls. They built a defensive structure called the Servian Wall, around the city of Rome, to protect it from any future attack. This wall effectively saved Rome when the Gauls launched their attack in 360, even though the Romans living outside the walled city in the surrounding towns and villages of Latium were terrified by these Gallic incursions.

Having defeated the Gauls, the Romans now no longer saw the Samnites as an ally, but instead as a growing threat to their ambition to conquer the fertile land of Campania, which was effectively in between Latium Rome and Samnium. They would ultimately fight three major wars with the Samnites for effective control of not only central Italy, but ultimately the entire Italian peninsula. This is such a major turning point not only in the history of the Molise region but also in the history of Rome and the subsequent development of Western civilization, that I will now outline the key events of these crucial wars.

Samnite Wars

Gauls

Umbrians

Etruscans

Samnites

Latins

Messapians

Campanians

Lucanians

Bruttians

Tarentines

(14) *Samnite warriors preparing for battle.*

The three Samnite Wars lasted from 343 to 290 BCE. During this time, the great powers in the region were the maritime trading civilization of Carthage in north Africa, whom the Romans were destined to fight for control of the Mediterranean in the three Punic Wars; Parthia, which is modern day Iran and Syria; and Macedonia which was first controlled by King Phillip II and then his son Alexander the Great, after Phillip was assassinated. Phillip took control of the Greek city states including Athens and Sparta and Alexander went on to conquer much of what is today the Middle East, including the Parthian empire, central and southern Asia all the way to India and into Afghanistan. Luckily for the Romans, Samnites and Carthage, Alexander did not turn his attention west to the Mediterranean, otherwise the course of history would have been very different. When Alexander died in 323 BCE the Samnite Wars were still raging.

At this time, the Italian peninsula was mainly occupied by a number of Greek city states along the coast of Sicily and the "heel" of the "boot" of mainland Italy. Then in the south there also were various Italic tribes including Messapians and Apulians. In central Italy as well as the Roman Latins and Samnites, there were Umbrians, Sabines and Campanians. Further north were the Etruscans and then the Celtic Gauls in the far

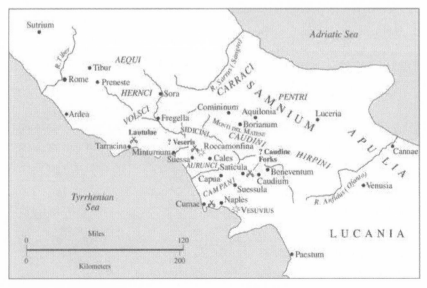

(15) *Samnium and surrounding regions of ancient Italy.*

north. Carthage also occupied the north-west portion of Sicily. Latium Rome was clearly intent on expanding its republican state, but it was prevented by the Samnites to its south-east, the Umbrians to its east, the Campanians to its south and the Etruscans to its north. Rome was effectively "sandwiched."

As we have seen, the Samnites had contact with the Romans before these wars. They had joined with the Romans in fighting the invading Gauls. It was during these battles that the reputation of the Samnites as fiercely courageous warriors was forged, to the point where the neighboring states, particularly the Umbrians, Campanians and Etruscans were fearful of them. If not fearful, the Romans certainly respected their fierce sense of pride, independence and fighting abilities.

The Samnites had also completed a treaty with the Romans in 354 agreeing to define the border between Latium Rome and Samnium to be the Liris River. This treaty had been necessary because the Romans were intent on expansion and had ventured into Samnium territory on numerous occasions, greatly angering the Samnites. Although the Samnites comprised five major distinct tribes, they would not hesitate to band together into a Samnite League in times of war, under the leadership of one commander selected by the tribes. This made them a very formidable military force.

The First Samnite War took place between 343 and 341 BCE and arose over territory in Campania. The Samnites had conquered Campania in earlier times to provide additional food for their people and many of them established farming settlements on the rich fertile Campanian plains. This lifestyle was very docile for the tribal mountain warrior Samnites, who were accustomed to living a tough and hard way of life. So over a period of time the Samnites living in Campania softened and settled into a lifestyle that was very different to that which their fellow tribespeople in the mountains lived. A dispute over food supply is what triggered the First Samnite War. The Samnites came from the mountains and laid siege to the Campanian capital city of Capua, causing much destruction and terror in the process.

The Campanians formally requested the assistance of the Romans, who sent a well manned and equipped army to Capua, and seized control of the city from the Samnites. They then kept a garrison of soldiers in Capua to maintain order. These soldiers did something that had not happened to the Romans before, they mutinied, refusing to follow orders, because they wanted a share of the war booty (valuables) which they were accustomed to receiving after achieving victory in a battle. This mutiny created great instability and damaged the reputation of Rome within Latium. As a result, the Romans agreed to sign a peace treaty with Samnium to end the war, and also passed a law in their Senate agreeing to share the Capua booty with the soldiers who had fought there. The Samnites were happy to conclude this peace treaty primarily because the Greek city state of Tarentum in the south of mainland Italy, recently reinforced with an army of Spartans from Greece, was posing a threat to them on their southern border which they needed to deal with urgently, so they did not want to be fighting a war on two fronts. It was a peace treaty of convenience for both sides.

Tensions continued to mount between Rome and Samnium over Roman colonies and also Campania. In a major provocation, the Romans established a colony at Fregellae in 328 on the Samnium side of the Liris river valley border. Rome tried to negotiate with the Samnites, but they outright refused to, instead demanding that the Romans leave the newly established colony. When the Romans refused to leave, the Samnites prepared for war. The second issue involved the Samnites providing military assistance to the Campanian city of Neapolis (modern day Naples) which was looking to conquer surrounding territory settled by the Romans.

At this time Neapolis was controlled by the Greeks but had the support of Samnium. There had been a change of power in the Greek city state of Tarentum and since then, the Greek city states in southern Italy saw the Romans as their greatest threat so reached out to Samnium to assist them. Even within the city of Neapolis, there was one faction within the power structure supporting Rome and another which supported Samnium. A Samnite military force was able to garrison (surround) Neapolis and from this strong vantage point urge their allies in Neapolis to attack the surrounding Roman colonies in Campania. Rome demanded that the Samnites remove their garrison, which they refused to do. As a result, war broke out again in 326.

In the first stages of the Second Samnite War, Rome did very well. The Romans invaded Samnium and won several battles. The city of Neapolis also fell to Roman control. At this point, the Samnites tried to negotiate a peace treaty but the Romans refused, sensing they were in striking distance of defeating and subduing the Samnites. But then things turned around dramatically when one of the Samnites' most famous military victories occurred in heavily forested mountain Samnium terrain in 321 BCE at the Battle of Caudine Forks where after fierce and ferocious fighting, an outnumbered Samnite army successfully trapped and totally disarmed a large Roman force of their armor, shields, javelins and swords. They also successfully blocked Roman communications and lines of retreat.

(16) and (17) *The Battle of Caudine Forks in 321BCE and the humiliation of Roman soldiers.*

The Romans had no choice other than to surrender. What made this victory so important is what the Samnites did next. They forced the Roman army to pass between a narrow passage in the Apennine mountains. The Samnites blocked this passage at both ends with felled trees and boulders. The Romans, stuck and surrounded, responded by setting up a fortified camp, but suffered a great humiliation because they had been subjugated, disarmed and trapped by the smaller Samnite force. After this victory, the Romans were forced to sign a humbling treaty admitting defeat and giving up their colony at Fregellae on the Samnite side of the Liris river, along with other settlements nearby. The Samnites kept 600 Roman hostages to make sure that the treaty was honoured. When it was, the hostages were released.

The peace treaty lasted for five years. During this time, the humiliated Romans made some major changes militarily and diplomatically, including re-arranging their legion battle formations from the Greek-styled phalanx to the more flexible and agile Samnite maniple system, which involved the legions fighting in smaller groups, having backup reserves and using their shields to provide greater defensive protection. It was typically Roman to take the best from other cultures and then refine it for their own use. Here they were doing it again with the Samnites! They were preparing for a massive counter-strike.

The Samnites underestimated the great dishonour and loss of prestige which the Romans had endured and failed to realize they were going to stop at nothing until Rome defeated and subdued their arch enemy. On the diplomatic front the Romans created alliances with the provinces of Lucania and Apulia, surrounding Samnium with enemies. They also reinforced a number of southern Latium cities that bordered Samnium.

The Second Samnite War resumed in 316 BCE when Rome suffered a number of early setbacks including a crushing defeat at Lautulae in Campania, after which the Campanians seriously considered abandoning their Roman allies, but instead hung in there by a thread. In 311 a number of Etruscan cities joined the war on the side of Samnium, and this alliance also won some battles. In 310, under the command of Fabius Maximus Rullianus, the Romans defeated the Etruscans, driving them out of the war by 308. Following these victories, the Roman legions were able to push the Samnites out of Campania and recapture all of the territory that they had previously lost to Samnium.

At this point, the Roman army was in a strong position to launch a massive invasion into Samnium itself, which they did with stunning success. In 304, a defeated and demoralized Samnium signed another peace treaty with Rome. In the peace agreement, the Samnites were forced to accept the takeover and colonization of a large part of their territory. After this humiliating setback, there was no doubt Rome was the most powerful military force in Italy at that time. Upon securing this peace agreement, the Romans proceeded to build the Appian Way to Capua. This major road gave them easier access to Campania and other areas in southern Italy, allowing for the Roman legions in the south to be resupplied faster, as well as more trade to be conducted.

The hostilities between Rome and Samnium were not over. There was to be a Third Samnite War between 298 and 295 BCE. Many of the provinces in Italy began to fear the military power and imperial expansionist intentions of the Romans. They wanted to combine their resources into one last ditch attempt to secure independence before Rome became even more powerful.

The Samnites were instrumental in putting together an alliance of Umbrians, Etruscans, Gauls, Sabines and various other tribal groups into joining them in a major military effort to defeat the Romans. The Samnites were to lead this combined military force. This undoubtedly was the biggest military threat that Rome had faced in its entire history to date. Realizing the imminent threat, the Roman Senate appointed two of its most decorated generals as Consuls in 298. These were Cornelius Scipio Barbatus and Fulvius Maximus Centumalus. Since the Romans were going to have to fight on multiple fronts, the two Consuls decided that Scipio would lead an army north to attack the Etruscans and Fulvius would launch an attack south into Samnium.

Scipio's army ravaged the entire Etruscan countryside, striking fear and terror with the people and taking control of a number of towns. Fulvius's army penetrated deep into Samnium and achieved a major victory in the Battle of Bovianum. These battles had definitely given the Romans the initiative in the early stages of the war.

In the second year 297, two new Consuls were appointed by the Roman Senate. They were Fabius Maximus Rullianus and Publius Decius Mus. Both Consuls led an army of legions against Samnium in the south, achieving a victory near the town of Tifernum, even though a number of Samnites survived this battle and were able to escape and head north to link up with their Gaul, Umbrian and Etruscan allies.

Samnium was left unprotected as the entire Samnite League Army also headed north. This allowed Decius's army to absolutely ravage and strike terror in the countryside of Samnium. The end result of the movement north though, was a combined allied force of 80,000 soldiers who were going to take on the Romans in a "last stand" battle to the death. This was the largest army ever seen on the Italian peninsula up to that point in history. The Romans were very concerned about this combined military force.

Consul Fabius decided that he needed to try and split the allied army by launching diversionary attacks into Etruscan and Umbrian territory. The strategy worked when the Etruscan army headed home to defend their territory. Now, the Samnite led allied army numbered 50,000 which was a much more manageable number for the Romans.

Both forces were ready to fight a decisive battle. It was the Battle of Sentinum, fought in 295 BCE. There were 50,000 Samnite led allied forces lined up against 40,000 Roman forces led by Fabius and Decius, who had both been re-elected as Consuls for that year because the Senate wanted the very best commanders to take on this allied force. The two massive armies literally stared at each other for the first two days, possibly seeking a psychological advantage. Eventually, the Romans attacked first with fierce brutal fighting, much bloodshed, screams of agony and war-cries all at very close quarters. Decius died during the early stages of the battle when the Romans were under tremendous assault. Fabius did not panic upon hearing of the death of his consular colleague and instead took command of the entire army.

After a barrage of ferocious fighting, the Romans were gaining the upper hand to the point where the allied forces were decimated and many Samnites and Gauls fled the battle. The Romans were killing as many of the retreating soldiers as they could. The Romans had secured

(18) *The Battle of Sentinum in 295BCE.*

a major victory in a battle in which 25,000 Samnites and Gauls had died and 8,000 Romans died. After this battle, the Romans finally succeeded in subjugating the Samnites and placing Samnium under Roman control. The Samnites had lost their independence. The unique culture and traditions of the Samnites was ultimately destroyed as the Romans ruthlessly implemented a policy of ethnic cleansing, wiping out much of their culture in the process and forcing the Saminites to assimilate into the Roman society and way of life. After this victory, the Romans become the dominant power in all of the Italian peninsula.

In spite of their defeat, the Samnites continued to be a thorn in Rome's side for the next two centuries. In 91 BCE the Samnites joined forces with many other Italian tribes and rose up in an armed revolt after the Romans refused to give them citizenship. This civil conflict was called The Social War. For a time Bovanium, the Samnites' largest town, even became the capital of a breakaway Italian state. The Romans eventually emerged victorious, but only after they gave the Samnites and their tribal allies, full Roman citizenship.

There was to be one last major Roman conflict in which the Samnites were involved. During the civil wars of the Roman generals

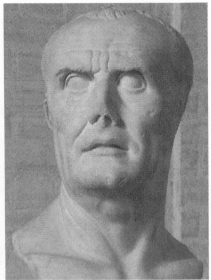

The Roman generals, Gaius Marius (above left, 19) *and Sulla* (above right, 20).

The Social War. (left, 21)

Gaius Marius and Sulla in 88-87 BCE the Samnites supported Gaius Marius with devastating consequences. A Marius backed force consisting mainly of Samnites fought Sulla's supporters outside the city of Rome at The Battle of Colline Gate. Before the battle, Sulla ordered his legions to show the Samnites no mercy and after his men won, many thousands of Samnites lay dead on the battlefield. All of the captured Samnites were brutally slaughtered.

Sulla did not stop there, as Strabo, a Greek historian writing over 100 years later, noted:

> He would not stop making proscriptions until either he had destroyed all Samnites of importance or banished them from Italy.

He said he had realized from experience that a Roman could never live in peace so long as the Samnites held together as a separate people.

Sulla's genocide against the Samnites was brutally and ruthlessly effective and never again did they rise up against Rome. Our people and towns were reduced to a shadow of their former prestige, and instead we were totally integrated into mainstream Roman society.

(22) *A Samnite tribal warrior showing the distinctive helmet.*

4

THE SAMNITE CULTURE

⚬⚬⚬

URING A TRIP TO ITALY IN 2012, I VISITED THE SMALL MOLISE TOWN
of Pietrabbondante. Just outside this town is a major Samnite
temple and sanctuary, founded in the sixth century BCE. It was the
centre for the Pentri, the largest of the Samnite tribes. My family
ancestry on my mother's side, is Pentri. The other tribes were the
Caraceni, Caudini, Frentani and Hirpini. All of these tribes originated
in what was then called Samnium, and they all shared the Oscan
language. Here at this sanctuary, on the slopes of Mount Saraceno
high up in the Apennine mountains, the five tribes gathered to discuss
their interactions and in particular, military tactics to be implemented
against their deadly common arch enemy, the Romans. The ancient
literature talks about a settlement near the sanctuary called Bovanium
Vetus, or the "Old City of the Bull," which is named after an ancient
Pentri origin myth. This myth tells the story of how the people sought
to appease their gods by sending away all children that were born in a
specified year. The children would follow an ox until it settled down
to rest alongside the source of a sacred stream of mountain water,
which they took to be a good sign and so they established a sanctuary,

(23 and 24) *The Samnite sanctuary and temple at Pietrabbondante.*

temple and settlement there. Bovanium was an important sacred place for the Samnites.

The original sanctuary and temple at Pietrabbondante was destroyed by the Carthaginian general Hannibal in 217 BCE during his raids into Italy after earlier crossing the Alps to invade with a large army and a herd of elephants. The temple was rebuilt by the Samnites with even more grandeur but it was again destroyed, this time by the very nasty and spiteful Roman general Sulla over the period 89-87 BCE. Whatever went on in the temple was only for those taking part in the rituals of worship and important decision making, because the remains show that there was no room for spectators. After visiting this site, I headed north where I encountered two more Samnite temples set in the breathtakingly beautiful countryside outside the town of Schiavi di Abruzzo. When I arrived, the site was deserted. Above me I saw that birds were hovering as I sat on the lush green slopes taking in the history, with a fresh mountain breeze cooling me, while enjoying a delicious traditional potato pizza and some Molise red wine. I sat there admiring the spectacle of an endless field of sunflowers ("girasoli") in the distance. Both of these temples date to the third century BCE. Although little remained of them, I can remember appreciating for the first time, just how formidable and well established my Samnite ancestors were. The Samnite tribes occupied their own fortified towns and villages high up, all over the Apennine mountains. All five of the Samnite tribes worshipped the same gods. This unified them to a common set of cultural and religious beliefs. During times of war all soldiers were united by a holy oath to protect their sacred soil. The religious beliefs of the Greeks were a major influence on the Samnites. The Romans and Samnites also

(25) *The God, Jupiter.*
(26) *The Sacred Agnone's Tablet.*
(27) *Castor and Pollux.*

worshipped the same gods. Although we cannot be certain where these particular gods originated, other than the fact that they were inspired by the Greeks, it is more than likely they were a part of the Samnite religious belief system first and then the Romans adopted them when they encountered the Samnites. After all, the Samnites were in Italy, centuries before the Romans! They worshipped Jupiter, Hercules, Mars, Mercury, Diane, Apollo, Castor, Pollux, Dyonisious and Ceres, amongst others.

The Samnites also had many cults. These included the "Ver Sacrum" or Holy Springtime which was very important for the protection of their crops and animals. Another one was the "Lex Sacrata" or Sacred Law which was the ritual of bonding men with their families and possessions. The Samnite gods were each worshipped for their own individual merits. A typical example can be found in the sacred Agnone's Tablet, which was inscribed in the Samnite language of Oscan, where 17 gods were worshipped in one single temple. This bronze tablet is today preserved at the British Museum in London. It is one of the most important Samnite inscriptions in the Oscan language ever recovered and can be traced back to around 250 BCE.

The Samnites worshipped all of their gods and semi-gods with equal fervour. These gods were not always represented in human-like form however and even their sex was not often known, although there were many more female than male gods. The gods would be called upon to protect Samnite homes including safeguarding the fireplace, the entrance door and the sleeping quarters. Other gods would protect soldiers in battle, the harvest in the fields, fresh water mountain springs and burial sites within their tribal territories.

The Samnites feared contagious diseases and practiced a form of exorcism to purify the body from these "demons." If they were invaded they believed their land would become contaminated. This is the reason why they carried out the famous "yoke ritual" when they trapped a Roman army in a narrow gorge in the previously described Battle of Caudine Forks. As a result of this Roman invasion the land needed to be purified and the people in contact with the defeated invaders had to be subjected to a cleansing ritual. For good luck and to keep away evil spirits the Samnites used amulets. These were small pieces of precious gems which were worn as necklaces and were believed to protect a person from any trouble or misfortune. During special occasions such as the harvest or a wedding, the "Sabella Carmina," or magic words calling upon the gods and spirits, would be invoked in special ceremonies. These practices were more magical in nature than religious and were a regular part of Samnite traditional life.

The five Samnite tribal groups could all trace their roots to ancient peasant and sheep farming communities. The Samnites were never formally organized into a collective nation or even city states, unlike the Romans and Greeks. Their society was one of small village commu- nities and fortified mountain towns. Wealth was quite evenly distributed amongst the people so there wasn't a wide gap between rich and poor and there certainly wasn't a significant land owning aristocratic class like the Patricians of Rome. Each of the five Samnite tribal groups elected their local leaders or magistrates. The people would also elect a supreme leader called the "Meddix Tuticus," for a one-year term, just like a Roman Consul. He enjoyed unlimited power and controlled the council of magistrates. The Meddix Tuticus did not have to follow the advice of the council when making his decisions. He was the commander in chief of the army, in charge of the judicial system and the highest ranking religious leader. Did the Romans copy aspects of their political structure from the Samnites? We just don't know for certain, but it is likely that they did.

One of the most famous Meddix Tuticus Samnite leaders was Gaius Pontius, who was a military commander during the Second Samnite War. He is mostly known for his victory over the Roman legions at the Battle of Caudine Forks in 321 BCE, previously described. This is the single greatest defeat inflicted by the Samnites over the Romans. At the beginning of the Second Samnite War, Gaius Pontius controlled a Samnite force of around 9,000 men, including 1,000 cavalrymen. With this force, he won a series of early victories, which included taking the towns of Canusium and Gnaitha, and defeating the Roman army under the command of Cornelius Lentulus. The sources describe him as a very religious and devoted family man who displayed much compassion for his tribespeople. He was also a fierce and courageous warrior who always led his army from the front.

Gaius Pontius did not ask anything of his men that he himself would not be prepared to do. As the Romans were moving into Samnium, Pontius discovered that the army led by two Roman Consuls was near the town of Calatia. He devised a plan to trap the Roman army, and quickly sent ten shepherds to the Roman camp. They told the Romans the Samnite army was laying siege to the town of Luceria, in the nearby region of Apulia. The Romans falling for this trap, rushed to the area and found themselves cornered by the Samnite army in a narrow pass. They were forced to surrender to Pontius.

Following the surrender of the Romans, according to the historian Livy, Pontius was at first unsure what to do with the Romans. He sent a letter to his father, the Samnite statesman Herennius Pontius, and the reply was that he should free them all and negotiate an alliance with Rome. Pontius did not like this idea and sent another letter to his father letting him know this. Herennius, in a seemingly hypocritical manner, told his son to execute the entire army, saying this would destroy the Roman threat for a long time. Pontius knew there were simply far too many Romans to have them all executed and sent his father another letter letting him know his thoughts. In the same letter, he asked his father to give advice on a "middle road" course of action. Herennius replied to his son that any "middle road" action would end up not only humiliating the Romans, but also leave them with the means to carry out revenge at a later date.

Pontius ended up ignoring his father's advice and forced the Romans to walk under a yoke composed of Roman spears, as we have seen. This was a supreme humiliation because it was considered cowardly for a Roman soldier to lose his spear. The army then returned to Rome, intact but severely embarrassed. Sure enough, Rome's revenge came soon after, when a significantly greater Roman force defeated the Samnite army and Pontius was executed.

(28) *The Roman town of Saepinum was originally a Samnite settlement.*

The following day I visited the archeological site of Saepinum. One of Molise's hidden treasures, the Roman ruins of Saepinum are among the best preserved and least known in all of Italy. This settlement was originally established by the Samnites but the Romans conquered it in 293 BCE. They expanded the city and turned it into a major trading centre also maintaining a relatively large army there to ensure the Samnites would not stir up any more trouble. When I visited the site I could see that the city originally had four gates, three of which had the arches still intact and well preserved.

In the centre there was a forum where the buying and selling of goods and produce would occur as well as for public announcements and a meeting place. The forum was surrounded by public buildings including a curia meeting place for the government and a basilica where the judicial courts were located, as well as a capitolium which was a temple dedicated to worshipping Jupiter. I also saw the site of the public baths and a carved stone amphitheater which could accommodate around 3,000 people. When I did more research on the layout of this city, I learnt that most Roman cities were planned and laid out in a similar fashion to Saepinum.

(29) *The transhumance herding of sheep is a Molise tradition originating with the Samnites.*

What do we know about the Samnite lifestyle and culture? We know that the Samnites were engaged in what was mainly a herding and mixed farming economy. They would move large flocks of sheep from summer pastures high in the Apennines to the warmer Apulian lowlands in the winter. As a boy and teenager, my father was a shepherd, herding and managing sheep on the Ferrone family farm. He was following an ancient custom that can be traced back to the Samnites, who also cultivated grape vines, olives, cereals and legumes; agricultural activities which still dominate Molise today. In addition to sheep, cattle and pigs were also domesticated and farmed.

A number of Samnite cemeteries have been excavated, showing that they buried their dead. We know that warrior princes played a major role in officiating at funerals, mediating between the tribal community and the gods. The Samnites had a custom of burying valuable posses-sions and heirlooms with their dead. Soldiers were buried with their weapons. Burial and death rituals often involved an idealized portrait of the deceased, reflecting their achievements and the wishes of the deceased.

(30) *Samnite cavalry soldier.*
(31) *Samnite battle helmet.*

(32) *Samnite hill fort.*

(33) *Samnite religious goddess.*

The Samnite culture placed enormous prestige on being a warrior. To fight in the army was the highest achievement a man could aim for. There were highly respected long standing families who held most of the power. These magisterial families possessed great prestige and influence which was passed on dynastically from one generation to another. They dominated the political and judicial system. They provided the military leaders in times of war with Rome and others. They also raised funds for public works, recreational facilities and religious temples. It seems that each of the five Samnite tribes was controlled by an oligopoly of the most powerful families. It was a competitive, hierarchical, image-conscious, aggressive, militaristic elite that held the power in Samnite tribal groups. But unlike their Roman counterparts, they did not accumulate great property wealth.

Just how militaristic were the Samnites? More than one hundred hill-forts have been identified across Molise Samnium by archaeologists, and there are others that still await discovery on remote and thickly forested mountain peaks. Samnite hill-forts were in naturally defensible locations on or near the summits of hills and mountains. Excavations have shown that these hill-forts supported permanent settlements nearby. Some of them have been dated to as early as the sixth century BCE. The larger hill-forts were home to ancient influential powerful families. The bigger the hill-fort, the more powerful the family was.

The ancient Roman historian Strabo writes that the Samnites once had great towns, but in time they dwindled into smaller villages. This coincides with the conquest and subjugation of the Samnites by the Romans, who destroyed many of the larger Samnite settlements in an endeavor to extinguish all signs of Samnite culture and building achievements. Some of the larger Samnite towns included Bovianum, Saepinum, Caudium, Larinum, Monte Vairano, Roccagloriosa, Pietrabbondante and Beneventum. Each town had a sanctuary which served as an economic, political and religious meeting point. These sanctuaries formed a hierarchy ranging in size from small shrines to the most prominent Samnite sanctuary of all at Pietrabbondante, which as previously mentioned, I visited. Animal sacrifices to the gods were an integral part of Samnite religious beliefs. It was mainly cattle, pigs, sheep, deer and goats that were sacrificed at the sanctuaries.

The Samnites are such an important part of the early history of Molise. The other very important groups that came later and heavily influenced Molise and Abruzzo were the Ostrogoths, Lombards, Byzantians, Franks, Normans, Spanish and Napoleonic French, who successively conquered southern Italy including Molise between the sixth and nineteenth centuries CE and whom I will be covering in this book, in some depth. I will then talk about the unification of Italy in 1861, firstly as a kingdom from 1861 to 1946 and then as a democratic republic; and what impact a unified Italian state had on Molise and Abruzzo.

The fall of the Roman Empire in 476 CE brought about a complete fragmentation of Europe into anarchical tribal fiefdoms and a destruction of an orderly cultural, legal, economic and political system which had been built by the Romans over many centuries. It was the Germanic barbarian tribal group, the Ostrogoths, ruled by Odoacer, who successfully toppled the Roman system and deposed the last emperor, the young Romulus Augustus. I can only imagine how many Samnites at the time would have thought the Romans got what they

(34)   *The Duchy of Benevento was a major Lombard Kingdom in southern Italy in the 8th century.*

deserved, payback for all the atrocities and bloodshed they inflicted not only on my ancestors, but so many other ethnic groups throughout the Mediterranean in their quest for world domination.

It was not to be until the Germanic Lombards commenced their invasion of the Italian peninsula in 568–569 CE under their king Alboin, that some stability was restored to Italy. The Lombards ruled Molise and Abruzzo from their Duchy of Benevento, which achieved the height of its power in the eighth century CE.

5

THE POETRY
OF HORACE

⟩⟨

ONE OF THE MOST PROMINENT PEOPLE OF ANCIENT ROME TO COME FROM the Samnite region of Italy was the Roman poet Quintus Horatius Flaccus, better known as Horace. He was born on 8th December, 65 BCE in the Samnium town of Venusia.

Horace was one of Rome's best loved and most influential poets who had a major influence on the subsequent development of western literature in Europe through the Middle Ages and into the Renaissance. Along with his fellow poet Virgil, he was a member of the inner circle of Emperor Augustus at the imperial palace, which also included Augustus' childhood friend Agrippa, who went on to become one of Rome's great tactical generals and Maecenas, a wealthy Roman patron of the arts. Horace was one of the world' first autobiographers. In his writings he told us much about himself, his personality, character, development and way of life.

Despite his early support for Marcus Brutus, one of the leading assassins of Julius Caesar, Horace eventually developed a close friendship

(35, 36 and, preceding page 37)
Quintus Horatius Flaccus, better
known as Horace.

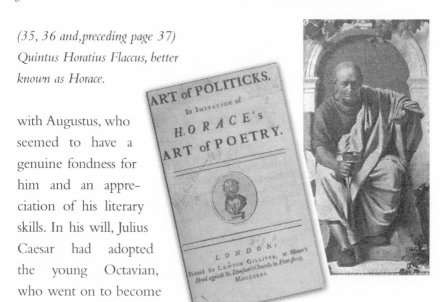

with Augustus, who
seemed to have a
genuine fondness for
him and an appre-
ciation of his literary
skills. In his will, Julius
Caesar had adopted
the young Octavian,
who went on to become
Emperor Augustus, as his
son.

The best source we have for the life of Horace is the Roman historian
Suetonius, who describes Horace's father as a plebeian freedman and
small landowner who worked part time as a public auctioneer of salted
food provisions and seemed to have made a financial success of it.
Various Italic dialects were spoken in the area surrounding his birth
which could have contributed to his love of language from an early
age. The dialect that he spoke was a form of Oscan, the language of the
Samnites. According to a local tradition that Horace referred to in his
writing, a colony of Latin Romans had settled in Venusia shortly after
the Romans had finally defeated the Samnites; but without a doubt,
Venusia was a Samnite settlement and this was Horace's ancestry.

His father, realizing the potential of his highly intelligent and
precocious son, accompanied the young poet to Rome to oversee his
education and moral development, spending a substantial amount of
money in the process. Horace later paid tribute to the role that his
father played in his early development and education, as can be seen by
this extract of a poem, from his *Satires*:

If my character is flawed by a few minor faults, but is otherwise
decent and moral, if you can point out only a few scattered blemishes

on an otherwise immaculate surface, if no one can accuse me of greed, or of prurience, or of profligacy, if I live a virtuous life, free of defilement (pardon for a moment, my self-praise), and if I am to my friends a good friend, my father deserves all the credit......As it is now, he deserves from me unstinting gratitude and praise. I could never be ashamed of such a father, nor do I feel any need, as many people do, to apologize for being a freedman's son.

It was while Horace was studying literature, philosophy and oratory in Athens at the famous Academy started by Plato, that he joined the army of Caesars's conspiratorial assassin, Marcus Brutus, as a military commander to fight against an army which had been assembled by Octavian, the future Augustus. The lower class plebeian Horace must have had a particularly close relationship with Brutus who had also spent time in Athens, because it was uncommon for people who were at least not from the

(38) *Marcus Brutus.*
(39) *Battle of Philippi in 42 BCE.*

higher class equestrian order, to be appointed as military commanders. Brutus eventually lost to Octavian at the Battle of Philippi in 42 BCE.

This defeat left the humiliated Horace with a deep distaste for warfare. We need to appreciate that at the time, commanding an army was one of the highest honors that a young Roman man could aspire to. His support of Brutus proved to be very costly because his family's property was confiscated by Octavian, who after winning the decisive battle of the civil war at Philippi, went on to become Emperor Augustus, transforming Rome from a republic to an empire in the process.

In spite of having supported the wrong side in the civil war, Horace returned to Rome where he was able to secure a position in the government as a "scriba quaestorius," an accountant, working under a quaestor (elected official) in the imperial treasury. The historian Suetonius claims that Horace was pardoned by Augustus and was able to buy his way into the position, a common practice at the time. If this is the case, the financial support to achieve this would most likely have come from his father.

It was at this time that Horace wrote his first series of poems and established contact with fellow poets Virgil, the author of the "Aeneid" a literary classic; and Varius Rufus, the author of "De Morte," a poem intended to comfort men about death and not to fear it. Rufus was a dedicated follower of the Greek philosopher Epicurus and his school known as "The Garden." Horace was attracted to the Epicurean philosophy which centred around the idea that the seeking of pleasure was the most worthwhile pursuit in life; totally opposite to the rival Stoic philosophy also popular in Rome at the time.

According to the historian Mary Beard, both Virgil and Horace represented "memorable and eloquent images" of the new Augustan "golden age" of Rome. In the words of historian Nigel Rodgers, Virgil, Horace and the controversial Ovid, created a classical style that was comparable to the greatest poets of ancient Greece.

Fortunately for Horace, his friendships with Virgil and Rufus paid great dividends when he was introduced by them to Gaius Maecenas, an influential man who would have a great impact on his life. As we have seen, Maecenas was very wealthy and a patron of the arts who gathered around him, a circle of young poets. He was also a personal friend and close advisor to Augustus, who Horace was introduced to, thanks to Maecenas.

Horace developed a close friendship with Maecenas, who genuinely enjoyed his company and poetry, to the extent that he gifted to Horace a fertile property in the Sabine Hills at Tivoli, not far from Rome, where once he became financially secure, Horace built a villa there.

Being true to the Epicurean philosophy, Horace's poems projected a joy for living life to its fullest and a love of the natural world. His first publication was the *Epodes* which comprised seventeen poems, released in 30 BCE when he was around thirty-five years old. These poems were written before he met Maecenas and were mainly about Octavian's (later to become Augustus) victory at the

(40) *Gaius Maecenas.*
(41) *Roman poet Virgil.*

Battle of Actium and his decisive humiliating defeat of both Marc Anthony and Egyptian Queen Cleopatra. The poems not only speak of politics and warfare but also of the simple joys of being in love and his yearning for the rural way of life. "Happy the man who far from business ploughs again his ancestral lands," he wrote. This excerpt particularly pleases me because it shows Horace had not lost his connection with the rustic lands of Samnium in which he was born, even though it would not have been fashionable for him to acknowledge his Samnite heritage in the imperial Roman inner circle of Augustus.

Soon after the *Epodes* he wrote two books of the *Satires*, which amongst other things included poems heavily criticizing the immorality and vices rampant in Rome at the time, and spoke about a journey he had undertaken with Maecenas to Brundisium in southern Italy to assist the resettlement of army veterans from the civil war into their own small farms, courtesy of Augustus.

Horace's next work comprised three books and eighty-eight poems, titled *The Odes*. These lyrical poems celebrated the leadership of Augustus and as we can imagine, were incredibly well received by the emperor, solidifying Horace's place in the inner circle of power. Augustus was now in regular discussion with Horace about writing a fourth book of fifteen poems, further celebrating the achievements of Augustus. I am torn by the thought that although Horace was clearly a creative and brilliant poet, was he allowing himself to be used as a tool for the emperor's propaganda, at the same time?

Horace said *The Odes* were a celebration of the Greek gods and that his inspiration for these poems came from his Greek poetic predecessors such as Alcaeus, Sappho and Pindar. Horace was deeply respectful of Greek literature and philosophy and admired Greek culture, believing it was far superior to Roman culture; something he wanted his fellow countrymen to appreciate. In *The Odes* he also again lavished praise on Augustus for his victory at Actium, for unifying Italy and for restoring tradition and morality in Rome. Was Horace using his poetry to help elevate the image of Augustus to the level of a Greek god?

His romantic poetic skills could also be seen in *The Odes*. Although he remained a bachelor for life, he seemed to deeply appreciate the act of long term commitment in a romantic relationship. This can be seen from this extract of poem 13 in *The Odes* book 1:

Three times blessed and more are they
who are united with an unbroken bond;
no wretched quarrels shall ever separate
our love before the final days of life.

This can be contrasted though, with what he had earlier written in his *Satires*:

Love has two evils, war and then peace.

Over time, Augustus and Horace became very close friends, to the extent that the emperor affectionately called him his "little charmer." In 17 BCE Augustus requested Horace write a public piece of poetry to celebrate the 800th anniversary of the founding of Rome by Romulus. He was also asked to joined the imperial staff of Augustus to help write correspondence on behalf of the emperor; but Horace declined because he believed this would limit his ability to pursue his own writing.

Horace died on 27th November 8 BCE, two months after his close friend and mentor Maecenas died. Horace was buried close to Maecenas. Even though among the social and moral reforms of Augustus, laws were introduced banning bachelorhood, Horace, having never married and leaving no heirs, left all of his estate to Augustus himself.

There is a footnote to this story which is to do with the death of the Emperor Augustus. The Augustan era was a golden age in Roman history. The peace which Augustus maintained during his long reign, the "Pax Romana," caused the economy, the arts and the standard of living of most free-citizens in the Roman Empire, to flourish. During his time as emperor, Rome had not engaged in any major military conflicts. He also oversaw an ambitious building program in which he completed many of the projects that had been conceived by his adopted father Julius Caesar and then he proceeded to initiate his own grand projects, particularly in central Rome around the forum. He claims to have restored or built eighty-two temples in just one year. Augustus expanded the public baths and opened them up for the enjoyment of many more citizens. We have also seen that he was a great patron of the arts and introduced a series of laws and decrees restoring morality to the Roman way of life, placing the family at its centre.

The much-loved Emperor Augustus died on 19th August 14 CE while visiting his estate in Nola, formerly a Samnite town. Both the historians Tacitus and Cassius Dio claim that his wife Livia may have played a role in his death, by poisoning his figs. They claim her motive for poisoning him was to bring about her son Tiberius as his successor, which in fact happened. We have no evidence that Livia killed him. Augustus' health had been declining for a number of months before he died and he had already made preparations for his succession by choosing his step-son Tiberius as his heir. Some speculate that Livia was nervous about the longevity of Augustus' reign and that he was becoming unhappy with his decision to appoint Tiberius as his successor.

On his death bed, Augustus' famous last words were, "*Have I played the part well? Then applaud as I exit.*" His last words to the public were, "*Behold, I found Rome of clay, and leave her to you of marble.*" An enormous funeral procession traveled with Augustus' body from Nola to Rome, and on the day of his burial, the entire city of Rome was shut down.

Clockwise from top

(42)   *Marc Anthony & Cleopatra in Egypt.*

(43)   *Marc Anthony committed suicide.*

(44)   *Roman Emperor Augustus.*

(45)   *Augustus on his deathbed at Nola, Samnium.*

Tiberius and his son Drusus delivered the eulogy while Augustus' coffin-bound body was cremated on a pyre close to his mausoleum, which can still be seen at the Roman forum today.

In my judgment, along with Marcus Aurelius, Augustus was one of Rome's greatest emperors. He reigned for over forty years, maintaining a continous period of relative peace and economic prosperity and unlike many subsequent emperors, was not murdered by members of the Pretorian Guard or other political rivals; that is, if we assume his wife Livia was not responsible for his death. The truth will never be known.

Rome was at the peak of its power at the time of the death of Augustus. Over the next century its prestige was heavily dented by the cruel tyrannical rule of such emperors as Tiberius, Caligula and Nero.

6

THE LOMBARDS, BYZANTINES AND FRANKS

⌒✦

*A*FTER THE DEMISE OF THE ROMANS, A BARBARIAN TRIBAL GROUP THE
Ostrogoths, who were instrumental in destroying the Western
Roman Empire, ruled much of Italy from 493 until 555 CE when the
Eastern Roman Byzantine Empire under the leadership of Justinian 1,

(46 and 47) *The Ostrogoths were responsible for
the collapse of the Western Roman Empire.*

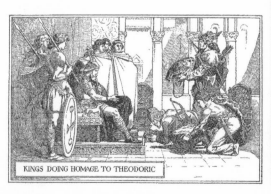

reconquered Italy after his army defeated the Ostrogoths, led by King Theodoric, in a series of pitched fierce battles.

In 568 the Lombards began their invasion of Italy. They were a Germanic tribal group who first originated from Scandinavia and then migrated to Pannonia, which is modern day Hungary. They divided the lands they conquered into duchies. The Lombard dukes of Benevento ruled Molise and Abruzzo as a kingdom. The Duchy of Benevento, also known as the "Samnite Duchy" was the southernmost Lombard duchy in the Italian peninsula. Lombard and Frankish dukes ruled Molise from 571 to 1077 CE, when it was conquered by the Normans. Much of what we know about the Lombard rule of Molise can be attributed to the historian Paul the Deacon (Paulus Diaconus) who wrote *History of the Lombards*. He was born to a rich and noble family in Fruili, northeast of Venice. Paul spent many years at the Lombard court in Pavia, south of Milan, serving as a counselor under King Desiderius. After the fall of the Lombard kingdom to the Frankish King Charlemagne, Paul and his brother were involved in an anti-Frankish plot. Their property was confiscated and his brother was taken as a prisoner to France.

Paul took refuge in Benevento near Molise, at the court of Duke Archis II, who had married Desiderius' daughter Adalberga, once Paul's pupil. Several years later when Charlemagne was in Rome, Paul wrote to

(48) *Paul the Deacon.*

(49) *Lombard military commander, Zottone.*

him begging for his brother to be pardoned and released. Charlemagne replied that he would release his brother if Paul agreed to join his court at Aachen Germany and regularly meet with him for learned discussions including philosophy, history and literature. In 786 Paul returned to Italy with Charlemagne, settling at the monastery of Monte Cassino, not far from Benevento, where he wrote his *History of the Lombards*.

A Lombard military commander by the name of Zottone led his troops into Campania in August 570 CE. He seized the city of Benevento from the Byzantine Eastern Roman empire and made the city the base of his operations. From this base, he marched his army south and attempted a siege on Naples in order to expand his territory further, but the siege failed in 581. Having lived an almost fully independent existence in Benevento since his arrival, Zottone submitted to the authority of the Lombard King Autharis in the north. Upon the death of Zottone in 591, the Lombard King appointed a noble by the name of Arechi as the successor Duke of Benevento. Arechi succeeded in conquering the towns of Capua and Venafro in the Campania and also territory further south in Calabria. He also took control of Salerno in the late 620s. This laid the foundation for Lombard rule of the region that today is Molise and Abruzzo, with the city of Benevento as the capital, right up until 774. The last Lombard duke was Arechi II, who took power after deposing the young Liutprand. Arechi's marriage to Adelperga enhanced his power because she was the daughter of Daufer, the last King of the Lombards.

During the time of Pope Gregory II from 715 to 731 the Papal States in Rome and central Italy were constantly threatened by the Lombards and Byzantines. Being the "meat in the sandwich," Gregory aligned himself with the Lombards and even prevented the levy of a tax on central Italy by the Byzantines. A military expedition sent from Byzantium to enforce the tax was defeated by the Papal army with the help of the Lombards. This Lombard–Papal alliance lasted until the death of Pope Gregory. The alliance could not last for much longer though, because at this point in time it was the Lombards who were accumulating more power and territory at the expense of the Byzantines and the Church. Pope Gregory III who reigned from 731 to 741, was acutely aware of the Lombard threat and as a result took the huge step of turning to the increasingly powerful Frankish Kingdom to provide him with military assistance to evict the Lombards out of central Italy, once and for all. But three successive visits by the Pope to Frankish King Charles Martel ("the hammer") did not succeed. It was Gregory's successor, Pope Stephen II who was able to enlist the support of Charles Martel's son, Peppin ("the short") in 751. Pope Stephen proceeded to anoint Peppin "Holy Roman Emperor," and in exchange Peppin promised to return to the Papacy all lands that had been taken from them by the Lombards and also to protect the Papal States from any further Byzantine territorial attacks.

Peppin kept his promise when he undertook two military campaigns against the Lombard King Aistuif, defeated the Lombards and returned all Papal lands. The Popes now had a militarily strong defender who had eliminated the Lombard threat and was going to protect them from constant threats coming from the Byzantine Empire, which still harbored ambitions to control all of Italy. But the Lombards were not totally done with yet. They still controlled the Duchy of Benevento in central Italy, including Molise and Abruzzo.

In 774, Peppin's son, King Charlemagne invaded Italy and created the Frankish Kingdom of Italy. Charlemagne was a member of what had become the Carolingian dynasty. They were a Germanic tribe that existed prior to France forming, but they did form a strong foothold of power in what is modern day France. He succeeded in uniting the majority of western and central Europe, being the first recognized emperor to rule western Europe since the fall of the Western Roman Empire in 476 CE. He was also a devout Catholic and closely aligned with the Church in Rome. The Franks became Roman Catholic after the conversion of the first Frankish King, Clovis I in 496. In 787 the Lombard Duke of Benevento, Arechi II was forced to submit to Frankish rule after Charlemagne's siege of nearby Salerno. However, following the death of Charlemagne in 814, centralized imperial authority in Italy including Molise and Abruzzo, began to disintegrate. This paved the way for the development of a quasi-feudal system of power where local lords and barons would become the masters of their own territories. During this time the dukes of Benevento began to call themselves princes of the Lombards; sometimes being loyal to the Franks and other times to Byzantium. Meanwhile by the early eleventh century the Normans from France were gradually gaining a foothold of power in southern Italy, taking part in mediating local disputes between Lombard princes, the dukes of Benevento, the Church and Byzantine governors. The Frankish Holy Roman emperors were concerned about the rising power of the Normans in southern Italy and sent military expeditions to attempt to block them, but they were defeated by the more aggressive, better organized and resourced Normans.

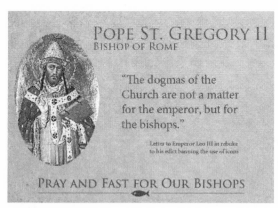

(50) *Pope Gregory II speaking about the dogmas.*

(51) *Pope Gregory II.*

(52) *Charlemagne.*

(53) *Charlemagne being crowned Holy Roman Emperor.*

7

BENEDICT AND
MONTE CASSINO

⟳

UST OVER ONE HUNDRED KILOMETRES FROM THE TOWN OF MY
parents' birth, is the historical town and mountain top monastery
of Monte Cassino. In 529 CE Benedict of Nursia, later to become the
patron saint of Europe, founded the monastery, where he formed his
Benedictine Order. It was built over a Roman pagan temple dedicated
to Apollo. Less than fifty years after its construction, the monastery was
attacked and badly damaged by invading Lombards, resulting in the
resident monks fleeing to Rome.

The monastery was re-established in 718 but was then abandoned
again in 833 after being sacked and burned down by the Muslim
Saracens. Under the direction of Pope Agapetus II, the monastery
was rebuilt in 949. In the eleventh century it became one of the most
important religious buildings in Italy and expanded by acquiring a large
area of surrounding territory. During this time, it established one of
the most comprehensive libraries in medieval Europe, housing many
ancient Greek and Roman manuscripts and some of the earliest literature written in the Italian language.

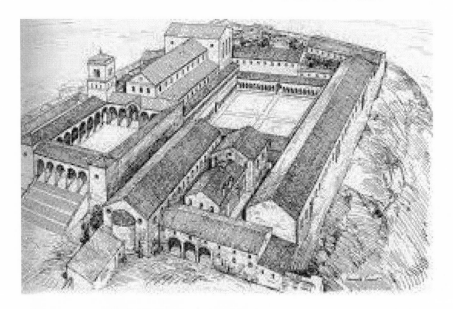

(54) *The Medieval Abbey*
      of Monte Cassino.

(55) *Benedictine monks*
      with manuscripts.

The monastery was destroyed again by an earthquake in 1349 and then was rebuilt twenty years later. During the seventeenth century, large renovation works were carried out, with the building complex redesigned in a Neapolitan Baroque architectural style. The cycle of destruction and rebuilding continued when in 1799 the monastery was again badly damaged, this time by the invading Napoleonic French army. The damage was carefully repaired and the monastery continued as a Benedictine sanctuary of meditation and learning for monks until 1866, when it was converted to a museum. But its troubled history did not end there.

In 1944 during World War Two, the monastery was the site of one of the fiercest battles of the war. The American led allies who had landed

(56) *Rebuilt Abbey of Monte Cassino.*

(57) *Abbey of Monte Cassino destroyed in 1943.*

in Italy in 1943 and were ruthlessly working their way up the Italian peninsula to remove the German forces and liberate Italy, mistakenly believed that German troops were hiding inside the monastery and heavily bombarded it. Instead, the monastery was being used as a safe shelter by many citizens who had sought refuge there. Tens of thousands of troops on both sides and hundreds of civilians were killed during the infamous Battle of Monte Cassino.

After the war, the Monte Cassino monastery was rebuilt for the last time. It remains perched at the top of the mountain overlooking the medieval town of Cassino. It is now a working monastery and is visited each year by hundreds of thousands of pilgrims and tourists. It houses the remains of Saint Benedict and also of his twin sister, Saint Scholastica. These remains have been preserved and remain undamaged, in spite of the turbulent history of the monastery.

Saint Benedict has been a major influence on the doctrine of the Catholic Church, which has been a crucial influence on the lives of the people living in Molise and Abruzzo, so it is worthy to examine his life, achievements and beliefs, in some detail.

Benedict was born in the Italian town of Nursia around 480 CE, four years after the Western Roman Empire finally collapsed when its last emperor, Romulus Augustus was overthrown by invading Ostrogoth barbarians. Most of what we know of Benedict's life was recorded in a book titled "Dialogues" written by Saint Gregory in 593-594.

After early schooling in Nursia, Benedict went to Rome to study literature and law. What he encountered there seems to have shocked and disgusted him, particularly the reckless and immoral lifestyle of many of his peers and the random street violence that was afflicting Rome at the time. So he decided to leave and retire to the tranquil, picturesque town of Affile, eighty kilometres outside of Rome.

At Affile, it is said that Benedict performed his first miracle, when he restored an earthenware wheat-sifter to perfect condition, after his elderly servant accidently broke it. By claiming this to be a miracle, he was ridiculed and humiliated by the townspeople, so much so, that he left the town to seek out a solitary existence of scriptural meditation in a cave near the town of Subiaco, where he began to live as a hermit.

Immersed in loneliness, his only contact with the outside world was with a monk called Romanus, who lived in a nearby monastery. He gave Benedict a monk's habit and religious manuscripts to read, also making sure that he had food and water.

(58) *Saint Benedict.*

During the three years that Benedict was living as a hermit, he began to formulate his teachings and philosophical beliefs, while going on long walks and encountering local shepherds. He shared his teachings with Romanus and the shepherds, who became the first followers of his Benedictine Order.

One of his followers was the daughter of a local shepherd who tried to seduce Benedict

(59) *Daily life in a Benedictine monastery.*

on a number of occasions, which he always resisted, despite the strong temptation. He remained chaste. He believed that the time had come for him to follow in the footsteps of the early fathers of Christian Monasticism. The nearby community of Vicovaro wanted Benedict to become the Abbot of their monastery, but after surviving an attempt by a resident monk to poison him, he returned to his hermitic existence, continuing to develop his Benedictine doctrines.

After a few more years, he decided the time was right to put his beliefs into practice and establish his Benedictine Order. This he did, by founding twelve monasteries in central Italy and assigning his twelve closest followers as the Abbots of each of these monasteries. He established his thirteenth monastery in the town of Subiaco, for the training of monks and the private tutoring of the sons of nobility. This is when the long standing tradition of Benedictine schools started, and continues to this day.

Benedict's fame spread throughout central Italy and took hold in Rome when two noblemen, Equizius and Tertullus, entrusted him with the education of their two sons, Maurus and Placidus. Benedict continued to claim that he performed miracles. He found water on

(60) *Benedictine monks in prayer
and meditation.*

a remote dry mountain top to quench the thirst of his monks while
they were on a meditational pilgrimage. It is also claimed that he was
able to make Maurus walk on water to save the younger Placidus from
drowning in a lake.

While living at the monastery in Subiaco, a rival and envious
priest called Florentius began to question and ridicule Benedict about
his supposed miracles, and was actively trying to take control of the
monastery. Benedict was clearly a person who did not handle conflict
well, because his response was to pack up and leave, despite the pleadings
from most of the monks for him to stay.

From Subiaco, Benedict traveled to the town of Cassino, where
as we have seen, starting in 525 he oversaw the construction of his
flagship monastery high up on the mountain overlooking the town.
Benedict possessed prodigious energy and determination, working very

long hours and surviving on four or five hours of sleep. He supervised the building of the monastery, further developed the philosophy of his Order and continued to perform miracles; including reviving a drowning young boy from certain death and producing flour and oil for the monastery in a time of acute shortage.

Benedict also seemed to be gifted with prophecy. During the autumn of 542 the Ostrogothic barbarian King Totila visited Cassino with his army, on his way to attack nearby Naples and then onto Rome. When Benedict met with Totila he warned him with this prophetic prediction, which has been quoted from his writings:

> You have hurt many and you continue to do it, now stop behaving badly! You will enter Rome, you will cross the vast sea, you will reign for nine years; however, in the tenth year, you will die.

This is exactly what became of King Totila.

Benedict devoted much of his time to converting the local population from pagan-worship to Christianity; as was the case with

(61) *King Totila.*
(62) *Benedict meeting Ostrogothic King Totila in 542 CE.*

(63) *Benedict and Scholastica.* (64) *Benedictine monks depicted in a jovial mood.*

his entire Benedictine order spreading throughout Italy, by this stage. Shortly before he died, Benedict claimed to have seen the soul of his sister Scholastica, rising to heaven in the form of a white dove. This vision came to him a few days after their last walk together at the foot of Monte Cassino. In another vision, Benedict saw the soul of Bishop Germanus of Capua taken by angels, while he was escaping fire.

Benedict died on 21st March 547. He had visions of his day of reckoning, informing his disciples throughout the Order, that the end for him was approaching. Six days before he died, he arranged to open the grave of his sister Scholastica, and in which he too would be buried. Then, completely exhausted, but at peace with his maker, he said his final prayers in the monastery chapel, where after taking his last Holy Communion, he died surrounded by his loyal and adoring monks, who buried him alongside his sister.

In 1964, in the acknowledgment of his many miracles and in recognition of the educational and charitable work performed by countless monks following the Benedictine Rule throughout Europe, Pope Paul VI proclaimed Benedict as the patron saint for all of Europe.

What were the major rules and doctrines of The Benedictine Order? The Benedictine Rule for monastic life was written by Benedict starting from 530 CE.

The Benedictine Rule was strict and mainly centred around absolute obedience by all monks to the Abbot. Benedict's emphasis on obedience was intended to stop monks from engaging in immoral or excessive behavior and also to provide monks with a blueprint on how

(65) *Rule of Saint Benedict,*
      manuscript.

(66) *Benedictine monk*
      preparing a manuscript.

to live a modest, disciplined and selfless life. Nevertheless, he envisioned his monasteries not as prisons of punishment but as loving communities where monks could come together, help each other and devote their entire lives to the will of God.

We need to appreciate that Benedict created The Benedictine Rule at a time shortly after the total collapse of the Western Roman Empire, when Europe had fragmented into tribal fiefdoms, overrun by an assortment of pagan barbarian groups led by chieftains, each contesting for a greater share of territory and resources. It was a total anarchic breakdown, the Dark Ages. Christianity was severely damaged and was on the verge of extinction during this time.

The establishment of Benedictine monasteries kept the doctrine and faith alive, with a set of clearly laid out rules that the devoutly faithful followers could adhere to and preach, in order to keep Christianity relevant in Europe. With the rise to power of the Christian Frankish King Charlemagne in the eighth century, Benedictine monasteries rapidly spread all over Europe under his protection. Substantial numbers of pagan barbarians were converted to Christianity by the Benedictine Order. Also, during this early medieval period, Benedictine monasteries and their educated monks were instrumental in transcribing ancient Greek and Roman literature into hand written manuscripts and in the education of the nobility, in order to keep western civilization and culture alive during these difficult and tumultuous centuries, at a time when almost the entire continent was illiterate.

The key sections of The Benedictine Rule were:

Section 5:   Obedience
Section 6:   Silence
Section 7:   Humility
Section 16:   Performing the Divine Office Throughout the Day
Section 20:   Reverent Prayer
Section 33:   Possessions
Section 48:   Daily Work
Section 53:   Receiving Guests
Section 54:   Receiving Letters
Section 55:   Clothes

I do not intend to cover these in much detail, instead I will outline the key message from each of the above rules. I am fascinated by how closely these rules align to the Molise and Abruzzo peasant way of life, and how my mother to this day in many respects, chooses to live her life. Obedience was the foundation of the Benedictine Order, as we have seen. The will of God as reflected in the teachings of Christ was paramount for all monks. The way this would be practiced was with strict obedience to the Abbot.

Silence was truly golden in the Benedictine world. The Bible states: I will take heed of my ways, so that I do not sin with my tongue. I have watched my mouth, dumb and humbled, and kept silent even from good things.

Humility was put into practice by the monks adopting a humble approach to all areas of their lives as reflected in this Bible quote: "*Every one that exalts himself shall be humbled: and he that humbles himself shall be exalted*". Benedict developed twelve steps on the path to humility for monks to follow in order to arrive at the love of God, which would then cast aside any doubt or fear.

Performing the divine office throughout the day was directly related to this quote from the Bible: "Seven times a day I praise you."

So it was expected that monks would perform meditative prayer seven times every day. These were set times during the day and evening which were given the names: Lauds, Prime, Tierce, Sext, Nones, Vespers and Compline. The set times were every two or three hours throughout the day and evening.

Reverent prayer required that the meditation was done sincerely and with humility. The prayers needed to be short and pure; and when they were performed by the monks as a community, the monks would be led in prayer by the Abbot.

The personal ownership of possessions was considered to be a corrupting vice by the Benedictine Order. Everything in a monastery was for communal use and sharing and nobody was permitted to give or receive anything without the permission of the Abbot.

Idleness was considered to be the enemy of the soul, so it was expected that all monks would divide their waking hours outside of meal times, between manual labour or devout prayer and reading. In the summer for example, they were expected to go out at dawn to work for four hours and then spend two hours reading. After lunch, they would rest in bed in complete silence or do further reading. In the middle of the afternoon the monks would gather for communal work in the monastery, or outside in the garden and the fields.

The Rule of Benedict regarding what to do with a lazy monk, was clear: "If, God forbid, such a monk is found, let him be punished on the first and second occasions. If he does not change, let him come under the correction of the Rule in such a way that others may fear." This usually meant being treated like an outcast in solitary confinement doing penance for a number of days. But if the "idleness" persisted, the monk could be expelled from the Order. The Rule on receiving letters prohibited monks from giving or receiving letters, tokens or gifts of any kind, either from family members or any other person, nor from each other, without the permission of the Abbot.

The Rule was explicit when it came to clothing. It stated that the Abbot should give clothes to the monks according to the climate in which they lived. Benedict went on to say: "I believe, however, that for a temperate climate, a cowl and a tunic are enough for each monk; a woollen cowl for winter and a thin or worn one for summer; along with a cloak for work, and socks and shoes. Monks should not worry about the color or the texture of these clothes; they should be whatever you can get most cheaply.""As for bedding, a straw mattress, a blanket, a bedspread and a pillow are enough. Beds must be frequently examined by the Abbot, to prevent personal goods from being stored. If anyone is found hiding something that he did not receive from the Abbot, let him fall under the severest discipline. Distribution must be made by the Abbot according to need. In the same way, he should bear in mind for the infirmities of the needy, and not the bad will of the envious. And in all of his decisions, let the Abbot remember God's retribution."

The Benedictine Order and its clearly defined rules enabled this religious movement to not only survive the Dark Ages, but to thrive in spreading the message of Christianity firstly throughout Europe, and then into the New World, with many Benedictine missionaries alongside and following the great maritime explorers.

Western Civilization owes its life blood to monks. In the early Middle Ages monasteries were at the centre of learning and culture in western Europe. The Benedictines were certainly at the forefront of this

(67) *Interior of the Benedictine Abbey of Monte Cassino.*

preservation of European culture; in their carefully crafted transfer of ancient knowledge into manuscripts, establishment of educational institutions and in their missionary work.

Benedict was a progressive reformer with much foresight. He is known as the "father of Western monasticism," having established his "Rule" which would become not only the accepted way of behavior for countless Christian monks and nuns that followed; but also embedded into the heart of European culture itself. This is why to this day Benedict remains the patron saint of Europe.

When I reflect upon the stoic, proud, humble, determined, modest and selfless attributes which I have observed in so many people from Molise and Abruzzo, I see the direct impact of Benedict's Rule, embedded within the culture of my ancestry.

Today, throughout the world, the legacy of Benedict and his passion for education continues with the many Benedictine schools which are still operating with the ethos of delivering not only an excellent academic education, but also instilling the importance of an ethical, moral and humanist approach to life.

8

THE NORMANS
MOVE SOUTH

⌒⤝

The Normans were an ethnic group that arose from ongoing contact between Norse Viking settlers of a region in France named Normandy, after them, and indigenous Franks and Gallic-Romans. These settlements in France were as a result of a series of Viking raids along the French coast which originated mainly from Denmark, but also Norway and Iceland. This group gained political legitimacy when the Viking leader Rollo agreed to swear an oath of loyalty to the Frankish King Charles III. The clearly distinctive cultural, traditional, linguistic and ethnic identity of the Normans initially emerged in the first half of the tenth century and then continued to evolve, despite their inter-marriages with other cultures. In 911 a Danish Viking chief named Hrolf led a large group along the French valley of the river Seine in search of booty and riches. However, the region had already been plundered by earlier Viking raids, so there wasn't much more of any value available. As a result, the Viking party moved further up the river, deeper inland until they arrived at the town of Chartres, which they unsuccessfully tried to

(68, left) *Norman King Rollo.*
(69, above) *Frankish King Charles III*
"the Simple."

raid and takeover. The local Franks put up a huge fight and successfully kept the Vikings outside the tall stone walls that surrounded the town. A stalemate had developed, but the Vikings would not go away, raiding the surrounding countryside and striking fear and terror amongst the peasants in nearby villages.

Charles III was King of the Franks at this time. He was known as "Charles the Simple" because of his straight-forward and humble demeanor. He sat down with Hrolf and was able to negotiate a compromise which involved the Vikings being given legal ownership of the surrounding land, later becoming "Normandy," in exchange for Hrolf swearing an oath of "fealty" to the Frankish king. This feudalistic promise of loyalty meant that the "Norman" Vikings would acknowledge Charles as their legitimate king, therefore becoming his vassals and agreeing to pay him taxes and provide military service as required. The end result though, was that these Vikings were to become the masters of their own destiny and create their own independent dukedom, which they were to name Normandy. Hrolf became baptized as a Christian and changed his name to Rollo.

The Normans brought their risk-taking, self-confidence, boundless energy, a love of travel, excellent commercial skills and an aggressive warrior spirit, to this new land. They also rapidly modified Frankish customs, traditions, culture, laws, political and military systems into a uniquely Norman form. This was a formidable combination because within a matter of three generations, Normandy became one of the wealthiest and most intellectually progressive societies in medieval Europe.

But right from the word go, there was an inherent limitation to how much could be achieved within the borders of the relatively small dukedom of Normandy. The Normans typically had large families, which often included numerous highly competitive, strong, fiercely independent and aggressive sons. Their tradition was that the eldest son would inherit all of the lands and possessions of the father. Soon what happened is that a large number of younger displaced Norman sons began to travel south and east in search of new lands that they could conquer, to build castles, accumulate wealth and start their own families. It is in this context that the Normans began to move into central and southern Italy.

As they travelled into Italy in small groups, the Normans hired themselves out as mercenaries to local Lombard, Frankish and Byzantine princes. Some gained power, taking or being granted land and castles. They would then arrange for additional Normans to make the trek south to join them as their vassals or servants. By the 1030s, a number of border castles were controlled by the Normans, who played off the rival ambitions of Byzantium, the Lombards and the Frankish Holy Roman Emperor, for their own political advantage. In 1038 a Norman adventurer by the name of Rainulf Drengot was given his own territory in and around the town of Aversa in the province of Campania, by the Frankish Emperor Conrad II, after vanquishing the Byzantines from the area, declaring himself a prince and formalizing his independence from the Kingdom of Naples and from his former Lombard allies. Rainulf had gathered a large military force of Italian Normans against Byzantine vassal forces and defeated them. After this decisive victory against the Byzantines, Norman power in Italy was officially acknowledged by the Holy Roman Emperor and the Church Papacy.

A new generation of Normans, prominent among them being members of the De Hauteville family led by Robert Guiscard, fought a series of wars between 1057 and 1091 which finally succeeded in

(70) *Norman nobility.*

expelling the Byzantines out of Italy altogether. The Norman way of waging war was not subtle. They were a tough, ruthless, focused and determined race who hungered for more land, trashing existing cultures and power structures in the process. They typically won their battles by the shock and awe tactics of heavily mail-clad armored horsemen with long spears who would lead battles, followed by a garrison of infantry warriors ruthlessly hacking into the enemy with swords, mace and axes, under the protection of the cavalry. Individual skill, courage and resourcefulness was prized in these battles. The Normans had mastered the art of siege warfare, which was backed up by formidable castles that they constructed in strategic defensive elevated positions throughout the lands that they controlled. To this day, many Norman castles can be seen in central and southern Italy, including throughout the Molise and Abruzzo region.

The Norman dynasties had a major political, cultural and military impact on medieval Europe. The Normans were renowned for their

(71) *Norman castle in southern Italy.*

superior fighting skills and tactical military prowess and eventually also for their deep faith in the Catholic religion. Norman knights, adventurers and mercenaries played a significant role not only in gaining control of large portions of southern Italy from the Lombards, Muslim Saracens and Byzantines; but also in conquering England under the leadership of William of Normandy in 1066.

(72) *Bohemond I.*

Norman cultural and military influence also spread from these new European conquests to the Crusader states of the Near East, where the Norman prince Bohemond I who was the son of Robert Guiscard, for example, founded the Principality of Antioch, when he was one of the leaders of the First Crusade from 1096 to 1099. The Crusades were

(73) *First Crusade – 1096 to 1099 CE.*

a series of religious wars fought between the Western Christians and Eastern Muslims for control of the holy lands, particularly Jerusalem. The first crusade had been requested by Pope Urban II in November 1095 in a speech at Clermont in southern France where he called on Western Christians to form an army of peasants, to be led by kings and knights, and to take up arms to aid the Orthodox Christian Byzantines who were being threatened by Muslim forces and then proceed to re-capture the Holy Land from Muslim control. Many Normans participated in the Crusades.

The main motivation for Norman knights, adventurers and mercenaries to seek to travel to and ultimately conquer foreign lands was the disorderly state of northern France during the tenth and eleventh centuries in particular. There was very little centralized stability and authority in Normandy at that time. Instead there were numerous aristocratic warlords who had carved out dynastic territories for themselves and were constantly fighting to expand their influence and landholdings. These aristocratic noble families often feuded among themselves, creating defeated and humiliated exiles who were banished and forced to seek their power and fortunes elsewhere. The Italian peninsula presented particular challenges for ambitious Normans because as we have seen, at the time it was divided up into a large number of kingdoms, duchies and principalities under the control of various Lombard lords, Muslim Saracens, Franks, the Catholic Church and the Eastern Roman Byzantine empire.

What is the earliest evidence that we have of Normans in central-southern Italy? In the year 999, Norman pilgrims returning from the holy lands in Jerusalem arrived in Salerno southern Italy where they were received with open arms by the local Lombard prince, Guaimar III. Under his reign Salerno had entered a period of economic stability and majestic grandeur. He ended up making Amalfi and Sorrento a part of his vassal states and also took over much of Byzantine Apulia and Calabria. During the time of the arrival of Norman pilgrims though, Salerno was under attack from an opportunistic group of Muslim Saracen pirates who had originated from north Africa. The Saracens deployed their usual tactic of demanding a large monetary tribute in exchange for

(74 and 75) *Lombard Kingdoms and Duchies in Italy 1000 CE, before the arrival of the Normans.*

their departure. The Normans were not accustomed to paying tribute as a ransom and considered the Lombard prince to be a coward for even considering this form of blackmail.

Since many of the Norman pilgrims were battle hardened mercenary knights, they were able to lead Guaimar's Lombard army into a successful attack on the Saracens, forcing them to flee empty handed. Guaimar was so grateful that he urged the Normans to remain in Salerno. They refused to stay, but instead they promised when they returned to Normandy, they would spread the word about the urgent need for capable fighting mercenaries in southern Italy. The reputation of the Normans as brave, fierce and effective fighters and therefore ideal mercenaries had now been forged and began to spread throughout southern Italy.

In 1017, a Lombard uprising occurred against the Byzantines in the southern Italian city of Bari. The Byzantines were Orthodox Christians who had emerged from the Eastern Roman Empire based in the city of Constantinople, now Istanbul in modern day Turkey. Under their former Eastern Roman Emperor, Justinian I, they re-conquered much of southern Italy from various barbarian tribal groups including the Ostrogoths, in the sixth century CE. The Lombard leader was Melus, the Duke of Bari. Melus recruited a group of Norman knights as mercenaries to assist him with the uprising.

The military campaign of 1018 ended in failure with only 10 out of a total of 250 Norman knights surviving the battle at the Ofanto River, near the site of the Battle of Cannae, in which Hannibal had defeated the Romans in 216 BCE. The Byzantine emperor had sent a detachment of his elite Varangian Guard and with their superior tactical and fighting skills, they had prevailed. It is ironic that these elite guards had a Viking ancestry, just like the Normans! This event is worth noting because it established a clear precedent for Norman mercenary activity in southern Italy. At this stage, the Normans were not particularly fussed about which side they fought for. In 1019 for example, the Byzantine garrison in Troy consisted mainly of Norman mercenaries.

During these years, as the Normans established a greater presence in southern Italy, they began to seize towns and carve out fiefs and territory for themselves. Often too small in number to directly assault well defended towns, the Normans proceeded to raid and burn outlying farming areas, slowly eliminating and starving their opponents of food supplies and commercial trade, until they surrendered. They even resorted to starting fires and then demanding payment of large ransoms before putting them out. They had clearly taken on the tactics of the marauding Saracen pirates whom they had detested in earlier times. The Normans introduced a systematic strategy of intimidation and terror in order to rapidly gain land in Apulia and in the area north of Naples. These tactics were successful, because in less than 70 years they were able to establish themselves as ruling lords and barons.

While the Normans often acted like pirates and robber barons, running amok and pursuing their own selfish and greedy interests, they could also show remarkable solidarity, cohesion and foresight when the situation required it. Even when arguing and fighting among themselves, they could quickly forget their quarrels and unify in order to confront a perceived threat. This ability to put their common interests ahead of their personal ambitions was one of the key reasons for their success in central and southern Italy. Another key to their success is that the strategic intelligence, capabilities, determination and tenacity of the Normans was constantly underestimated by their Lombard, Papal (at times), Muslim, Frankish and Byzantine adversaries. Rarely superior in military numbers, the Normans instead would use their heavily armored cavalry and "rapid surprise attack" tactics to outsmart their opponents and take advantage of even the slightest windows of opportunity.

The Normans were also capable of treating their opponents with the utmost respect. For example, when Pope Leo IX ventured south from Rome in 1053 with an army to deal with the Norman confiscation of Church property, he soon found himself as their virtual prisoner, following the crushing defeat

(77) *Pope Leo IX.*

(76, below) *Battle of Civitate in 1053 CE.*

of his army near the town of Civitate. In spite of this, the devoutly Catholic Normans showed the Pope deep respect while he was held captive and were able to negotiate a mutual settlement with him that legitimized their property holdings and also upheld the prominence of the Church in Norman controlled dukedoms. The Normans would continue to pursue the intrigue of Papal politics, including when the Norman Duke Richard of Capua invaded Rome in 1059 and ensured that his ally, Nicholas II was elected the new Pope.

9

ROBERT GUISCARD'S CONQUEST

HE NORMAN CONQUEST OF SOUTHERN ITALY REALLY TOOK HOLD IN THE eleventh century when large numbers of knights and adventurers from the coast of Normandy France began to hire themselves out as mercenaries to the rival Lombard rulers of Benevento, Salerno, Naples and Capua. During this time the various Norman mercenary groups banded together to defend their newly established territory. By the mid eleventh century Robert Guiscard ("the Wise") had established a Norman kingdom in southern Italy when he conquered Calabria in 1053, followed by Benevento in 1054. He then allied himself with Pope Nicholas II who ruled from 1059 to 1061 and protected him from being dominated by Frankish Germanic rulers. As a reward for this protection, Guiscard was given papal sanction to rule Calabria, Puglia and the island of Sicily. He sent his younger brother Roger to conquer Sicily while he himself set out to conquer Puglia from the Byzantines.

With Puglia conquered, and as a result Byzantium's rule in southern Italy ending in 1071, a few years later Robert Guiscard set out to conquer

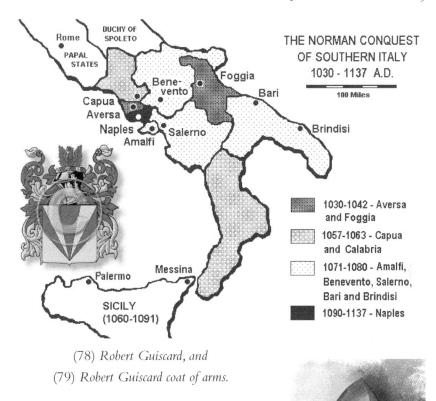

THE NORMAN CONQUEST
OF SOUTHERN ITALY
1030 - 1137 A.D.

100 Miles

1030-1042 - Aversa
and Foggia

1057-1063 - Capua
and Calabria

1071-1080 - Amalfi,
Benevento, Salerno,
Bari and Brindisi

1090-1137 - Naples

(78) *Robert Guiscard, and*
(79) *Robert Guiscard coat of arms.*

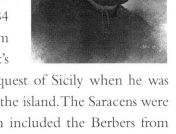

the Byzantine capital of Constantinople (now Istanbul). But before arriving he was called back by Pope Gregory VII to defend the papacy against the Frankish Holy Roman Emperor Henry IV. In 1084 Guiscard captured the city of Rome from Henry IV's army. Meanwhile, Robert's younger brother Roger, secured his conquest of Sicily when he was able to defeat and evict the Saracens from the island. The Saracens were a diverse group of Muslim people which included the Berbers from North Africa and Spanish Moors.

Let us examine the life and achievements of Robert Guiscard in more detail, because he was a very significant influence on Molise and Abruzzo at this time. There is no doubt that the arrival of Robert Guiscard in Italy in 1047 was a major turning point for the influence and power of the Normans in southern Italy. Robert was born in Normandy in 1015 into a noble family of knights. When he arrived in

Apulia southern Italy in 1047 to join his half-brother Drogo, he found that this region, although flourishing with agriculture, trade and a pleasant climate, was riddled with factional political instability, intrigues and disturbances. Robert's arrival was not unusual because at the time, the region including Molise and Abruzzo was full of opportunistic Norman knights, adventurers and mercenaries seeking to accumulate wealth, power and property. These immigrants, led by Robert Guiscard were destined to transform southern Italy, politically, economically, culturally and militarily.

In Campania, Abruzzo and Molise, the Lombard duchies were launching wars against the Byzantine dukes of Naples in order to gain control of that strategically important seaport. Meanwhile, in the southern Italian region of Apulia (now Puglia), William ("Iron Arm") De Hauteville, Robert's eldest half-brother, had been elected Count of Apulia in 1042 after having successfully led an army and defeated the Byzantines who had controlled that region. In 1046, after his death, he was succeeded by his brother Drogo.

When Robert Guiscard joined his brothers, they initially sent him to Calabria to attack Byzantine-held territory. Robert began his campaign by pillaging the countryside and ransoming its people. In 1053, as the head of a combined military force of Normans from Apulia and Campania, he defeated the disorganized and haphazardly led forces of the Byzantines, the Lombards and the Papacy near the town of Civitate.

Because of the deaths of his three half-brothers William, Drogo and Humphrey, Robert returned to Apulia in 1057 and seized control of the dukedom from Humphrey's feuding sons. This feud continued to simmer for some time and not only involved the sons, but also a number of prominent Norman barons who were all very upset over land and power that had been taken away from them by Robert. After becoming the legitimate leader of the Apulian Normans of southern Italy, Robert travelled south to resume his Calabrian military campaigns. His brother Roger's arrival from Normandy enabled Robert to further extend and solidify his territorial conquests in southern Italy, which he ran from his base in Apulia.

During his progression from adventurer to commander of mercenary troops and finally to conquering duke, Robert had emerged as a shrewd, cunning and powerful political leader. In 1059 he entered into a concordat with Pope Nicholas II in the town of Melfi. This was a significant agreement and achievement on the part of Robert. Until that time, the Papacy had been hostile towards the Normans in southern Italy, considering them to be a band of opportunistic anarchists who were hell-bent on upsetting the balance of power in southern Italy; a delicate structure based on shared power between the Byzantines and the Lombards; and no interference in their affairs by the influential and powerful Papacy and the Catholic Church.

The religious schismatic split that had occurred between the Greek Orthodox and Catholic Latin churches in 1054 had worsened the relations between the Byzantine Emperors and the Popes. Eventually, the Papacy realized that Norman conquests over the southern Italian possessions of the Byzantines could work to the advantage of the Catholic Church. Robert's plan to expel the Muslim Arabs from Sicily and to restore Christianity to the island also won the endorsement of Pope Nicholas II. This Norman expedition into Sicily which as we have seen, was led by Robert's younger brother Roger, commenced in 1060 shortly after Robert had completed his conquest of Calabria. Until this time, Robert's relationship with Roger had been strained, primarily because the younger brother did not want to be subordinate to his older brother. So Robert's decision to allow Roger to lead the military expedition into Sicily went a long way towards restoring harmony and mutual respect between the two brothers.

Meanwhile, Robert Guiscard continued to expand his southern Italian duchy, culminating with the capture of the city of Bari in 1071 which resulted in the end of Byzantine rule in southern Italy. Robert then turned his attention to the neighboring territory of Salerno, which was controlled by the Lombards. Instead of fighting with them, Robert dissolved his first marriage and married Sichelgaita, the sister of Salerno's last Lombard prince Gisulf II. However, soon after the marriage, hostilities broke out between the two rulers when Gisulf tried to convince the Byzantine's to fight a counteroffensive against Robert and his Normans. Fearing that the Norman advances into Campania, Molise and Abruzzi would threaten the power base of the Papal states, Pope Gregory VII excommunicated (expelled) Robert from the Catholic Church and provided Gisulf with substantial military support. The struggle came to a head when Gisulf, determined to hang on to his power, advanced towards the commercially prosperous city of Amalfi. Robert responded to the city's cry for help in 1073 and sent in military forces in order to successfully defend it. This was a fatal blow to Gisulf. In December 1076 Robert Guiscard completed his conquest of Salerno and made it the capital city of his southern Italian duchy.

(80) *Pope Gregory VII crowning Lombard prince, Gisulf II.* (81) *Pope Gregory VII coat of arms.*

Having driven the Byzantines out of Italy, how did Robert Guiscard achieve his strategically important conquest of the Duchy of Salerno and begin the process of driving the Lombards out of central and southern Italy once and for all, and securing his control of southern Italy? At this point, I want to deviate a little and introduce you to the life of a courageous and fiery, passionate woman, Sichelgaita, the warrior princess. She played an important role in Robert's determination to create a southern Italian kingdom and then to seek to conquer Byzantium.

How did an attractive intelligent young princess end up being married to the mighty Robert Guiscard? What series of events culminated in this young armor-clad princess riding alongside her husband to the imposing walls of her native city of Salerno which was ruled by her brother, and demanding his surrender?

During this time there were five major players all vying for control of southern Italy. We have already been introduced to them. There was the Germanic Holy Roman Empire; the Catholic Church of Rome; The Eastern Byzantine Empire; the Normans and the last remaining Lombard duchies, including Salerno.

To better understand the story of Sichelgaita and what she and her husband ultimately were fighting for, I will give you a little more perspective of what the state of play was with each of these competing (and sometimes co-operating) five powers in southern Italy. The Holy Roman Empire was created by the Frankish King Charlemagne in 800 when he was crowned emperor of Europe by the Pope. This empire basically replaced a loose assortment of barbaric tribal groups that fought for control of western Europe in the aftermath of the collapse of the western Roman Empire in 476. This Holy Roman Empire was the predecessor to the nation states of France and Germany and lasted until 1806 when Francis II abdicated after Napoleon Bonaparte took control.

The Catholic Church of Rome exercised its secular political power through its Papal States, which took up much of central Italy, including Molise and Abruzzo at times, and came into being as a result of territory that was granted to it in 756 by the Frankish King Pepin "the short," who was Charlemagne's father, as we have seen. This was known as the Donation of Pepin. That initial gift of land transformed the Church into a major secular military and political power. It also deepened the relationship between the Popes and Holy Roman Emperors, culminating in the crowning of Charlemagne as emperor by Pope Leo III in a lavish ceremony at St. Peter's Basilica in Rome on Christmas Day, 800. This event marked the beginning of widespread involvement by the Catholic Church in the political and military affairs of Europe right up until the Holy Roman Empire itself was dismantled one thousand years later by Napoleon. This situation also laid the foundations of a deep rift that developed between the devout, spiritually religious elements of the Catholic Church and the political/military elements of the Papal State, which pitted the "Guelph" spiritual Church supporters against the "Ghibelline" secular imperial State supporters after the monk Hilderbrand called for a Church Imperial Theocracy to control all of Catholic Europe, spiritually, politically and militarily, with the Holy Roman Emperors totally subservient to the Church, providing them mainly with military support when they required it. Hilderbrand went on to become Pope Gregory VII, who tried very hard to put this absolute power structure into place.

The third major player in the political and military affairs of central and southern Italy at this time was the Byzantine Empire, also known as the Eastern Roman Empire. It started under the Roman Emperor Constantine, who ruled from 306 to 337 CE and laid the foundation for a formidable empire which lasted up to 1453 when the Ottoman Turks scaled the walls and conquered the city; creating the Ottoman Empire first led by Sultan Mehmed II. The Ottoman Empire lasted until the end of World War I, when it collapsed and led to the creation of the nation state of Turkey and the name of the city of Byzantium being changed first to Constantinople and then to Istanbul.

(82) *Roman Emperor Constantine.*

Starting from the collapse of the Western Roman Empire in 476 CE and continuing through the years of Lombard rule in southern Italy from 568 to 774, Byzantine military forces were actively engaged in many regions of central and southern Italy and did not totally and permanently withdraw from the peninsular until the 1100's. Of course, we already are familiar with the story of the Lombards and then the subsequent Norman incursions into southern Italy.

(83) *Ottoman Sultan Mehmed II.*

10

SICHELGAITA THE
WARRIOR PRINCESS

ET US NOW TURN TO THE LOMBARD DUCHY OF SALERNO, THE CITY IN
which Sichelgaita was born in 1035 and over which first her father
Gaimar V and then her brother Gisulf, ruled. The independent Duchy
of Salerno was created by the Lombards in 839. During the course of
the next two centuries Salerno became one of the finest cultural centres
of Europe. It was famous for its medical school, the first in Europe
to exclusively focus on training doctors. It was at this school that the
understanding of diseases and their diagnosis, treatment and potential
cure, was first studied, using a scientific evidence-based approach to
replace the previous Christian monastic treatments involving prayer and
bleeding of the flesh. This medical school included a group of female
students who were known as the "Ladies of Salerno," within this group
was a woman called Trotula, who taught at the school and wrote some
important early medieval literature on the medical conditions of women.
She attracted the attention of many women who enrolled to study there.
One of these students was Sichelgaita. It seems that much of the medical

(84) *Sichelgaita studying at the Salerno medical school.*

(85) *Trotula, teacher of medicine.*

knowledge that was accumulated at the Salerno school originated from knowledge coming from the eastern Muslim world as a part of trading networks, including the Silk Road, where medical science was significantly ahead of that from western Europe, during this time.

As we have seen, Sichelgaita was born into the Lombard ruling family of the Duchy of Salerno. She was the daughter of Duke Gaimar V who was brutally murdered by a rival noble family in a palace coup when she was a young girl. Her brother Gisulf raised a formidable army and retook control of the Duchy. When this happened, Sichelgaita became the most privileged woman in Salerno. She devoted a lot of her time to studying medicine and pursuing her passions for military strategy, horse-riding and swordsmanship.

Meanwhile the Duchy of Salerno was again under threat in 1050. The Byzantines and the Normans were both threatening to attack.

Robert De Hauteville was given the name "Guiscard" which meant "resourceful," by his first wife's nephew because it was claimed that he knew whom to marry and also for his sublime ability to know when to behave in an aggressive ruthless manner and when to be humble modest and forgiving. There is no doubt that Robert Guiscard had inherited the Norman sense of urgency and thirst for battle, but at the same time he could be charming, patiently strategic and diplomatic. His wisdom extended to not being vindictive to his enemies after securing victory in a battle.

His wisdom and strategic sense also extended to his formidable enemy, Salerno. Rather than an outright military attack, he reasoned, why not merge the Lombard and Norman dynasties in southern Italy by a marriage, which would combine the ancient noble Lombards with the aggressive warrior Normans. All he needed was a beautiful willing princess to marry – Sichelgaita!

There is no evidence to suggest Sichelgaita was forced to marry Robert Guiscard against her will. Instead, the sources seem to indicate that although it was a political marriage of convenience, she was genuinely fond of and attracted to the charismatic, handsome Robert. She was astute enough to realize the time was up for Lombard power in southern Italy and it was now the Normans who were on the rise. So she could not have found a better dynastic match than Robert Guiscard, who by that time was effectively the most powerful Norman in Italy. At the same time, his cousin William was emerging as the most powerful Norman in Normandy, with his eyes set on taking control of England, which he did after defeating the Saxon King Harold at the Battle of Hastings in 1066.

Robert and Sichelgaita were married in 1058. Her brother Gisulf was not thrilled by the union, but he too was smart enough to realize this marriage would secure some ongoing semblance of Lombard power in southern Italy, albeit with the Normans having the upper hand by holding the real power. In order to clear the way to marry Sichelgaita, Robert had to annul his first marriage, which he did by admitting to a fabricated charge of incest. After their marriage, Robert took his young bride off to Melfi, which was the capital city of his Duchy of Apulia. In the meantime,

(86 and 87) Sichelgaita, Lombard princess and the wife of Robert Guiscard.

Gisulf was left alone to continue his rule of the Duchy of Salerno.

For the next eighteen years Sichelgaita was constantly alongside her husband Robert as he continued to consolidate his control of southern Italy through an astute calibration of diplomacy and military conquest. Robert respected the advice of Sichelgaita to the extent that she became his trusted adviser and confidante. Being a very devout Catholic, she also played a crucial role in helping Robert improve his often turbulent relationship with the Church. She expressed concern about his wavering faith which resulted in his excommunication on more than one occasion and what she considered to be his reckless invasions of Papal lands.

She had played an important role in smoothing over his rocky relationship with Pope Nicholas II to the point where he ended up anointing Robert as the legitimate ruler of the southern Italian lands he had conquered to that date, including much of Molise and Abruzzo. In return Robert had sworn an oath of allegiance to the Pope and to the Church. This represented a major turning point in the relationship between the Normans and the Church from mutual mistrust and suspicion to a positive symbiotic relationship. This can be illustrated by the hostility that Pope Stephen IX exhibited towards the Normans in

1057-58, including the conducting of military campaigns against them; to the great reformist Pope Gregory VII, who reigned from 1073 to 1085, was a good friend of Sichlegaita and was initially a supporter of Robert Guiscard before Robert displayed his intentions to conquer Salerno.

In 1076 Robert Guiscard had reached a point in his power when he believed he was ready to make a play for the Duchy of Salerno, which was still under the control of his brother-in-law Gisulf. By this time, Salerno was the last remaining large Lombard duchy in southern Italy. Sichelgaita did not want Robert to take Salerno by military force, so she went to visit her brother Gisulf and begged him to surrender. He refused to, so as a result Robert Guiscard lay siege to the city of Salerno, blocking off all food supplies until the population reached a point of starvation. He then expelled Gisulf and took control of the city and the Duchy of Salerno. After pleading with Robert, Sichelgaita managed to save her brother's life by arranging for him to be exiled in Rome under the protection of Pope Gregory VII.

Under the combined rule of Robert and Sichelgaita, Salerno's fortunes improved markedly, with even the medical school regaining its reputation of excellence when one of the great medical scholars of the time, Constantine of Carthage, was hired to teach at the school. Robert also oversaw the construction of a new and more secure city wall to further protect the city from future attack and a grand cathedral as a gesture of goodwill towards Pope Gregory VII, who was clearly annoyed with the manner in which his ally and friend Gisulf was evicted from Salerno.

Now that Robert Guiscard was at the peak of his power in central and southern Italy and with the help of his resourceful wife who had patched up his relationship with the Church, he turned his attention to the Eastern Byzantine Empire. Earlier, in 1074 he and his wife had arranged for their daughter Olympiade, to marry into the ruling dynasty of Byzantine Constantinople. He believed that this marriage would lay the foundation for the eventual Norman rule of the Eastern Roman Empire, creating the most powerful empire in all of Europe; even surpassing the achievements of his cousin

William the Conqueror who in 1066 had taken control of England and along with his control of Normandy, ruled over a powerful and influential empire.

There clearly had developed strong rivalry between Robert and his cousin William. It was this ambition which solidified his relationship with Pope Gregory VII who ultimately forgave him for his "unchristian" conduct towards Gisulf. If he was to be successful in securing Norman control of the Eastern Roman Empire, Robert would go down in history as the man responsible for re-uniting the divided Christian world back into one true holy Catholic faith. The great schism between the western Catholic and eastern Orthodox churches had occurred in 1054 when Pope Leo IX and the Greek Orthodox Patriarch Michael Cerularius, mutually excommunicated each other. Robert would unify the Christian world! The prospect of this excited Pope Gregory VII.

But, out of left field, there came a spanner in the works. There was a palace coup in Constantinople and the new Byzantine dynasty backed out of any arrangement to merge with Norman Italy. Robert then realized that in order to fulfil his ambition he would have no choice other than to conquer Byzantine militarily. His prestige and reputation was now on the line, so even if he wanted to, he could not back down now. It was during this Byzantine military campaign that Sichelgaita developed her reputation as a fierce and courageous warrior when she joined her husband Robert and fought alongside him on this long drawn out campaign. He trusted her to lead a contingent of his men into battle, which she did admirably.

There is an often told story which has been passed down, of her exploits describing her as the "Valkyrie-like blonde berserker princess throwing herself into the jaws of death, charging into battle, spitting fire and railing at her men to stand their ground and fight." This vivid description describes her exploits at the Battle of Durazzo on the Albanian Adriatic coast in October 1081. It was at this battle where Robert Guiscard was determined to inflict militarily what he had failed to do diplomatically, when his plan for his daughter to marry into the Byzantine power elite, failed.

(88) *Anna Komnene, daughter of Byzantine Emperor Alexis Comnenus I and author of* The Alexiad.

There is an excellent description of Sichelgaita in battle from Anna Comnena, the daughter of Alexis Comnenus I, who was the Emperor of Byzantine at the time of Robert's invasion. This passage comes from her 15-volume history, "The Alexiad," which Anna wrote around twenty years after the actual events took place. This is what she had to say about Sichelgaita:

"Directly Gaita, Robert's wife (who was riding at his side and was a second Pallas, if not an Athene) saw these soldiers running away. She looked fiercely after them and in a very powerful voice called out to them in her own language an equivalent to Homer's words 'How far will ye flee? Stand and fight like men!' And when she saw that they continued to run, she grasped a long spear and at full gallop rushed after the fugitives; and on seeing this they recovered themselves and returned to the fight."

Even though she was badly wounded, Sichelgaita continued to fight with the utmost courage and was able to keep the enemy forces at bay until Robert arrived with reinforcements. The battle was ultimately won by the Norman forces, but the conquest of Byzantium had to be abruptly aborted. A serious situation had developed back in Italy. The normally symbiotic relationship between the Papal States and the Holy Roman Empire had fractured for two significant reasons. Firstly, Pope Gregory VII had thrown his total support behind the Norman invasion of Byzantium because he saw this conquest as a means of ultimately unifying Christianity under the Catholic faith again; and also as a way of stopping the Muslim Seljuk Turks from harboring any attack on Constantinople and Western Europe thereafter.

(89) *Sichelgaita in battle against the Byzantines.*

The Seljuk Turks were a clear and present danger because they already spectacularly defeated Byzantine forces further east and as a result the Byzantine emperor had already requested that Pope Gregory declare a Crusade against the Muslims. The end result of this is that a Norman victory would also be a Papal victory, which the Germanic Holy Roman Empire could not allow to happen because its power in Europe would be significantly weakened and this power vacuum would be filled by the Normans. The second reason for the rapid deterioration in the relations between the Church and Empire was Pope Gregory's previously mentioned intention to create a Roman Catholic Papal theocracy in Europe, in which the princes and kings of the Holy Roman Empire would be vassals to the Pope of Rome.

As a result of these looming threats, the Holy Roman Emperor Henry IV formally declared that Pope Gregory VII be deposed. The emperor backed this declaration up by invading Rome and installing his own "puppet" Pope Clement III. This created a dangerous situation for Robert Guiscard because the entire foundation of his southern Italian Duchy was based on the Church controlled Papal States and the Empire acting as an equal buffer to his territory. His wife also continued to maintain close ties with the Catholic Church hierarchy.

To protect his power base in Italy Robert rushed to Rome, but in doing so made a rare tactical mistake. He did not have enough soldiers to effectively conquer a large city like Rome, so he hired Saracen Muslim mercenaries who were scattered around southern Italy. Although this decision paid off for him militarily because he succeeded in taking Rome back for the Pope after the imperial forces were evicted; the Saracen Muslim's displayed outrageously cruel and brutal behavior towards the population and offended them greatly with their looting and pillaging.

The people of Rome therefore turned against Pope Gregory and blamed him for unleashing the "Muslim hoards" on them. The Pope was forced to flee to Salerno under the protection of Guiscard, leaving the "anti-pope" Clement III in control of Papal Rome. Pope Gregory VII died in Salerno in 1085, a sad and broken man who had failed in his ambition to reform and strengthen the power of the Church.

Meanwhile, in 1084 Sichelgaita returned to the battlegrounds of the Adriatic coast with her husband in an endeavour to finish off the enemy once and for all. They defeated a combined Venetian–Byzantine naval force in what was a fiercely fought series of battles, taking control of the islands of Corfu and Cefalonia in the process. Tragically, it was in Cefalonia where the life of the great Norman conqueror Robert Guiscard came to its ending, when he became ill from a disease and died suddenly in the arms of his devoted and loyal wife, in July 1085. His remains were returned to Italy to be placed in the De Hauteville family crypt in the Cathedral of Venosa in Apulia (Puglia).

Sichelgaita died in her beloved Salerno in March of 1090. After her husband's death she devoted much of her time in religious seclusion at the Abbey of Monte Cassino close to Molise, a place that she was devoted to for most of her life, and where she was buried. Since her death, two particularly vicious rumors have persisted. Firstly, that she had tried to poison Bohemond, her husband's son by his first marriage, so as to stop him from being a threat to her maternal children's dynastic claims to power; and secondly, that she had poisoned her husband Robert, and that is how he died rather than contracting a disease. There is absolutely no evidence for either of these claims. It is unfortunate that the reputation of such an inspirational, devout, intelligent and courageous woman is tainted by these persistent unfounded claims.

She allegedly tried to poison Bohemond, when in fact shortly after the death of Robert Guiscard, Sichelgaita and Bohemond reached an agreement in which her maternal son Roger Borsa, was anointed to succeed his father Robert as the ruler of the Duchy of Apulia and Calabria, covering most of central and southern Italy. This had been the wish of Robert Guiscard.

Roger Borsa went on to rule the duchy from 1085 until his death in Salerno in 1111, while his uncle Roger ruled most of southern Italy and Sicily. Unfortunately, he was not as skillful as his father in military, political and diplomatic matters, so during most of his reign, the duchy fell into feudal anarchy with numerous Norman nobles and lords carving out their own fiefdoms within the duchy and actively undermining Roger at every opportunity.

Roger was also in conflict with his half-brother Bohemond, who against the wishes of his late father and step-mother, contested Roger's rule by initiating an armed revolt with the assistance of a number of Norman nobles and lords, and seized part of the duchy territory for himself. This conflict with his half-brother continued until 1085, when Bohemond left to join the first crusade as one of its leaders.

Roger Borsa was a weak ruler who, in spite of the support of the Papal States, presided over the gradual disintegration of his duchy.

It was a sad ending to what had been a glorious achievement of conquest and rule by Robert Guiscard and his heroic wife, Sichelgaita.

II

THE FEUDAL SYSTEM

obert Guiscard is an important person in this story of Molise and Abruzzo. He was an attractive, charismatic and highly intelligent man who displayed great strategic military and political skills. Robert was able to unify much of central and southern Italy at a time when it consisted of people with diverse ethnic backgrounds including Latins and Germanics in the former Lombard territories and Greeks in the former Byzantine territories. He built a new political and social structure based on a patronage based monarchical-feudal system, which was uniquely Norman in nature.

This structure laid the foundation of life in Molise and Abruzzo for many centuries to come, only waning in the mid-twentieth century. Robert was also a devoutly religious man who sought to keep the Roman Catholic faith strong within all of the territories that he controlled. It was definitely a low point in his life when he was excommunicated from the Catholic Church. But he was able to repair his damaged relationship with Pope Gregory VII and come to the rescue of the Papacy and Church when its very existence was under threat. It is no coincidence that the people of Molise and Abruzzo, including my mother, are the most devoutly Catholic of any region in Italy.

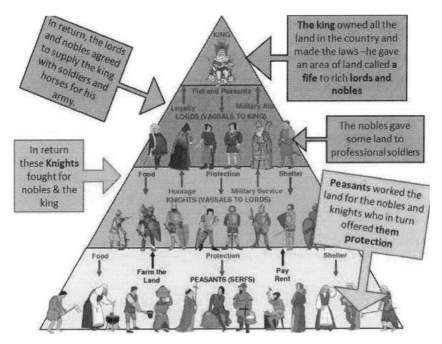

In return, the lords and nobles agreed to supply the king with soldiers and horses for his army.

The king owned all the land in the country and made the laws—he gave an area of land called a fife to rich lords and nobles

KING

Fief and Peasants

Loyalty   Military Aid
LORDS (VASSALS TO KING)

The nobles gave some land to professional soldiers

In return these Knights fought for nobles & the king

Food   Protection   Shelter
Homage   Military Service
KNIGHTS (VASSALS TO LORDS)

Peasants worked the land for the nobles and knights who in turn offered them protection

Food   Protection   Shelter
Farm the   Pay
Land   PEASANTS (SERFS)   Rent

(90) *The Feudal System introduced by Robert Guiscard into Molise, Abruzzo and southern Italy.*

With the death of Robert Guiscard in 1085, his younger brother Roger became the supreme ruler of Norman Italy which covered southern Italy and Sicily. Roger reigned until his death in 1101, when Roger II, a nephew took control. During the reign of Roger II he was able to add Naples and Capua to the Norman kingdom. He also succeeded in recapturing Molise and Abruzzo from the Holy Roman emperors, who had taken control of these regions shortly after the death of Robert Guiscard; and North Africa, from Tripoli to Tunis, from the Saracens. In 1130 Roger II changed his title from count to king and made Palermo Sicily the capital city of his newly expanded kingdom.

By 1194 Roger II's heirs, who had already lost the Norman's North African possessions, ended Norman rule in southern Italy when they surrendered the entire kingdom ("the kingdom of the Two Sicilies" as it was known) to the Germanic Holy Roman Emperor Henry VI under the pretext that Henry had married a woman from the Norman court.

In 1230, Henry VI's son, Frederick II united the Kingdom of the Two Sicilies with the Holy Roman Empire, under himself as the one supreme king, and established his court in the southern Italian city of Foggia, where he built a spectacular castle and palace. He reigned as an absolute monarch and introduced a new code of law which preserved all of the baggage of feudalism, including the rights of barons and lords over their peasant serfs. He also surrounded himself with non-Italians and founded the University of Naples. In 1237 Frederick II declared war on the Lombard cities of northern Italy and on the Papal States with the ambition of creating a New Roman Empire. As part of this war, the forces of Frederick seized control of the papal city of Benevento. This ongoing war created great division between the faction that supported Emperor Frederick, called the Ghibellines and the faction that supported Pope Gregory IX called the Guelfs. This war continued until Frederick's death in 1250. His son Manfred then became the Regent of Italy.

In an endeavor to end the war between the Ghibellines and the Guelfs, Pope Urban IV offered the Two Sicilies to King Louis IX of France in 1264. The king allowed his brother Charles of Angevin to accept the Pope's offer. Charles marched into southern Italy with a French army in 1266, defeated the forces of Regent Manfred, secured control of the Kingdom of Two Sicilies and established the French Angevin Kingdom of Naples, which ruled southern Italy including Molise and

Guelfo   Ghibellino

(91) *Pope Urban IV.*   (92) *King Louis IX of Naples.*

Abruzzo. In 1282 the tyranny of Charles of Anjou's French kingdom and army incited the bloody "Sicilian Vespers" people's rebellion. Fearing the vengeance of Charles and Pope Martin IV, the Sicilians offered their island to the Spanish King Pedro III of Aragon. After twenty years of war, Pedro's Spanish army established the rule of the Kingdom of Aragon over the island of Sicily. As a result, the "Two Sicilies" was divided in two again, with the Kingdom of Naples continuing to be ruled by the French House of Angevin and Sicily by the Spanish House of Aragon.

As we have seen, the greatest contribution the Normans made to the Molise and Abruzzo region was the introduction of the feudal system of hierarchical power, societal structure and land ownership, shortly after they established their kingdom there from their base in Benevento from 1054. Prior to the Normans, there was a system of centralized authority in Molise and Abruzzo which had been in place since the collapse of the Western Roman Empire in 476. First it was various Ostrogothic tribal groups, then the Lombards, Franks and finally there was Papal authority centralized from Rome. This all changed with the Norman conquest.

The feudal system the Normans introduced gave rise to a loosely clustered system of local baronial power, which was described as feudalism. This involved the establishment of numerous manorial estates throughout Molise, each controlled by a local lord or noble, in Italian they were known as *barone* (barons). The system was very hierarchical, with each lower level being vassals (or servants) of the higher level. So, sitting at the top of the hierarchy was the king. He would have an entourage of very loyal men, lords and barons, who in exchange for being granted large tracts of land, would assist the king in administering the kingdom, including maintaining law and order, collecting taxes and raising an army when the king required it.

As an agricultural based economy blessed with exceptionally fertile soil and climatic conditions, Molise and Abruzzo consisted of large areas of farming land out of which came the production of a wide variety of plant and animal produce. A person's position in this society was determined by the amount of land that person's family owned and farmed, if any. The *latifondisti* large land estate holders

(93, above) *Feudal Nobles and Barons.*
(94, right) *A Noble marriage.*

have held much influence in Molise and Abruzzo from the eleventh
century, to the present day.

There were four main levels of society in the Molise and Abruzzo
feudal system. Firstly, the "galantuomini," well-off noble barons with
historical family connections to the ruling Normans, who controlled
large areas of prime farming land as well as large tracts of land in the
towns and villages. They were positioned at the top of the regional
feudal hierarchy, and comprised around two percent of the total
population. These families typically lived in luxurious "palazzo's", often
with adjoining castles to offer protection from any outside invaders.

Secondly, there were the artigiani-mercanti class. These were artisans
or merchants who possessed particular skills either in the professions,
trades or in conducting business. It included professionals such as
doctors, lawyers and teachers; skilled people like blacksmiths, carpenters
and stonemasons; as well as small businesses selling a variety of food and
hand crafted products. They would normally be congregated within a
particular precinct or street in a town or village and comprised around
ten percent of the total population.

The next group comprised the "contadini" or peasants. They represented around thirty-five percent of the population and were land
owning smaller farmers. My family were from this class. They would
typically focus on particular produce or animal farming, building up
much skill and expertise over many generations. The entire family
would work on the farms, including the children when they completed
their compulsory four or five years of primary level education. They

worked from sunrise to sunset, typically six days a week, with Sunday being the day of religious festivities and rest.

At the lowest level of the feudal system were the "giornalieri" or day laborers, working mainly on farms. This group comprised around fifty-three percent of the population, owned no land, and often lived in poverty because they could not secure regular work, particularly in the winter months.

Each of the four groups in this feudal system had very little social contact with each other, except at an economic level when they provided labor or in their capacity as consumers. It was virtually impossible for a member of a lower strata to advance higher up the hierarchy. The "giornalieri" for example were not given opportunities to become land owning small farmers. Even if a "giornalieri" or "contadini" was to qualify in a particular trade, skill or profession, they would still be viewed by the rest of society as belonging to their feudal class level at birth. But if their children went on to continue with a particular family skill, they would then be viewed as belonging to the higher level strata.

One exception to this general rule appeared to

Artigiani-mercanti

(95) *carpenter*

(96) *blacksmith*

(97) *bakers*

(98), (99) and100) Contadini *and* giornalieri *peasants in medieval southern Italy.*

apply when a man from a higher strata married a lower strata woman. In those cases, the woman and her future children would automatically belong to the higher strata at the time of her marriage. Some more enterprising *contadini* peasants including my family on my mother's side, expanded their farming interests by utilizing more farming land. They typically did not have the financial resources to acquire this land. Instead they would rent the additional land from *galantuomini* or *artigiani-mercanti* families who would provide them with surplus land. In these instances, the rent would not be paid in the form of cash, but in produce instead.

Molise and Abruzzo were quite unique amongst the agricultural regions of central and southern Italy in that so many peasants actually owned the land they farmed. This was not the case in regions like Calabria and Sicily. These other regions developed a system of landed estates with absentee landowners. So as a result most of the peasants there were day laborers who never had the opportunity to own land.

Although it was the Normans who introduced the feudal system in Molise, it must be said that the legal right of individual land ownership can be traced to the reforms of the "Napoleonic Code" introduced into the region around 1806 when Napoleon Bonaparte's family gained control of southern Italy, including Molise and Abruzzo. The present system of local peasant families owning small farm land holdings has prevailed ever since.

At this point I should mention that although the Catholic Church was not formally a part of this feudal system, it wielded immense power at two levels. Firstly, it was a substantial land owner in its own right and therefore employed many *giornalieri* day labourers, as well as renting out much of its land to the *contadini* peasants. Secondly, it also derived much power because the vast majority of the people of Molise and Abruzzo were "God-fearing" devotional Catholics who participated fully in the activities of the Church, from attending weekly mass and the numerous religious festivals conducted in all of the villages and towns; to the various "life-event" ceremonies including baptisms, confirmations, weddings and funerals. In addition to this, everybody was expected to contribute as much as they could to the Church, regardless of their position in the feudal hierarchy.

The basic pattern of farming in Molise and Abruzzo differed from most of the other regions in central and south Italy. The peasant farmers strived towards self-sufficiency. Each family would grow everything they required for their own food needs, and would also produce relatively small surpluses which they could sell at the town market. So the primary motivation was to grow and produce enough food for the survival of the family. It was also important for these families to produce enough food surpluses to ensure they survived the particularly cold 6-8 week, peak winter period when no farming could be done, families remained indoors around an open fire place and the village was effectively cut-off from the outside world.

The large land-owning and professional/artisan/commercial upper classes of the feudal system considered themselves as superior to the lower class peasants and day-labourers. Members of the lower classes for example, were not invited to any social, religious or family functions arranged by the upper classes, and vice versa. There was a distinctive form of segregation going on in these towns and villages at the time. Even at public functions like attending mass or at religious festivals, the two distinct groups would be divided, with little social interaction. An example of this social divide in action was card playing. The lower classes were considered to be too intense in their card playing. Men would often congregate at the local village *cantina* or wine cellar and commence playing cards mid-afternoon on a Sunday for example, and would continue playing late into the evening, drinking red wine and gambling their hard earned money, even though they would need to leave their homes for the fields at sunrise the next morning.

The upper classes viewed this behaviour with disdain and believed that lower class men lacked the discipline of prioritizing family and work obligations ahead of card playing, gambling and drinking. On Christmas Eve, there was a tradition in many Molise and Abruzzo villages where the lower class men would play cards, drink and gamble all through the night into the early hours of Christmas morning, then with little sleep, attend the morning mass with their families. The women did not like this practice because the men would often be grumpy through lack of sleep, hung over and to top it off, often lost much of the precious family savings from gambling.

The lower classes viewed the uppers as aristocratic snobs who thought they were superior to the lowers. The lowers believed they worked much harder than the uppers and that the wealth accumulated by the uppers was due to their exploitation of the blood, sweat and tears of the common people. It is not hard to see why many lower class peasants and day laborers at the time were die-hard communists even before Karl Marx appeared on the world political scene in the mid-1800s. Another example can be found in the accents the two differing social groups spoke. The lower classes regarded their dialect and accents as softer and more "Italian-like" than the harsher "French-like" accents they believed the upper classes spoke. Here we see the French Norman and Napoleonic influence infiltrating the very heart of Molise and Abruzzo village life.

When it came to marriage, it was not common for people from one class to marry somebody from another class; even though these

(101, 102 and 103) *Molise peasant village life.*

marriages did occur from time to time throughout the region. The upper classes were very suspicious of men who courted their women. They believed these men were looking to gain upward economic mobility and access to the significant dowries and property that upper class families often possessed. Upper class women rarely married lower class men because it would mean a downward step in their social and economic standing, much ostracizing from their peers; and having to live in an inferior home, often out in the countryside rather than within the town or village. Also, on the rare occasions that marriages of this nature occurred, the daughter would literally be disinherited by her father, and the family home would be closed off to her and her children.

(104) *A Molise village wedding.*

Let's explore in more detail, the attributes of the social classes in Molise and Abruzzo. At the local level, the upper classes were given labels such as *nostri signarotti* (our lords) or *nostri baroni* (our barons). These labels were coined by the lower classes and were used in a derogatory fashion as a way of scorning and ridiculing the upper classes. These titles were originally used only for the lesser nobility, but later they were also used for any large land-owning families. They can be traced back to the earliest times when the feudal system was first introduced. In many Molise and Abruzzo villages to this day, the term "Don" is used to refer to and address prominent citizens and members of the Catholic clergy, even if they come from the lower classes. We need to appreciate that the large land-owning nobility (*baroni*) held immense power in Molise and Abruzzo.

There are many stories throughout the region of noble families treating the lower classes with much cruelty and disrespect. The children of the nobility were never allowed on the streets to play with the children of the lower classes. The children of the nobility did not attend public schools but instead were privately tutored by "men of letters." The girls and young women from the nobility were forbidden to leave their homes for an evening stroll in the town square or piazza ("the *passeggiata*") unless they were accompanied by their fathers or older brothers.

All contact between the nobility and lower classes, regardless of the circumstances or reasons, was conducted on a highly formalized basis, with the lower classes addressing them in the proper manner and showing complete reverence and respect to the nobility, wherever they encountered them. There were even subtle differences between the two classes. In addition to obvious differences in styles of clothing and grooming, many male members of the nobility for example, had extended fingernails on one of their little fingers, in order to symbolize their social ranking and the fact they did not do any manual labor.

Upward mobility, although possible, was incredibly difficult. For example, if the son of a peasant was to break out of his normal social strata, somehow raise sufficient money and seek to educate himself beyond the usual four years; and then attend a university and qualify as a doctor or lawyer; he would not be accepted as a member of the upper class. He would still remain the son of a *contadino* peasant, even though he could freely practice his profession.

There were different scales of ranking within the *artigianti / mercanti* social class. This class was often referred to by its French name, "the bourgeoisie" (or *borghesia* in Italian). There were two major sub-groupings within this class. There was an upper level which typically consisted of artisans, merchants, the flour miller, truck owners and professionals such as doctors, lawyers, teachers and accountants. Then there was the lower level which mainly consisted of part-time artisans and merchants who also farmed land. Also in this lower group were government bureaucrats such as postal clerks, tax assessors and municipal administrators. The national police (*carabinieri*) were an interesting omission. They were not classified within the class system at all because they typically came from other regions of Italy and did not reside in Molise and Abruzzo for long periods of time, often being transferred throughout the country. They were viewed as outsiders.

What was life like in a typical Molise and Abruzzo village in the early 1950s? There was a survey done by the Abruzzo-Molise regional government at the time, to examine the standard of living, particularly of the peasant families. The survey focused on the material goods possessed by a typical village home at the time. Here is some of the data from the survey. Only nineteen percent of homes had internally connected running water. Six percent had their own wells. The remaining households had to source their potable water from public wells, often traveling a great distance each day to get to the mountain spring water wells, like my mother did for a number of years as a young girl.

Only thirteen percent of homes had indoor toilets. For the rest of the homes, the outdoor garden served as the place for excrement, garbage and waste water. Less than two percent of homes at the time had bathtubs; although eighty percent of homes were connected with electricity. Typically, this would consist of one 25 Watt bare light bulb,

(105 and 106) *Abruzzo-Molise village housing and family life.*

suspended in the middle of the combined dining room, kitchen and bedroom. Around fifty percent of the homes were equipped with bottle-gas hot plates for cooking and heating water.

It was difficult to ascertain the social class and standing of a person by simply looking at their clothing. Some of the poorest looking people often had money hidden away in their mattresses. This was an attitude of mind borne from a deep mistrust of authority and power, including the State and banks. Is it any wonder that people held a deep mistrust of authority when we consider the history of this region being one of continuous exploitation by so many different groups?

Conversely, it was not uncommon for members of the upper classes to be cash poor, even though their families may have owned extensive property holdings. It was often difficult to establish the political ideologies of the people of Molise and Abruzzo. For example, monarchists who believed in the God given absolute power of kings, the nobility and the maintenance of the feudal system could be found scattered amongst the lower classes; even though the majority of the upper classes were certainly supporters of monarchy. It was a similar situation with communism, but the other way around. Although the majority of people from the lower classes were fervent believers of communism in the late nineteenth and early twentieth centuries; there were a scattering of more intellectually learned and enlightened people from the upper classes who held similar beliefs, even though the ideology of communism would imperil their privileged status if it was ever introduced into government.

Nowadays, the feudal system in Molise and Abruzzo does not exist in the rigid form that was the case from the eleventh to the nineteenth centuries. But the remnants of this hierarchical system are still there to be clearly seen. This is one of the fundamental reasons why Molise for example, continues to have this perception within the remainder of Italy in particular and the wider world in general, of being a "backward" place that is locked into a medieval way of life and thinking. Many people in positions of power and authority within Molise often retain these feudal attitudes with no interest in sharing and dissipating this power amongst others. Those in authority are still supported by a rigid

(107) *Molise village priest
at the market.*

(108) *Molise elderly lady
in her home.*

regional and municipal government bureaucracy which is invested in maintaining the status quo and not open to progressive change.

The emigration of a large proportion of the Molise and Abruzzo population to other regions of Italy and to countries around the world has played a major role in preserving village hierarchies, social life and traditions, for the sake of maintaining stability. Also, a stagnant and ultimately shrinking population has acted as a major disincentive for the Italian federal government and corporations to invest in the region, resulting in an economy which is still largely agriculturally based and traditional in nature. The strong Roman Catholic mentality that exists to this day in Molise and Abruzzo with all of its traditions, rituals and fears, has also contributed to a way of thinking which is deeply resistant to change, engrained within the psyche of many people in the region.

Another contributor to the maintenance of centuries old traditions in Molise and Abruzzo is the incredible solidarity of the family structure, which although is an enviable social trait, has created an insular way of thinking which has definitely stifled entrepreneurialism and hence the economic development of the region. Finally, there is an ingrained mindset in Molise and Abruzzo that is referred to as "la miseria," the misery. It is the tendency to allow negative thoughts and fears to overwhelm a person, producing an apathy on the part of many people from the region. This attitude creates a resistance to change and risk taking, so the economy remains stagnant and unemployed people uprooted from a traditional farming life that has gone on for centuries, experience great difficulty in re-inventing themselves and changing their way of life. It is this mindset that largely prevents the man on the street ("uomo qualunque") to better their life, to seek new opportunities and to venture beyond the stifling yoke of their families. "La miseria" reinforces the long standing attitude of the lower classes in Molise and Abruzzo to be suspicious and resentful of those that hold excessive power and authority.

12

THE BLACK DEATH STRIKES

NE OF THE GREATEST DISASTERS TO AFFLICT EUROPE DURING THE Middle Ages was the Black Death, a pandemic bacterial plague which originated in what is now Mongolia in central Asia, and was transported along land and sea trading routes into Europe by fleas on rats. By the time the pandemic ran its course, three years after it started, around 30% of Europe's population had been wiped out.

The Black Death arrived in Italy on sailing ships which berthed in the port of Messina Sicily in October 1347. By January 1348 the pestilence struck the mainland of Italy and had a devastating impact on the lives of the people living in central Italy and beyond.

The plague came mainly in two forms. The most common was the bubonic variety which got its name from the dark colored swellings or buboes that would appear on a victim's neck, armpits or groin. These buboes could grow to the size of an apple. Usually, when an unfortunate victim developed buboes, it indicated they had only about a week to live before they would be fatally stricken by the disease. Infected fleas that had

(109, 110, 111 and 112) *Scenes from the Black Death.*

the bacterial disease in their intestines would attach themselves to rats and then bite humans, transferring the disease into the blood system.

The second type was the pneumonic plague, which attacked the respiratory system and would spread rapidly in the air, from the breath of one human to others. It was much more virulent than the bubonic type, usually causing death within one or two days of the infection.

Of course, during the fourteenth century medical science was very crude and there was no understanding or even awareness of bacteria and no knowledge of the cause and any effective treatment of the plague.

The Italian writer Giovanni Boccaccio lived through the plague. His experience inspired him to write the classic text *The Decameron*, a story about seven men and three women who escape the disease by fleeing to a villa in the countryside of Italy. In his introduction, Boccaccio provides a graphic description of the symptoms for the bubonic variety, from his first hand observations, which I have quoted here:

The symptoms were not the same as in the East, where a gush of blood from the nose was the plain sign of inevitable death; but it began both in men and women with certain swellings in the groin or under the armpit. They grew to the size of a small apple or an egg, more or less, and were vulgarly called tumors. In a short space of time these tumors spread from the two parts named all over the body. Soon after this the symptoms changed and black or purple spots appeared on the arms or thighs or any other part of the body, sometimes a few large ones, sometimes many little ones. These spots were a certain sign of death, just as the original tumor had been and still remained.

Boccaccio goes on to explain how hopeless the situation was because of no known effective treatment for the disease:

No doctor's advice, no medicine could overcome or alleviate the disease. An enormous number of ignorant men and women set up as doctors in addition to those who were trained. Either the disease was such that no treatment was possible or the doctors were so ignorant that they did not know what caused it, and consequently could not administer the proper remedy. In any case very few recovered; most people died within about three days of the appearance of the tumors described above, most of them without any fever or other symptoms.

His description of the rapid spread of the disease is very sobering. In this excerpt he is referring to the pneumonic variety:

The violence of this disease was such that the sick communicated it to the healthy who came near them, just as a fire catches anything dry or oily near it. And it even went further. To speak to or go near the sick brought infection and a common death to the living; and moreover, to touch the clothes or anything else the sick had touched or worn gave the disease to the person touching.

Boccaccio then talks about the way people resorted to isolation, as best they could, considering the crammed circumstances most peasants lived under, in an attempt to escape the plague:

(113), 114 and 115) *Giovanni Boccaccio, author of* The Decameron.

Such fear and fanciful notions took possession of the living that almost all of them adopted the same cruel policy, which was entirely to avoid the sick and everything belonging to them. By doing so, each one thought he would secure his own safety.

The Black Death created a major breakdown in medieval society and put on display an incredible amount of cruelty that was based on blind fear, ignorance and terror. Boccaccio describes it as follows:

One citizen avoided another, hardly any neighbor troubled about others, relatives never or hardly ever visited each other. Moreover, such terror was struck into the hearts of men and women by this calamity, that brother abandoned brother, and the uncle his nephew, and the sister her brother, and very often the wife her husband. What is even worse and nearly incredible is that fathers and mothers refused to see and tend their children, as if they had not been theirs.

A terrible aftereffect of the Black Death was the sheer number of dead bodies that needed to be dealt with in villages and towns throughout central Italy and beyond. Here, in his *The Decameron*, Boccaccio paints a stark picture:

The plight of the lower and most of the middle classes was even more pitiful to behold. Most of them remained in their houses, either through poverty or in hopes of safety, and fell sick by thousands.

Since they received no care and attention, almost all of them died. Many ended their lives in the streets both at night and during the day; and many others who died in their houses were only known to be dead because the neighbors smelled their decaying bodies. Dead bodies filled every corner. Most of them were treated in the same manner by the survivors, who were more concerned to get rid of their rotting bodies than moved by charity towards the dead. With the aid of porters, if they could get them, they carried the bodies out of the houses and laid them at the door; where every morning quantities of the dead might be seen. Then they were laid on biers or, as these were often lacking, on tables.

Such was the multitude of corpses brought to the churches every day and almost every hour that there was not enough consecrated ground to give them burial, especially since they wanted to bury each person in the family grave, according to the old custom. Although the cemeteries were full they were forced to dig huge trenches, where they buried the bodies by hundreds. Here they stowed them away like bales in the hold of a ship and covered them with a little earth, until the whole trench was full.

A second wave of the plague struck central Italy over two centuries later, in 1657. Here is a firsthand account of the impact of this plague on the village of Pescocostanzo, approximately 100 kilometres from my family village of Montagano:

In Pescocostanzo the plague arrived much later than in other places, and in a couple of months, disappeared, taking away whole families. Those making a will often were the last of their family alive, and appointed cousins, uncles or churches as heirs.

From 15th May to 11th August 1657, Notary Giovanni Tomaso Colecchi, after sunset and when the heat of the day gave way to lower temperatures, with seven witnesses and in the company of the local judge, almost every night walked through the deserted streets of the town, to stop in front of a half-closed door where some poor souls, facing untimely death because of the plague, would dictate their last will. The death toll was surely much higher than the 55 wills here recorded. Some did not have the time, or did not believe they were going to die. Children died without leaving any trace in documents, those who were too poor would not call a notary, but, as many declared in their wills, since there is no place for wealth and property in the other world, they wanted to leave things in order, and avoid enmity among their heirs."

Each deed takes two or three pages. The great majority of those affected by the plague, at least as recorded in the wills, was made up of women; the disease as history books record, was brought to Pescocostanzo that thanks to its administrators and isolated position had almost escaped the contagion throughout the year 1656, from a merchandise seller of cloths and ribbons coming from Naples.

The Black Death had a number of positive and negative consequences which were cultural, religious and economic in nature. It should be pointed out that this pandemic led to the decline of the feudal system, a major loss of faith in the Catholic Church and the emergence of the Renaissance leading to enlightened thinking and the prominence of science over religious doctrine.

From a cultural point of view, the art and literature of the period took on a dark ironic humorous tone as a means of coping with the tragedy afflicting great numbers of people. Much of the art was bleak and morose, highlighting death and destruction.

During and immediately after the plague, many people struggled with maintaining their faith in a Church which was seen to be helpless

(116) *The power of the Church diminished during the Black Death.*

(117) *The Flagellants.*

in saving its followers from the disease. This led to many Christians losing faith in the strict doctrine of the Church and being prepared to consider alternative ideologies and philosophies on how best to live their lives. The power and influence of the Church began to decline, as a result.

As we have seen, during the time of the Black Death the state of medical science was very crude and doctors did not understand the origin of the disease and how it was transmitted, so it was common for many people to believe that magical supernatural powers were responsible for the plague.

Jews were unfortunately singled out for persecution during the Black Death. They were accused of conspiring to spread the plague, since many prominent traders at the time were Jews, traveling from town to town, bringing the rats with them, it was alleged. Of course the Jews had been persecuted in Europe for centuries, going right back to the crucifixion of Jesus Christ, for which they were blamed; so they were easy scapegoats in a time of ignorance, fear and panic, as existed during this time.

The Black Death also resulted in a major reduction in the population of central Italy and wider Europe, and an immediate decline in economic activity. However, with the extremely large number of deaths, there was an acute shortage of workers, so wages and living conditions increased for those who survived. This was the main reason the feudal system began to collapse, replaced by the development of a working class with greater freedom and rights.

The Black Death had a tragic impact on Europe for many centuries. Around 30% of the population of Europe was wiped out, although in some towns and villages over 50% died from the disease. It directly contributed to a significant reduction in the production and consumption of goods and services, bringing about the deepest economic depression in the history of western civilization.

As mentioned, we can trace the devastating impact of the Black Death on a major loss of faith by the people in the Catholic Church, one of the side-effects being an almost complete halt in the construction of churches and cathedrals. With an opening up in progressive critical thinking, filling the large void vacated by the loss of faith in the Catholic Church; the Black Death is directly responsible for the end of the Middle Ages and the beginning of the Reformation, which ultimately led to a Renaissance in the arts, literature, science, medicine, philosophy and political ideology; paving the way for the emergence of the modern world as we know it.

To this day, countless folklore and legends told around an open fire in the villages of Molise and Abruzzo by the wise elderly, can trace their roots to the devastating plague which afflicted and forever changed the lives of so many people.

The Black Death also serves as a reminder that humanity is constantly at risk from pandemic disease, regardless of our state of medical and technological development, as again experienced by the world during the 2020 Covid19 pandemic. We are at the mercy of bacteria and viruses.

13

FERDINAND I OF NAPLES

❦

I N 2012 I VISITED THE MONFORTE CASTLE IN THE MOLISE CAPITAL of Campobasso. It is located on a high rocky cliff on the outskirts of the city. Erected on the site of a previous Lombard tower, it is of Norman origin and was built as a defensive fortification.

It is named after Count Nicola Monforte, who restored it after the earthquakes of 1456 and 1458. During Norman times Campobasso became an important centre in the feud between the de Molisio family and the Ugone family, who moved their residence there.

Both families were vying for control of this city and the surrounding villages (including Montagano) in the mid-1100s. Control was fledgling and intermittent, passing from one family to the other. After 1237 Campobasso became the property of the Gambatesa family and later of the Monforte family who retained control until 1495.

One of the earliest Norman Counts of Campobasso was Hugo de Molisio who in the mid-1100s appears to have been given a sovereign grant of a very large area of land, which included Campobasso. In later

(118, above) *Monforte Castle in Campobasso, Molise.*

(119, right) *Campobasso Baron Monforte.*

years, this land was passed onto the Gambatesa family, by marriage. Then ultimately it fell into the hands of the Monforte family, who were the descendants of the renowned Norman, Simon de Monforte, who was a nobleman and soldier taking part in the Fourth Crusade from 1202 to 1204 and who died in the siege of Toulouse France, in 1218.

This very ambitious family continued as Counts of Campobasso, exerting great influence throughout the area, including my family village of Montagano. The last Monforte Count who bore the title under the Spanish Aragon ruling dynasty was Nicola Monforte.

He was active in the political affairs of the mid 1400s when he provided military and financial assistance to a number of regional barons, along with princes in the House of Aragon who ruled various principalities in southern Italy all within the Kingdom in Naples and were looking to overthrow Ferdinand I (also called Ferrante) who ruled Naples with an iron fist from 1458 to 1494.

According to the sources, Ferdinand I was gifted with great courage and real political ability, but his method of government was vicious, cruel and disastrous. His financial administration was based on creating oppressive and dishonest monopolies and he was mercilessly severe and utterly treacherous towards his enemies. Ferdinand had many enemies, especially considering his kingdom's importance to other rulers at the time. He responded ruthlessly to any perceived threat, often paranoid about his enemies and their intentions.

Ferdinand even plotted to overthrow Pope Alexander IV, after he realized the Pope could not guarantee the security of his reign and his kingdom. It is against this background of political intrigue that Count Monforte was joined in the clandestine effort to topple Ferdinand, by the barons of Salerno, Bisignano, Venosa and Melfi. Unfortunately, mutual jealousies and rivalries undermined their efforts and King Ferdinand not only prevailed, but was able to identify many of his conspirators and either execute or exile them. Count Nicola Monforte went into exile and his Campobasso property was seized by the King. The military reputation that he had, secured Nicola commanding roles in the armies firstly of the French Duke of Lorraine and afterwards, Charles the Bold of Burgandy. But he was never able to remove the stain of his involvement in the attempted overthrow of King Ferdinand 1 of Naples.

Nicola Monforte's son succeeded afterwards in recovering the favour of his legitimate sovereigns and was reinstated in his Campobasso estates and honorary titles, after having taken part with the French in the military campaigns of Charles VIII, who succeeded Ferdinand I as the King of Naples. After the end of French control of Naples, the Monforte lineage was denied any ancestral possessions and titles in Campobasso and ended up living in the town of Nola. Hence, the Monforte dynasty well and truly ended.

At this point it is worthy for us to examine the life of Ferdinand (Ferrante) I in greater detail because in his long reign as the King of Naples, he was very influential in determining the course of events in the Molise and Abruzzo regions, which came under his control. He was King of Naples from 1458 to 1494 and was the illegitimate son of Alfonso V of the Spanish kingdom of Aragon. His mother was Alfonso's mistress Giraldona Carlino. In order to set young Ferdinand up with a bright future, Alfonso arranged for Ferdinand to marry Isabella of Clermont in 1444. She was from a powerful feudal family, being the eldest daughter of Tristan di Chiaramonte, the Count of Copertino and Catherine of Baux, who was the niece and presumed heir of her childless uncle, prince Giovanni Antonio del Balzo Orsini of Taranto. Ferdinand's wife Isabella, stood to inherit a large area of feudal land in southern Italy which was controlled by her uncle.

In accordance with his father's will, Ferdinand succeeded his father Alfonso as King of Naples in 1458 at the age of 35. He faced an immediate obstacle though, when the Pope at the time Calixtus III, from the Spanish Borgia family and a rival to Alfonso V, declared that the Spanish Aragon dynastic line ceased to have any legitimate claim to the Naples throne, upon the death of Alfonso; and instead the Pope claimed the possession of the Kingdom of Naples as a territory belonging to the Catholic Church and attempted to place one of his nephews on the throne. But this was not to eventuate because Pope Calixtus III unexpectedly died in August 1458, and the new Pope Pius II immediately recognized Ferdinand as the legitimate King of Naples. Were Pius and Ferdinand involved in a conspiracy that killed Calixtus? We will never know.

(120, left)
Alfonso V,
King of Aragon
Spain.

(121, right)
Pope
Calixtus III.

With the full backing of the new Pope Pius II, Ferdinand achieved the legitimacy and recognition he so desperately had craved. Pius was very keen to maintain peace and stability in southern Italy while he was planning a major crusade against the Ottoman Turks, who had only recently taken control of the great city of Constantinople, which had led to the collapse of the Orthodox Christian Byzantine Eastern Roman Empire.

Shortly after becoming king, Ferdinand faced a significant challenge from a number of nobles and barons in the kingdom, including the previously mentioned Monforte family of Campobasso, who strongly objected to his intention to restrict their ancestral feudal power and instead to greatly enhance his own power. Ferdinand put a lot of effort into trying to suppress the first baronial revolt, including building close ties to some of the most powerful ruling families in Italy; including the Duke of Milan, Francesco Sforza, whose daughter Ippolita, was married to Ferdinand's son Alfonso.

To solidify their opposition to Ferdinand, these southern Italian nobles led by the Prince of Taranto, allied themselves with the French Angevins, a dynasty with a long standing claim to the Kingdom of Naples. The French claim to the throne originated in 1266 when Charles, the Count of Anjou and Provence, conquered southern Italy at the request of the Catholic Church. The heir to the Angevin dynasty Jean of Anjou, rode into southern Italy from France in July 1460 with an army, to enforce his family's claim and fought Ferdinand's forces at the Battle of Sarno, which Jean decisively won, but failed to capitalize on, retreating back to France instead.

This enabled Ferdinand to regroup his military resources to the extent that when Jean of Anjou invaded again in August 1462, this time he was soundly defeated by Ferdinand's army at the Battle of Troia. Nevertheless, the fatal blow to Jean was not delivered until 1465 when a French Angevin naval fleet was destroyed by a joint Ferdinand led Neapolitan and Spanish Aragonese fleet. This event finally solidified Ferdinand's legitimacy and authority over the Kingdom of Naples.

Ferdinand could be absolutely ruthless to those whom he perceived were out to undermine him. A classic example is the way in which he dealt with the celebrated and highly ambitious mercenary captain, Jacopo Piccinino. He was intriguing, manipulating and positioning to establish a principality for himself within the Papal States, around the town of Assisi; a location that was very close not only to the borders of the Kingdom of Naples, but also to other powerful noble lands, such as the Duchy of Rimini held by Sigismondo Malatesta, and the Duchy of Urbino held by Federigo da Montelfeltro; both close friends and allies of Ferdinand. Feeling like he was being sidelined by these powerful nobles, and not supported by Naples, Piccinino decided, along with his formidable army, to join the Franch Angevin military forces that were attempting to overthrow Ferdinand.

(122) *Battle of Troia, 1462.*

(123) *Jacopo Piccinino.*

At the end of the above mentioned war in 1465, the jubilant Ferdinand invited Piccinino to his castle for a series of dinner banquets. Piccinino had just married an illegitimate daughter of the Duke of Milan, who was a close ally of Ferdinand.

Piccinino had no reason to be suspicious of Ferdinand's apparent act of goodwill because it was not uncommon for mercenaries to fight for both sides in conflicts. They were not seen as having any political or ideological attachment to any conflict, but instead were professional soldiers who would fight for the highest bidder of their services.

It was in this context that Piccinino was happy to accept Ferdinand's invitation, thinking he would be offered a lucrative commanding position

within the army of Naples, on the basis he had fought so bravely, skillfully and courageously, even though he fought

(124) *King Ferdinand I of Naples holding court at a banquet.*

for the other side. To make him feel even more secure, Ferdinand had arranged for a number of his soldiers to safely escort Piccinino to Naples.

After a month of feasting and celebrating when all seemed to be going so well, Piccinno was suddenly placed

(125) *Castel Nuovo, Naples.*

under arrest. The next thing that happened was he "mysteriously" fell out of a high window in the king's Castel Nuovo prison in highly suspicious circumstances and died from his injuries. This method of execution was called "defenestration" and was a popular medieval Neapolitan way of getting rid of enemies if one desired to make it look like suicide. This was Ferdinand's way of exacting retribution from a mercenary whom he considered not only to have betrayed him by fighting for the other side, but who was now also causing political instability by attempting to establish a power base close to his kingdom's borders and upsetting the power structure of some of his closest noble allies.

These were allies he needed badly, to counteract the revolt that was still brewing with many other nobles within the Kingdom of Naples who were agitating for Ferdinand's removal as the king. This was a very powerful message to those southern Italian barons who were considering further acts of resistance; if a mercenary captain from outside the kingdom could be dealt with so brutally, so could they. After this event, one noble fled for France and left a note on the front gate of his palace in Salerno which simply said, "the bird has flown."

Ferdinand's ambition of maintaining peace and stability in Italy was easier said than done. The balance of power was unhinged on 26th April 1478 when there was a brazen assassination attempt aimed at Lorenzo Medici, the ruler of Florence, one of the most powerful leaders in Italy at the time, while he was attending a high mass at the Duomo

(126) *Assassination of Giuliano Medici, Florence, 1478.*

Cathedral before a large crowd. His brother Giuliano was stabbed 19 times and received a sword wound to his head. As Giuliano bled to death on the cathedral floor, Lorenzo escaped with serious, but not life-threatening injuries. The attempted coup had failed. But who was behind it and why?

It turned out to be a conspiracy by the Florentine Pazzi family, great rivals to the Medici's, who were determined to end what they claimed was the tyranny of the Medici dynasty and replace it with a government which would be more respectful of the republican constitution. Upon failing in their assassination attempt, key members of the Pazzi family and their co-conspirators were hunted down and swiftly executed under the orders of Lorenzo. There is evidence that Pope Sixtus IV and Ferdinand of Naples were aware of the conspiracy to kill Lorenzo and supported it, believing the Medici family was becoming far too powerful and influential in Italy, to the detriment of the Church and Naples. Realizing that he needed to reach some kind of compromise with his perceived enemies, Lorenzo Medici traveled to Naples

(127) *Pope Sixtus IV.*

to personally negotiate a peace settlement with Ferdinand. This was a risky venture for Lorenzo to undertake and he fully understood he could suffer the same fate as Jacopo Piccinino at the hands of the highly volatile and unpredictable Ferdinand. In fact, the great political Florentine writer Machiavelli stated that some of Lorenzo's enemies in Florence were hoping Ferdinand would in fact dish out to Lorenzo the same treatment he had given to Piccinino. Lorenzo himself realized the risk he was taking and said, "if our adversaries aim only at me, they will have me in their power."

Upon meeting face to face a great mutual respect developed between the two highly ambitious men; it was obvious that both Lorenzo and Ferdinand were well aware of the importance of achieving a peace settlement for the stability of Italy as a whole, and for their respective power bases in particular. It would be no exaggeration to state that at this point in the history of the Italian kingdoms, the Medici were the dominant force of northern Italy and Ferdinand of southern Italy, with the Catholic Papal State the proverbial meat in the sandwich.

The two leaders came out of the peace settlement with their respective holds on power firmly secure. The loser from the settlement was the Church. The Papal States felt threatened by the heightened power of Medici Florence, Ferdinand's Naples and his ally, Sforza Milan.

Tensions came to a head in 1482 when a war broke out between the Papal States led by Pope Sixtus IV, backed by their Venetian ally; and the Duchy of Ferrara which was supported by Ferdinand of Naples. The war arose as a result of a resurgent Venice taking possession of the town of Forli, near the Ferrara territory in September 1480. Venice had ended its long conflict with the Ottoman Turks in 1479 and was seeking to capitalize on its military strength by seizing more territory in mainland Italy. After having taken control of Forli, Venice received Papal blessing to extend its influence into Ferrara territory. Hence a war broke out.

The war came to an end with the signing of the Treaty of Bagnolo on 7th August 1484 which involved Ercole I d'Este, the Duke of Ferrara, giving up some conquered territory to the Papal States and Venice completely withdrawing from Ferrara occupied territories. The end result was a significant lift in the prestige of the Papal States in general and Pope Sixtus IV in particular, even though Ercole success-fully avoided the total absorption of his Ferrara kingdom into the Papal States. It was the influence of Ferdinand of Naples that prevented the Papal States from taking full control of Ferrara.

Meanwhile, back in Naples, Ferdinand had to contend with a second and much more serious baronial revolt in 1485-86. The newly elected Pope Innocent VIII supported the rebel nobles. His father had close ties to the French Angevin dynasty and had fought for Rene of Anjou against the Spanish Aragons. The barons of southern Italy were becoming increasingly agitated by the tight grip on power that Ferdinand was exercising out of Naples, which continued to weaken their own feudal power within their respective territories.

To make matters worse, Ferdinand had also significantly increased taxes. This second revolt included new leaders who had risen to power from modest backgrounds solely because of royal favors given to them by Ferdinand, which particularly angered him. The two most prominent of these leaders were Francesco Coppola, the Count of Sarno and Antonello Petrucci, who served as royal secretary within the court of Ferdinand.

Yet again, Ferdinand was able to destroy this baronial opposition with one of his favorite ploys; which was to reach out to every one of them, forgive them for any disloyalty and then invite them all to a huge marriage feast in the lavishly decorated great banquet hall at his Castel Nuovo in Naples to celebrate the marriage of the son of the leading rebel, the Count of Sarno, to Ferdinand's own grand-daughter. In the middle of this marriage celebration, the Count, his noble allies in attendance and many other powerful barons and members of their families throughout southern Italy who had resisted him, were arrested and either publicly executed or privately murdered in prison by his henchmen.

It is incredible that in spite of Ferdinand's ruthless reputation for brutally exacting revenge by "forgiving and inviting" enemies to feasts and celebrations, this group of barons fell for his ambush and trap, yet again! Ferdinand was determined that this time, not a single baron was going to survive and go into exile. He had extinguished the revolt of the barons, once and for all.

There was another side to Ferdinand I, he was also a progressive and enlightened Renaissance prince in the true spirit of that time. When his Aragon royal relatives, King Ferdinand and Queen Isabella of Spain expelled the Jews from Spain and Sicily in 1492, Ferdinand openly welcomed many of these Jews into his Neapolitan kingdom, genuinely sympathetic to their persecution by the Christians and also appreciative of their valuable artisan skills, particularly in the production of clothing. There were few other Christian princes in Europe who were showing this tolerant and welcoming attitude to the Jews at that time.

Ferdinand showed great enthusiasm for the establishment of a wide variety of manufacturing activities in his kingdom, including the creation of a silk industry. He actively encouraged merchants and entrepreneurs from all over Europe to establish themselves in Naples. There is an argument that this was all part of an attempt by Ferdinand to diminish the power and influence of the feudal system and hence the barons by creating a new "bourgeois" entrepreneurial class as an alternative to the feudal barons.

Ferdinand's close adviser Diomede Carafa, a highly respected nobleman, urged his king to reduce taxes so that businesses could thrive; "*for a king cannot be poor to whose power wealthy men are subject,*" he said. He went on to say, "*where one just rule flourishes, there the cities flower and the riches of the citizens grow.*"

"*Money is struck not for the profit of the prince, but for ease of buying and selling, and for the advantage of the people,*" Carafa said. Here it can be seen he was promoting the power of free markets, early signs of consumerism market economics and empowering the entrepreneurial spirit in Naples. He was well ahead of his time in promoting liberal economic policies as a replacement to medieval feudalism. All of this diminished the power and influence of the barons even further. Ferdinand implemented Carafa's economic policies and as a result his kingdom experienced significant economic and population growth.

Ferdinand was also a great patron of the arts, attracting talented people such as the painter Antonello da Messina, the sculptor Guido Mazzoni, the poet Giovanni Pontano and the Flemish composer Johannes Tinctoris, to his Neapolitan court. Ferdinand also brought the nearly dormant University of Naples back to life by attracting firstly, acclaimed scholars and then students from throughout Europe. He built it into one of the great universities of Europe.

Ferdinand I died in early 1494 at the age of 63, as the sound of French war drums could be heard beating from across the Alps. He had left instructions for his body to be preserved and mummified. In 1994, five hundred years after his death, his preserved body was

(128)   *Giovanni Pontano.*

exhumed in the Basilica of St. Domenico Maggiore in Naples.

During the autopsy that was conducted, part of a hollow organ came to light, which was identified as the rectum. After re-hydration and cutting of the rectal specimen, a biopsy confirmed that Ferdinand I had died from bowel cancer.

(129)   *Guido Mazzoni sculpture.*

Encouraged by the Duke of Milan Ludovico Moro, who was suspicious of Ferdinand's ambitions for more control of Italy; the French King Charles VIII planned to enter Italy and reclaim the Kingdom of Naples as the rightful Anjou heir. By the time his army approached Naples, Ferdinand had died and his son Alfonso II had taken over as king. But Alfonso panicked and fled Naples, leaving the vulnerable city to be meekly defended by his son, Ferrante II.

Although Charles VIII succeeded in becoming the King of Naples, French rule did not last for long. The Spanish Aragon dynasty briefly re-established its control of Naples and then was yet again removed from the throne by another French invasion. Out of all this chaos though, emerged Ferdinand II, King of Aragon who also claimed the right to rule southern Italy in 1504.

Ferdinand II was born on 10th March 1452 and was the son of John II of Aragon and Juana Enriquez. Ferdinand II had a number of royal crowns, including King of Aragon from 1479 to 1516, King of Sicily from 1479 to 1516 and King of Naples from 1504 to 1516. As if this wasn't enough, as a result of his marriage to Isabella I of Castile, he also became the King of Castile and Leon from 1474 to 1516.

As the King of Castile and Leon, Ferdinand was to play a critical role in the discovery of the New World when he and his queen wife Isabella met Christopher Columbus in 1486 and agreed to finance his planned expedition to reach Asia by a westward route. Of course, the

(130) *King Ferdinand I
of Naples.*

(131) *King Charles VIII,
entering Naples.*

rest is history when Columbus inadvertently sailed and landed in North America in 1492. Upon the return of Columbus to Spain, Ferdinand and Isabella secured a papal bull (Church decree) from Pope Alexander VI that granted them full title and ownership to these newly discovered lands.

The latter part of Ferdinand's life was mainly taken up with the Italian Wars, which were disputes the Spanish monarchy had over the control of Italy with successive kings of France. In 1494 as we have seen, Charles VIII of France invaded Italy and expelled Ferdinand's cousin Alfonso II from the kingdom of Naples.

In 1501 Ferdinand II entered into an agreement with Charles VIII's successor Louis XII to partition the Kingdom of Naples between them, with Campania, Abruzzo and Molise, including the city of Naples itself, going to the French; and Ferdinand taking control of Apulia and Calabria.

This agreement soon fell apart and over the next few years Ferdinand's brilliant general, Gonzalo Fernandez de Cordoba conquered the French portion of the Kingdom of Naples, including Molise and Abruzzo, by 1504. When Ferdinand II died in 1516, he was still the King of Naples.

14

BARONS OF CAMPOBASSO AND BENEVENTO WITCHES

～✕

N ADDITION TO THE MONFORTE CASTLE, THE CITY OF CAMPOBASSO
has an abundance of monuments depicting different periods in the
history of Molise. Among the many churches is the Church of Saint
Antonio Abate which was built in 1572 and displays a late Renaissance
façade and Baroque interior. It is embellished with paintings and frescoes
by various seventeenth century artists. I feel a real sense of wonder
whenever I am walking through the historical centre of Campobasso,
with its medieval stone cobbled streets and alleys.

The province surrounding Campobasso has numerous important
archaeological sites, including a burial ground and Hellenic tombs
which are preserved at the village of Larino, continuously inhabited
since the fifth century BCE. This was the location of the Roman
defeat of Hannibal in 217 BCE. The village of Larino also contains an
assortment of monuments from different periods in history, including
a well preserved Roman amphitheater and accompanying baths; a

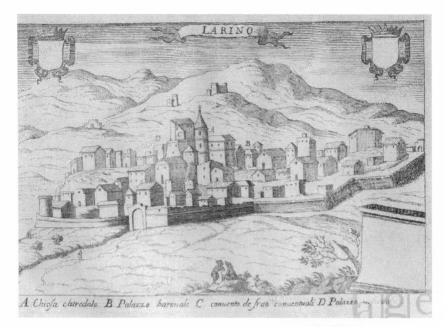

A Chiesa cattredale B Palazzo baronale C convento de frati conventuali D Palazzo

(132, above) *Medieval Larino, Molise.*
(133, right) *Medieval Larino.*

fourteenth century Gothic styled cathedral with an adjacent tower; and the Palazzo Comunale, which began as a Norman castle.

The nearby valley of the Tammaro River contains many Samnite sites, including the settlements of Monte Vairano and Cercemaggiore and the fortifications of Gildone, Vinchiaturo-Mirabello, Duronia and Terravecchia di Sepino.

During my visit to the region there were a number of castles which stood out for me. These were the Castle of Gambatesa dating from the mid-twelfth century, built by the de Molisio family, whom Molise is named after and as we have seen also controlled Campobasso as Counts for a period of time in the twelfth century.

Then there is the Castello d'Evoli in Castropignano, which was built in the mid-fourteenth century over the remains of an ancient

Samnite fortress. I also visited the Castello di Tufara, which began as a Norman stronghold, was destroyed in 1220 and then was rebuilt and expanded during the next two centuries.

The Castle of Riccia is particularly interesting. It was built in 1500 by Bartolomeo II De Capua. The De Capua's were a noble family and the castle they built was elegant. This noble family had a reputation for being very fair and generous to the peasants who came under their rule at that time. However, over the next two centuries, subsequent generations of the De Capua family dominated the peasants in such a harsh and cruel manner that in 1799 the townspeople revolted and burned the castle down. Today, only a few ruins of the castle with its medieval watchtower can still be seen in the historical centre of Riccia.

While I was in Italy in 2012 I also visited the city of Benevento, fifty kilometres northeast of Naples. The city is attractively located, surrounded by the Apennine mountains. It lies on a ridge between the Calore, Irpino and Sabato rivers. It originated as the settlement of Malies during the time of the Samnites and was later known as Maleventum. The city held great importance to the Samnites, who took refuge there after their defeat by the Roman Republic in 314 BCE.

When the Romans seized control of this area after the Samnite Wars, they renamed the city Beneventum for the sake of superstition and eliminating all references to the Samnites. It became an important stopping point and trading centre along the Appian Way, the road the Romans built connecting Italy; and a base from which the Romans further expanded into southern Italy. Beneventum remained in Roman hands during both the Punic Wars with Hannibal's Carthage and the Social Wars between the Roman Generals Sulla and Marius. It was conquered by the Ostrogoths led by Totila, after the collapse of the Western Roman empire in the fifth century and its walls were razed in 545 CE. As we have seen, it was later occupied by the Lombards when they conquered southern Italy, with Benevento becoming their capital city.

While I was in Benevento I visited numerous sites of historical significance. Trajan's Arch was built by the Romans in 114 CE in impressive marble with ornate decorative carvings, largely commemorating the life and times of the Roman Emperor Trajan himself and built to celebrate the importance of the town as a trade route. The workmanship and detail in the stonework are of exceptional quality. I also visited a Roman amphitheater built during the time of Emperor Hadrian, which could hold 10,000 spectators and is still in excellent condition. I spent some time at the Santa Sofia church, unusually circular in design and a rare example of Lombard architecture, dating to around 760 CE. The church has attractive cloisters along with frescoes that although damaged, can still be seen inside. At the top of the town I visited Benevento Castle which consists of a sturdy stone tower built by the Lombards in the ninth century and an adjoining small palace that was added by the Normans in the fourteenth century. The castle is strategically positioned at the highest point of the town to keep a watch on all the routes entering the town.

(134) *Trajan's Arch Benevento.*   (135) *Benevento Castle.*

During medieval times Benevento was known as a meeting place for the witches of Italy. Before examining this Benevento phenomenon in some detail, we need to understand the reasons for the Witch Craze, which spread in Europe, particularly between the fourteenth and seventeenth centuries. The root cause can be traced to the Black Death Plague which devastatingly struck Europe, beginning from 1347.

The single greatest political and ideological impact of the Plague was its serious erosion of Catholic Church power. The argument goes like this. If God was concerned with the wellbeing of his devout followers, why would he have allowed such a horrible pandemic to decimate Europe? Initially, the Church tried hard to counteract this concern by claiming the pestilence was God's way of punishing humanity for deviating away from the teachings of Jesus. This was little consolation to the millions of true believers who had strictly adhered to the doctrines of the Church. So gradually, more and more normally compliant people began to question the power of the Church and actively rebelled by refusing to attend Mass and not adhering to Church sacraments and doctrine. In response to this threat, the Church initiated a number of measures designed to enforce their power over the people. The Church Inquisition had a major impact in shutting down the influence of radical scientific thinkers like Giordano Bruno and Galileo Galilei. Another measure they introduced was to aggressively persecute witches, whom they considered to be heretical enemies of the Church and lovers of the Devil.

This persecution of witches led to the Witch Craze, aimed fairly and squarely at unmarried women, whom the Church felt threatened by, with marriage being the central sacred tenet of Christianity. Single women were an easy target because they held no power in the Church hierarchy and could easily be used as a scapegoat in order to frighten the people and reinforce Church power over them. As an incentive to local

(136) *Hecate.*   (137) *Diana.*   (138) *Proserpina.*

villagers to identify and report single women suspected of worshipping the Devil, the "Malleus Maleficarum" was published in 1486 with the full blessing of the Catholic Church. This was effectively an operating manual on how to identify, persecute, put on trial and punish a witch.

Let us now investigate how Benevento came to be so influential for the practice of witchcraft in Italy. The legend of the witches of Benevento can be traced back to the pre-Roman era, when the area was settled by Samnite tribal groups who practiced pagan rituals as part of their religious beliefs, particularly to do with magic and spirit beings. Three Greek goddesses also had a major influence on these early Italian tribal rituals; they were Hecate, Diana and Proserpina.

Here is an excerpt from Greek literature, in the *Tale of Medea*, highlighting a ritual performed by early medieval Italian witches as part of their invoking ceremonies. Notice the strong connection between the natural world and the three female goddesses:

> *Diana, who commands silence when secret mysteries are performed, I invoke you.*
> *Night, faithful keeper of my secrets, and stars who, together with the moon, follow on from the fires of the daylight, I invoke you.*
> *Hecate of the three faces, who knows all of my designs, and comes to help the incantations and the craft of the witches, I invoke you.*
> *Earth, who furnishes witches with powerful herbs, and you, breezes, winds, mountains, rivers and lakes, and all the gods of the groves and all the gods of the night, be present to help me.*
> *Proserpina, night-wandering queen, I invoke you.*
> *Hecate, Diana, Proserpina, look kindly now upon this undertaking.*

The idea here was that inanimate objects possessed consciousness and power, and could be invoked or called upon for assistance. We have seen earlier when we examined the religious practices of the Samnites that they would call upon the Gods to assist them with many aspects of their lives including family unity, good harvests and preparations for battle. So it is clear witchcraft was practiced in Italy from the earliest ancient times and was a rustic tradition of the peasants, not one of the noble classes.

Having said that, we know the noble families of Italy also took on aspects of witchcraft in the Middle Ages, when they began to hire Court magicians and astrologers to enlighten them in the mystic occult arts. One example from the medieval sources is the powerful Visconti family who rose to power in Milan, ruling the city state from 1227 to 1447 as lords and dukes. The Visconti's helped popularize the Tarot, a pack of 78 playing cards each with unique mystic powers to predict the future. After being embraced by the Visconti's, Tarot cards became very popular and were taken seriously among the noble families of Europe.

Another example of the medieval nobility taking on mystic beliefs was an old and powerful secret society in Italy known as the "Madre Natura" ("Mother Nature"). It was founded by a small group of bishops and priests from the early days of the Church. The society had to be secretive because its beliefs were not in line with Christian doctrine, instead their beliefs were pagan Neoplatonist. One of its goals was to "restore the usurped altars to the god of the silver bow and the radiant daughter of the foaming wave." This is a reference to ancient Roman pagan gods. The Medici family of Florence were members of the "Madre Natura" and in later years, this group developed connections with the Freemasons and the Carbonari, another Italian secret society. For a brief period during Roman times, the Cult of Isis, the Egyptian Sun god, was popular in Benevento with the Roman Emperor Domitian erecting a temple there, in her honour. Within the Cult of Isis, the Greek goddesses Hecate of the underworld and Diana of the hunt, both connected with magic, were also worshipped.

The Benevento witch legend itself though, can be traced back to the seventh century when Benevento was the capital of the Lombard Duchy which controlled much of central Italy at the time, as we have seen. Although officially converted to Catholicism, the Lombards did not give up their traditional pagan religious beliefs. Under the leadership of Duke Romuald I, they worshipped a winged, two-headed golden viper snake, which appears to have been connected with the earlier Cult of Isis, since that goddess had the power to control serpents.

(139, 140 and 141)

The witches of Benevento.

The Lombards began to celebrate their pagan rituals near the Sabato river, which the Lombards dedicated to Wotan, the father of their gods. At this site near the river, they would hang the hide of a goat on a sacred walnut tree. The warriors would earn the favor of Wotan by riding frantically around the tree on horseback while striking the goat hide with their lances, with the intention of tearing off shreds, which they would then eat.

The Christians in Benevento began to connect this strange ritual with their already existing beliefs about witches. In their eyes, the women who participated in this ritual were witches, the warriors were warlocks, the goat was the incarnation of the Devil and the cries and chants were orgiastic rites. A local priest, later to become Saint Barbatus of Benevento, accused the Lombard rulers of being heretics. Saint Barbatus cut down the sacred walnut tree, tore out its roots, and on that very spot arranged for the church of Santa Maria to be built. According to the legend, the Lombard duke Romuald continued to worship the golden viper in private, until his wife Teodorada, handed it over to Barbatus, who then proceeded to melt the gold down and use it to make a chalice for his church.

In the following centuries, the legend of the Witches of Benevento spread throughout Italy. Starting in 1273, reports began to circulate of witches' gatherings in Benevento. Based on the testimony of a local woman Matteuccia da Todi, who was put on trial for witchcraft in 1428, the rituals took place under a walnut tree, believed to be the incarnation of the tree that had been cut down by Barbatus many centuries earlier and restored by the Devil for the worship of his cavern of witches. During numerous witch trials conducted in Benevento mainly in the fifteenth century, many accused witches would recant this magic spell:

Unguent, unguent,
Carry me to the walnut tree of Benevento,
Above the water and above the wind,
And above all other bad weather.

According to the legend, witches who were totally undistinguishable from other women by day, would anoint their underarms and breasts with an "unguent potion" at night and take off by flying on brooms and recounting the magic spell quoted above. At the same time, the witches would disintegrate their bodily form, becoming spirits of the wind, which would propel them, so unsurprisingly they favored windy stormy nights when flying.

It was believed there was a bridge from which the witches of Benevento would launch themselves into flight. This bridge was called the "bridge of the janaras" and was destroyed during the Second World War. Others claimed that at night the witches would steal horses from stables and after plaiting the horses' hair, they would race them at a frantic gallop until foam would form around the horses' mouths; the witches then rubbing the foam all over their bodies. The citizens of Benevento would be frightened by stories claiming the witches were able to cast spells, causing abortions, creating deformities in newborn babies and inflicting terminal illnesses. In numerous villages in Campania, Abruzzo and Molise, rumors were circulating among elderly village women that the Benevento witches were kidnapping newly born babies from their cradles and sacrificing them to the Devil in fire rituals.

The peasants believed the witches ("janaras") could cast a spell converting them into a form of wind, allowing them to enter homes under the door. For this reason, there has been a long standing tradition in many villages in central Italy, including the village of my parents' birth, to leave a broom or some salt, outside the front door at sunset, to prevent witches from entering, because they would be compelled to count all the fibres on the broom, or count the grains of salt, before entering the house; in the meantime, sunrise would be approaching and so they would be forced to fly away. The broom and salt have strong symbolic value amongst the believers of witchcraft in central Italy. The broom is a phallic symbol of fertility, which is the opposite of the spell of sterility that witches were believed to often cast. As for salt, it was connected to the Latin word "salus." Salus was the Roman goddess of safety, wellbeing, good health and prosperity.

(142) *A witch being burnt at the stake.*

(143) *A witch casting a magic spell.*

Besides the *janaras* witches described above, there were believed to be other types of witches in Benevento. The *zucculara* ("lame person") haunted the area of Triggio, the medieval Lombard quarter of Benevento in which the Roman amphitheater was located. Legend had it, the people could hear the noisy clogs of the *zucculara* when she was out prowling at night. It is believed this witch legend comes from the Greek goddess Hecate, who wore only one sandal and was worshipped at the crossroads. The name "Triggio" is derived from the word "trivium," crossroads in Latin.

There were also the *manalonga* ("long hand") witches who lived in wells and would mercilessly pull down passersby into the well, their terrified screams echoing throughout the surrounding area. The legend of this witch is believed to have come from people having a fear of pits, which were imagined to be passageways to hell.

All of these witches' legends still hold strong belief in Molise and Abruzzo, being passed on from generation to generation, particularly by elderly women, who strongly believe that these witches really exist and are casting spells on many people as they go about their daily lives. In a later section of this book, I have recounted the story of when my mother was cast with an evil spell, weeks before she was about to depart Italy, to join my father in Australia. Her story is a sober reminder of just how engrained these superstitions still are within the culture and traditions of Molise and Abruzzo. As if that wasn't enough of a traumatic experience, my mother Carmelina also experienced the power of witchcraft in Australia. This story is retold later in the book as well.

(144) *An elderly village "good witch."*

(145) *Malleus Maleficarum (1486).*

15

CELESTINE V –
THE HERMIT POPE

URING THE THIRTEENTH CENTURY THE MOLISE REGION PRODUCED
its only Pope, Celestine V. The story of his life and how he became
the Pope is fascinating. Only two Popes in history have resigned or
abdicated willingly. The most recent was Pope Benedict XVI who
resigned in 2013. But the first was Celestine V.

Born in 1215 as Pietro Angelerio in the small Molise town of
Sant Angelo Limosano near Isernia, he lived most of his adult life as a
self-flagellating hermit in a cave in the Apennine mountains of Molise.
Born into a peasant family, Pietro began his career as a priest at the
Benedictine monastery of Santa Maria di Faifoli, which is close to the
town of Montagano where my parents were born. Within a few years
however, monastic communal life lost its appeal to him and he withdrew
to a cave on Mount Morrone, where he lived alone and devoted himself
to quiet meditation and prayer. Ironically, it was Pietro's desire to live a
solitary life, far from worldly concerns, that led to his eventual election
as Pope, as we shall see.

Traditional religious hermits at the time rejected the trappings and temptations of the material world, seeking to know God and receive wisdom through living a life of extreme modesty, selflessness and simplicity. Religious hermits often became objects of great curiosity and interest to nearby peasant locals. As their fame spread, they drew the attention of pious pilgrims as well as the official Church. Rather than being left alone to pray and meditate quietly, they became the centre of attention. Pilgrims begged them for advice and miracles. Monks asked to join them. Priests looked to them for spiritual guidance.

Pietro, in his small cave, was no different. After about fifteen years living in solitude on Mount Morrone, he decided to withdraw to an even more remote and inaccessible location in the Maiella mountains of the Abruzzo region of Italy. But disciples continued to flock to him and eventually were formally included into the Benedictine order of monks, which later became known as the Celestines. Under Pietro's guidance, the brothers followed the Rule of St. Benedict and were completely independent from the local bishops.

Over time, this new order accumulated money and property. Pietro became the abbot of Santa Maria di Faifoli, which as I have said, is just outside of my parents' birth village, Montagano. His reputation as a miraculous healer, an ascetic and an effective leader grew, and so too did his contact with the outside world, to the extent that during this time he became so popular that he stood out amongst the religious hermits in Italy. Charles II, the King of Sicily and Naples extended his official protection to Pietro's monastic order. His name became well known to the Cardinals within the Papal Curia and also to the powerful aristocratic families of Rome.

In 1293 Pietro moved back to Mount Morrone where he built the Santo Spirito monastery at the base of the mountain, outside the town of Sulmona in the Abruzzo province of L'Aquila. There, he chose to live in a small grotto halfway up the mountain, relinquishing any official position in his order. Finally, he seemed to have achieved the quiet and solitude that he had so longed for. Unfortunately for Pietro though, his retirement coincided with a period of chaos within the Papal Curia in Rome. Pope Nicholas IV had died suddenly on April

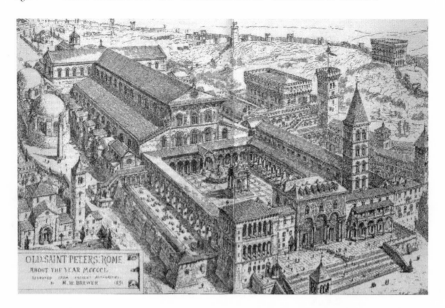

OLD SAINT PETERS ROME
ABOUT THE YEAR MCCCCL
RESTORED FROM ANCIENT AUTHORITIES
BY H. W. BREWER   1891

CÆLESTINVS·V·PP·SAMNIS·

(146, right) *Pope Celestine V.*
(147, above) *Saint Peter's Basilica Rome in the 13-14th century.*

4th 1292. The twelve Cardinals of the College gathered to elect a successor but they were divided by personal family feuds. To succeed, a candidate needed to secure two thirds of the votes. Months passed and the twelve Cardinals failed to reach an agreement on any candidate.

The heat of the Roman summer made them ill. Twice the conclave broke up so the Cardinals could escape to the cool breeze of their countryside villas. During one of these periods in 1293, the faction led by the Colonna family took advantage of the absence of their enemies to push for the election of their own candidate. But even in the absence of one of the factions, the Cardinals still failed to elect a new Pope. The situation was now becoming urgent. Charles II, King of Sicily and Naples decided that enough was enough and he personally intervened in March of 1294 by putting forward four candidates of his choice. But still, the Cardinals could not agree. In a tense meeting on July 5th 1294, Cardinal Latino Malabranca declared a holy hermit from Molise had made a prophecy that if the conclave continued to disagree, God would punish them. Malabranca had enormous influence, being a member of the Orsini family, one of the most powerful in Rome. At this meeting, Malabranca revealed the name of this hermit was Pietro Angelerio. Then, to the complete surprise of the other Cardinals, Malabranca proposed that the college break the deadlock once and for all by electing Pietro as Pope.

In desperation, and under enormous pressure from King Charles II, the Cardinals elected this reclusive monk to the position of supreme leader of the Catholic Church and Christ's representative on Earth, the Pope. With great reluctance and after a lot of pressure put on him by the conclave, Pietro accepted his election as Pope. A relieved Charles II arranged for the Hermit Pope to be escorted into Rome riding a donkey, imitating Jesus Christ's entry into Jerusalem. He took the name Pope Celestine V and was widely viewed as ushering in a more-humble, simple and spiritual papacy in contrast to the aggressively militaristic and politically active Popes that Rome was becoming accustomed to. Rome had a Molisani Pope!

Unfortunately, the very qualities and attributes whch had made him a revered hermit made him a weak and ineffective Pope. Celestine was naive, passive, unsophisticated and poorly educated. Instead of taking up residence in Rome, Celestine V was based in Naples where he fell under the complete control of King Charles II, who amongst other things, convinced him to appoint twelve new Cardinals, including seven Frenchmen, all loyal to Charles. This infuriated the great powerful families of Rome, who had become accustomed to wielding enormous power including appointing and controlling Popes. Celestine was so poorly educated that for the first time ever, meetings with the Cardinals were in Italian rather than Latin. He had little interest in the political intrigues of the papacy or the day to day running of the Church, which resulted in confusion and chaos. For example, he was so indecisive that he frequently appointed more than one priest to the same official position. Worse still, the new Pope blatantly favored his own monastic order, granting them unprecedented privileges and power, even attempting to transfer the ownership of rich monasteries to the Celestines.

After five months, Celestine was completely overwhelmed with the burden of the papacy. He requested to hand over the administrative power to three Cardinals for the 28-day period of Advent, which marked the beginning of the Christian year, so that he could devote all of his time to meditation and prayer. The College of Cardinals turned down his request. Exasperated and at his wits end, Celestine finally sought the advice of Cardinal Benedetto Caetani who was highly respected for his expertise in Canon law. On this occasion though, it seems that Caetani incorrectly advised Celestine that Canon law allowed for a Pope to voluntarily resign. Together, they proceeded to draft a statement of abdication which detailed the reasons Celestine wished to resign.

On December 13th 1294 at a full meeting of the Cardinals, Celestine read his statement of abdication, removed his papal ring and formally resigned as Pope, declaring himself to be Brother Pietro again. On the following day, the College of Cardinals formally elected Benedetto Caetani to the papacy. Caetani had blatantly benefited in a big way from the advice he had given Celestine, becoming Pope Boniface VIII at a lavish ceremony held on December 24th 1294. Unlike Celestine, Caetani was ambitious, cunning and clever. He knew the threat a former Pope could be to creating a schism (division) within the Catholic Church. Although Pietro wanted nothing more than to return to his previous life as a hermitic monk, Pope Boniface placed him under house arrest. Escaping briefly, Pietro spent several months as a free man on the run. He was recaptured when he tried to hire a boat to take him to Dalmatia on the Adriatic coast. The former Pope spent the remainder of his life in solitary confinement in the tower of Castel Fumone, outside the town of Ferentino. There he died in mysterious circumstances on May 19th 1296.

Celestine's legacy has endured to this day. The great Italian writer Dante Alighieri, placed him in Hell in his classic literary work of 1320, "The Divine Comedy," with the following words:

I saw and knew the shade of him
Who from cowardice made the great refusal.

Dante, along with many other medieval commentators at the time, viewed Celestine's abdication as a grave and unforgiveable sin. A refusal to submit to God's will. This is why they believed he was destined to spend eternity in Hell.

On the other hand, Celestine also had many supporters, including those whom he had showered with favours while Pope. They viewed him as a martyr, who was manipulated, forced out of the papacy and then persecuted by Boniface VIII. This view eventually prevailed and on May 5th 1313, Celestine was canonized by Pope

Clement V as a Saint. The people of Molise, including my parents, certainly view him as a courageous martyr.

The death of Celestine has been shrouded in mystery for centuries because of the rumor that Boniface ordered his murder. This speculation was fueled by a mysterious hole at the top of Celestine's skull which many thought was evidence of a traumatic blow to his head with a sharp object. Many people believe he was murdered with a nail that was driven through his skull, while he was asleep.

The suggestion that Pope Celestine V was murdered under the orders of his successor Pope Benedict VIII is not so unusual in papal intrigue and politics. As many as twenty popes have been murdered throughout history. Up to one-third of these murdered popes were elected between the years 872 and 1012 CE. Here are four of the more interesting cases.

(148) *Pope Boniface VIII.*   (149) *Dante Alighieri.*

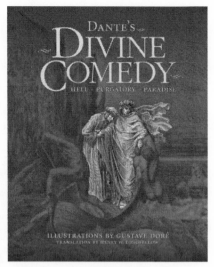

(150) *Dante's* Inferno.

(151) *Dante's* Divine Comedy.

John VIII (872-82) was poisoned, beaten-up and left for dead. Stephen VI (896-970) was put into prison and then strangled by his political enemies. John XII (955-64) was a warrior who became pope at the age of seventeen. Extremely corrupt and immoral, he was murdered by the jealous husband of one of the noble women he had been having an affair with. Clement II (1048) didn't last long as pope when he was poisoned with a mixture of sugar and lead.

16

GIORDANO BRUNO – A RADICAL THINKER

⟵⬤⟶

WHEN IT COMES TO CONTRIBUTIONS TO THE BODY OF SCIENTIFIC and philosophical knowledge during the Renaissance, one of the greatest and most original thinkers of the sixteenth century was Giordano Bruno, a man who held ideas that were surprisingly progressive for his time, and too radical for the Church, as it turned out. He was born in the town of Nola in 1548, which is in Campania not far from its border with Molise and was very much a part of the Kingdom of Naples. Readers will remember this town as the location where the great Roman Emperor Augustus had his country villa, and where he died.

Every time I visit Rome, I will go to the Campo di Fiori in the city centre. This square, or piazza as we call them in Italian, is one of the most beautiful and historically significant in the eternal city. It gets its name because it was traditionally where the florists of Rome would set up their market stalls, selling an assortment of flowers from all over Europe. At the centre of this piazza, looming over all of the cafes,

(152) *Giordano Bruno* (left).
(153) *Giordano Bruno statue in Rome.*
(above)

trattorias, pasticcerias, remaining flower stalls and many other specialty food outlets, stands an imposing statue of a dark sullen Giordano Bruno. Where the statue is, marks the spot where Bruno was burnt at the stake by the Catholic Church for not recanting his heretical scientific beliefs.

His life and story is a fascinating insight into the sheer dominance of the Catholic Church doctrinal belief system at that time, and how the onset of the Renaissance and the Enlightenment created a scientific revolution which threatened its power base and influence. The Church was particularly fearful of scientists and philosophers who were gaining a following amongst the nobility and intellectual classes for spreading information which they believed directly contradicted the teachings of the Church. After all, it was this dogma that the Church relentlessly drilled into the people when they regularly attended Mass, in order to maintain control and influence over them; so any form of enlightened, progressive critical thinking was a clear and present danger to them.

Giordano Bruno's father was a mercenary employed by the Spanish Bourbons who had ruled over the Kingdom of Naples since the beginning of the 1500s. The sources indicate that Giordano was a lonely, bookish boy who was respectful of his family and firmly indoctrinated into the beliefs of the Church. In 1562 at the age of fourteen, he left his humble family farmhouse when his parents decided to send him to Naples to further his education. Giordano had never traveled outside of his birth town of Nola to this date, let alone seen a thriving city like Naples. During the time of Giordano's visit, Naples was the fifth largest city in the world by population and was one of the great political, social and economic centres of Europe.

The city was a magnet for bakers, fishermen, seamstresses, farm produce vendors, hotel porters, laundresses, carpenters, sausage makers, blacksmiths, stonemasons, wheelwrights and water sellers who went barefoot in the mild climate and lived largely on bread and figs. Sitting above this group of enterprising small time artisans, traders and entrepreneurs were the ruling class of nobles, counts and barons surrounding the king and his family. At the bottom of this sprawling social ladder were the impoverished peasants, beggars and prostitutes who could be seen on the streets and in the side alleys, literally begging and scraping to stay alive. The streets of Naples would have overwhelmed the senses of the young Giordano, while he was holed up in crowded and unhygienic student quarters, immersed in his world of theology and philosophy, inside his squalid room.

At the age of seventeen, Giordano Bruno was admitted to the Dominican monastery of San Domenico Maggiore in Naples. This was a prestigious place of learning attended by many sons of the noble classes throughout Europe. So it is here where for the first time in his life, Bruno begins to lay the foundations for his connections with members of the ruling class. From all accounts, Giordano loved the intellectual rigor of this conservative institution. It is here where he was taught Scholastic Philosophy which included the teachings of Aristotle, as interpreted by the Catholic Thomas Aquinas and other prominent Christian thinkers of the Middle Ages. He was also exposed to the renaissance rebirth of Neoplatonism, the ideas of the classical Greek philosopher Plato, whose manuscripts were in the monastery library and he would devote endless hours to reading, in the evenings. Bruno took strands from each of these philosophic traditions and wove them into his own unique philosophy, as we shall see. It was a spartan existence for him that involved rising very early in the morning at 4am for prayer and meditation, then after breakfast, tending to the monastery vegetable gardens followed by countless hours of educational instruction primarily in Christian theology and philosophy. The students would be confined to their quarters, the chapel or library, by sunset.

In her book, *Giordano Bruno: Philosopher/Heretic,* the author Ingrid Rowland, writes that Giordano had three personalities. One was based on "scholastic, strict, system-building." The second was a "Platonist's poetic exaltation" and the third was "a dark wit born in his parents' little house and the stiletto-sharpened streets of Naples." Interestingly, in his own writings, Giordano described himself as "irritated, recalcitrant and strange, content with nothing, stubborn as an old man of eighty, skittish as a dog that has been whipped a thousand times." He claimed that his nickname was "the exasperated."

At the age of twenty-four Giordano Bruno became a priest and then received the equivalent of a doctorate in Theology, three years later. Bruno's non-conformist thinking was concerning the officials at the monastery. Even at this early stage, although a brilliant student, he was displaying his rebellious side and coming into the firing line of the Church, when for example, he got rid of all the religious art in his student cell at the monastery, including pictures of the Virgin Madonna and St. Catherine of Siena. On another occasion, whilst having a discussion with an older priest, he defended the logic of an argument made by the fourth century priest Arius, that Jesus Christ was not fully divine. He was expressing doubts

(154) *Plato.*

(155) *Aristotle.*

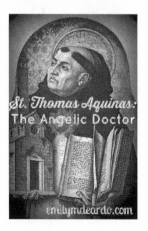

(156) *Thomas Aquinas.*

that Jesus was the son of God, a central teaching of the Catholic Church. What he was defending was the Arian heresy, which was highly controversial within the Church hierarchy at the time.

The head abbot of the monastery discovered a copy of the controversial anti-Christian philosopher Erasmus's "Commentaries and Paraphrases of the New Testament," a book that was proscribed as banned by the Catholic Church, which at the time strictly followed the Old Testament. Giordano had scribbled supportive notes in the margins of the book, which was found in the latrines that he used. This matter was reported to the Catholic Church.

At age twenty-seven, Giordano Bruno was formally advised that he was being investigated by the Catholic Inquisition. Upon hearing about this, Giordano escaped from the monastery and traveled north to Switzerland. As far as the Church was concerned, his actions amounted to a confession, so as a result, he was removed from the priesthood and excommunicated. He was now a wanted man.

Over the next fifteen years, Bruno traveled throughout Europe, always beyond the clutches of the Church. He visited Geneva, Toulouse, Lyon, Paris, London, Oxford, Wittenberg, Prague, Helmstedt, Frankfurt, Zurich, Padua and finally, Venice. He never stayed in any city for much more than a year or two.

During this time, Bruno established a reputation for his philosophical work on artificial memory and techniques that he developed to enhance one's memory. His mastery of this technique and his own phenomenal memory impressed many scholars and powerful people who he encountered during his travels.

While in Geneva in 1577 he converted to Protestantism and secured a position at the university as a professor of Sacred Theology. While at this university, he could not resist attacking the philosophical ideas of a rival professor, in a pamphlet which he had written and arranged to publish. Bruno was arrested for this and spent over two weeks in jail. He was only released when he agreed to get on his knees while apologizing to the senior professor whom he had defamed.

While in Paris he conducted a series of public lectures on logic and metaphysics. He also published a book on memorization techniques.

Intrigued by this book and his radical ideas, the French King Henry III appointed Bruno as his private tutor and royal reader. His job was to instruct the king and members of his court on the art of memory enhancement, logic and metaphysics. This time in Paris appears to have been enjoyable and creative for him. He was active in his literary pursuits, also writing a black comedic play about life in Naples, "The Candlemaker." Rumours were circulating that the Inquisition was coming to France, so he packed up and left.

Bruno moved to England where he seemed to feel out of place. His experiences at Oxford University for example, left a sour taste in his mouth. At a public lecture at the university there, the audience laughed at his heavy Neapolitan accent and the manner in which he spoke with hand movements. After this humiliation, he professed to hate the English. *"They look down their noses, laugh at you and fart at you with their lips,"* he wrote. Nevertheless, while at Oxford, Bruno developed his ideas about the universe and developed a reputation as a highly original deep and creative thinker. He was able to combine the then controversial Copernican idea of the sun-centred solar system with his neo-platonic thinking to produce a theory on the universe that was entirely original. In London, he formalized his theory by publishing a dialogue which suggested that the universe was far larger than Copernicus ever imagined. Bruno saw a universe which was inhabited by millions of planets, all revolving around "sun-like" stars. In his dialogues, Bruno argued that once people became aware they live in a vast inhabited, infinitely old universe, their lives would be transformed for the better. It is difficult to overstate how absolutely "mind-blowingly" radical Bruno's ideas would have seemed to ultra-conservative people of faith, at the time.

(157, left)
Nicolas
Copernicus.

(158, right)
Galileo Galilei.

Bruno's thoughts were not confined to the vastness of the universe. He was also thinking about things that were infinitely small, the micro-world down to what we now understand to be the sub-atomic level. He promoted an "atomic theory" which proposed that every physical thing is made up of identical particles, which he called "seeds."

By the late sixteenth century, Giordano Bruno had connected the dots and developed a new philosophy, one that was outside the scope of any previous western intellectual thought. His philosophy was able to connect the unimaginably large with the unimaginably small. He was not an empirical scientist who would rely on experiments or mathematics to test theories of the natural world, like Galileo was; he was instead, a natural philosopher who relied on rigorous intellectual thought to develop his theories, similar to Newton and Einstein, who would come later.

Bruno spent two years in England, but then in 1585 his friend and patron in London, the French ambassador, was recalled to Paris; so Bruno followed him. Upon his return, he soon realized that it was no longer the Paris which he had come to love. The city was caught up in a major religious war, so after staying for a year, he fled to the Germanic states. He ended up in the town where Martin Luther had created the Protestant Reformation, Wittenberg.

He led a quiet life there, lecturing at the university for a year before moving on to Prague and then to the Lutheran university at Helmstedt, but again, religious wars were raging here too, between the Protestant Lutherans and Protestant Calvinists. These religious disputes deepened further Bruno's cynicism of religious dogma. So again, he moved, this time to Frankfurt, which was to be his last northern European visit.

By the time he arrived in Frankfurt, he had reached the age of twenty-eight and had written and published most of his material, producing over thirty titles in the form of treatises, pamphlets, dialogues, poems and plays. The central theme that was emerging from his lectures and writing was his belief the Earth and Sun were not at the centre of the universe, but instead the universe was unimaginably vast and that all of the stars were like our Sun, with planetary systems revolving around them. This was incredibly radical thinking for the time and of course, his beliefs directly contradicted the Catholic Church's doctrine of the Earth and mankind being at the centre of the universe.

From a scientific point of view, Giordano's theory was a significant advancement from the 2,000 year Ptolemic earth centred-heliocentric view, which aligned perfectly with the doctrine of the Church. The common theme of Giordano Bruno's radical beliefs was immensity. The immense vastness of the universe and the insignificance of humanity within it, fascinated him. He gained strength from this deep insight, which seemed to put his persecution by the Catholic Church, into its right perspective. He was not about to give up his beliefs. There is a particular excerpt in a dialogue which he wrote, that gives us a good insight into his state of mind in his determination to resist the onslaught brought upon him by the Church. He is talking about an incident that occurred in his home town of Nola, and states:

Fate has decreed that Vasta, wife of Albenzio Savolino, when she means to curl her hair at her temples, shall burn fifty-seven hairs for having let the curling iron get too hot, but she won't burn her scalp and hence shall not swear when she smells the stench, but shall endure it patiently. That from the dung of her ox fifty-two dung beetles shall be born, of which fourteen shall be trampled and killed by Albenzio's foot, twenty-six shall die upside down, twenty-two shall live in a hole, eighty shall make a pilgrim's progress around the yard, forty-two shall retire to live under the stone by the door, sixteen shall roll their ball of dung wherever they please, and the rest shall scurry around at random. Albenzio Savolino's bitch shall conceive five puppies, of which three shall live out their natural lifespan and two shall be thrown away, and of these three the first shall resemble its mother, the second shall be mongrel, and the third shall partly resemble the father and partly resemble Polidoro's dog. Albenzio, when he bends over to pick up a broken needle, shall snap the red drawstring of his underpants, and if he should blaspheme for that reason, I mean for him to be punished thus: tonight his soup shall be too salty and taste of smoke, he shall fall and break his wine flask.

I have quoted the above excerpt because it gives us an idea of how random he believed the universe was. It paints a vivid picture of chaos and a lack of any defined order and structure. We can see that he views the things of this material world as comprising random events and numbers, beautifully illustrated by his complete disinterest in mathematically accounting for the dung beetles that he writes about. In Giordano Bruno's view of cosmology, disordered randomness applied not just to the trivial things that were going on in his hometown of Nola, but also to profoundly great and sacred things like the workings of the universe.

In his book, *The Song of Circe* written in 1582, a mystical sorceress calls the universe into order, starting with the sun:

> Apollo, author of poetry, quiver bearer, bowman, of the powerful arrows, Pythian, laurel-crowned, prophetic, shepherd, seer, priest, and physician. Brilliant, rosy, long-haired, beautiful-locked, blond, bright, placid, bard, singer, teller of truth. Reveal, I pray, your lions, your lynxes, goats, baboons, seagulls, calves, snakes, elephants. The turtle, butterfish, tuna, ray, whale, and all your other creatures of that kind.

What comes through loud and clear in this excerpt is the sheer joy that Giordano derives from exquisite randomness and his outright refusal to believe that an omnipotent God who has placed mankind at the centre of the universe created a systematic order purely for the enjoyment of man; when in fact he believes the reality is a vast universe created from random brilliance, which he celebrates with vivid expressive prose.

Giordano Bruno's vision of a vast universe containing an abundance of intelligent life was heresy at its worst, as far as the Church was concerned. If there were a vast number of other civilizations, this made an absurdity of the Christian creation story. It also eliminated God's difference from humanity. Giordano had written that he started having doubts about Christianity at the age of eighteen. In his philosophy, a man-made god has no place, neither does the doctrine of original sin. Very importantly, his philosophy laid the foundations for modern physics, cosmology and astronomy.

(159) *Venice.*
(160) *Giovanni Mocenigo.*
(161) *Venetian gondola.*

In 1592, after fifteen years away from Italy, and with the full knowledge that the Catholic Church was hell bent on making an example of him, he did something very strange; he came back to Italy. Was he homesick? Did he believe that he was safe in progressive Venice? In any event, regardless of his true motives he went to Venice where he secured a job tutoring a Venetian nobleman Giovanni Mocenigo, who had read many of his works. He particularly wanted Bruno to help him master his advanced memory recall techniques.

They seemed to have had a falling out when Mocenigo was not progressing at the rate he wished to, and also he was annoyed with the excessive attention Bruno was giving to his wife. As a result, fully aware that he was a wanted man, according to the later testimony of Bruno, one morning Mocenigo ordered five of his servants to lift Bruno out of his bed and carry him to the attic of the palazzo. Locked in the attic, Bruno was told by Mocenigo that unless he revealed his best and most secretive techniques for memory enhancement, something unpleasant would happen to him. Bruno replied: "*I have taught you enough, more than I was obliged to, and I do not deserve to be treated like this.*"

The next day, Mocenigo reported Bruno to the Church authorities, who then collected him and delivered him to the Inquisition. During the Inquisition hearing held in Venice, Mocenigo wrote a three-page statement claiming Giordano Bruno said it was a great blasphemy for Catholics to say that bread transmutes the flesh and that Catholic opinions were the teaching of asses. He accused Bruno of being an enemy of the Church, by claiming that Christ was a wretch and that the Virgin could not have given birth. In his statement he also wrote that Bruno had plans to make himself the head of a new sect under a new philosophy.

In his own testimony, Bruno admitted having some doubts about Catholicism, but he denied holding heretical positions. He did however, make what in hindsight appears to have been an unwise admission, when he told the Venetian Inquisitors that ever since he was a young man, he harbored doubts about whether Jesus was the son of God. It is this admission that seems to have mostly offended the Inquisitors and motivated them to keep him in prison, even after Bruno gave his final testimony on 30th July 1592 in which he retracted all of the heretical statements that were attributed to him by his Venetian accusers.

On his knees, before the three Venetian Inquisitors, Bruno said:

> I humbly beg pardon of the Lord God and your illustrious Lordships for all the errors that I have committed, and am ready to carry out whatever your prudence shall have deliberated and judged expedient to my soul.

But Bruno still could not stop himself. While being held in his cell in Venice, awaiting a decision of the Inquisition of a request by Rome for his extradition, he got into yet another heated religious argument with his fellow prisoners, both of whom were priests. The argument concerned a statement that the Bible states Jesus made on the cross: "*Father, let this cup pass me by.*" Bruno argued that this statement proved that Jesus was mortal. The priests were horrified.

It took a few more months for the decision to extradite Bruno to Rome, to be made, but in February 1593 Venetian authorities loaded Bruno on a ship bound for Rome. For the last seven years of his life, he lived in a solitary prison cell, close to St. Peters square in Rome.

The Roman Inquisitors made it clear to Bruno, that in addition to his many blasphemous statements against the Catholic doctrine, they were particularly disturbed by his theory of the universe where he claimed that:

there are many worlds, and all the stars are worlds, and he thinks that anyone who believes that this is the only world is extremely ignorant.

The Roman Inquisitors closely examined the transcripts of the Venetian Inquisition as well as reading all of Bruno's published literature. In 1599, the highly regarded Jesuit Robert Bellarmine, was made a Cardinal by Pope Clement VIII. After being appointed Cardinal, Bellarmine was also appointed to the Roman Inquisition. Once there, Bellarmine plotted to use his new power and his incisive mind to turn the screws heavily on Giordano Bruno, who he detested. Cardinal Bellarmine refined all of the heretical charges against Bruno down to eight propositions and stated that Bruno would need to convince the Inquisition that he was willing to recant all eight of them, if he wished to save his life. Unfortunately, the transcripts of what the eight propositions included, have been lost, but we have a summary of four general areas of concern, in which Bruno refused to budge. These were:

His rejection of the divinity and incarnation of Jesus Christ
His belief in the existence of multiple worlds
His belief in the souls of animals
His rejection of the art of divination

These four areas of concern became the central focus of Bellarmine's and the Inquisition's investigation and questioning.

In the end, Giordano Bruno gave his inquisitors a clear ultimatum. He told them that if Pope Clement VIII confirmed that the actions he was charged with were definitely heretical, then he would recant. If there was no such confirmation coming from the Pope, he declared he would not recant. This demand was considered by the Inquisition to be a gross act of disrespect for its authority and power, so it did not help his case. As expected, the Pope did not reply to Bruno's request. During a series of heated exchanges, Bruno said to Bellarmine: "*You lie through your throat.*" Frustrated by his intransigence, the Inquisitors debated whether they should have Bruno tortured. As his biographer

Ingrid Rowland put it: "*In his own way, in his own terms, Giordano Bruno now began to prepare for his own martyrdom.*"

Bruno was forced to kneel before his Inquisitors while hearing the verdict:

"*We declare you, the aforementioned Giordano Bruno, to be an impertinent, pertinacious, and obstinate heretic. We now expel you from our ecclesiastical bar and from our holy and immaculate Church, of whose mercy you have now rendered yourself unworthy.*"

Bruno's reply was:

"*You may be more afraid to bring that sentence against me, than I am to accept it.*"

It took some time for the Inquisition to decide to burn Giordano Bruno at the stake. The Church had to weigh the risk of offending Bruno's powerful friends around Europe including kings, ambassadors and dukes, some of whom were allied with the Pope; with the necessity of sending a powerful message that the Church would not tolerate radical heresy coming from thinkers who dared to question the very foundations of the Catholic doctrinal belief system.

The Church had good reason to be concerned that executing Bruno would have negative repercussions to their prestige and political power. Also execution could be viewed as a failure on the part of the Church for not succeeding in their stated aim that Inquisitions should not be used for punishment but instead to re-educate those who had been led astray from the core beliefs of the Church through admonition and persuasion.

On 8th February, 1600, Church officials performed what was called a "solemn degradation." In this ceremony, Bruno was stripped of his priesthood, his deacon's stole, his manipole, his acolyte's candle, his Dominican scapular and his habit. Then he was shaved all over his body, dressed in the clothes of a common layman and turned over to a Bailiff. The Bailiff represented the secular branch of the Roman government. It was they who did the dirty work of execution, not the Church officials. Giordano Bruno was imprisoned for eight days at the Castel San Angelo in central Rome, during which many of his supporters made unsuccessful pleas and attempts to convince him to repent his heresies.

In the early morning of the 17th February 1600, the day after Ash Wednesday, the primary Christian day of penance, a courageous scientist from the humble town of Nola near Molise, Giordano Bruno, rode to the Campo di Fiore on a mule, the traditional animal to transport people going to their deaths. He was accompanied by Papal guards and walking behind him were a number of Cardinals led by Robert Bellarmine and other Church officials. Many of his supporters were there yet again pleading with him to abandon his obstinacy and admit to his heresies in the hope his execution would not go ahead.

He could not speak because he had been gagged with a leather bridle to prevent him from shouting out heresies to the crowd which had assembled in the piazza that day. When he arrived at the centre of the piazza, the guards stripped Bruno naked and tied him to a wooden stake that was erected at the centre of a pyre lit up in flames of charcoal and firewood. A priest held up a crucifix to Bruno's face, but he instantly turned his head away. As the crowd watched in utter silence, the heretic was totally consumed by the raging fire. Witnesses there that day claim they did not hear any sound coming from Bruno. When the job had been done and the fire was exhausted, his remains were taken away and literally dumped into the nearby Tiber river. By carrying out this barbarous act, the Church appeared to have failed the objectives of its

162)
Robert Bellarmine.

163) Roman
Catholic Inquisition.

Inquisition which was to "admonish and persuade" people found guilty of heresy, not to punish them with death.

The Catholic Inquisition would arrive unnannounced in a town and give people accused of heresy an opportunity to admit their grave sin. Those who confessed received an immediate punishment ranging from banishment away from their town to a whipping. If the heretic did not confess, extreme torture and execution were inevitable. We don't know how many people were executed by the Catholic Inquisition during the Middle Ages, but estimates are that at least 300,000 people died.

Giordano Bruno paid the ultimate price for his ideas and beliefs which were dramatically inconsistent with those of the Church. Did the Church overreact by executing him? It seems they believed they did, because when the Church had to deal with another "obstinate heretic," Galileo Galilei, fifty years later, and put him on trial for his scientific beliefs, although finding him guilty, rather than execute him, they imprisoned him in the Castel San Angelo dungeon prison in Rome.

Today, Giordano Bruno is widely respected as a martyr who died for the causes of freedom of speech and enlightened science. On the pedestal of the statue of Giordano Bruno in the Campo di Fiori Rome, bronze engraved letters read: "*To Bruno, from the generation he foresaw, here, where the pyre burned.*"

On the 17th February every year, the Mayor of Rome lays a wreath, draped in red and gold ribbons, at Giordano Bruno's feet.

The burning of Giordano Bruno came to haunt the man who was the most responsible for it, Cardinal Robert Bellarmine. Within a decade of Bruno's execution, Galileo Galilei was using his telescope to observe the heavens. He became the first human to see the moons of Jupiter, the rings of Saturn, Sun spots and the craters of the Moon.

What Galileo saw, convinced him that Copernicus had it right when he stated that the Earth revolved around the Sun, rather than the other way around, as Catholic doctrine dictated.

This is what Cardinal Robert Bellarmine wrote:

In Genesis, the Psalms, Ecclesiastes, and Joshua, you will find all agreeing that the sun is in heaven and turns around the earth with great speed, and that the earth is very far from heaven and sits motionless at the center of the world.

(164) *The Castel San Angelo in Rome, where Galileo was imprisoned.*

(165) *Giordano Bruno burnt at the stake in Camp di Fiori, Rome.*

Having learnt a lesson in the Bruno case, Cardinal Robert Bellarmine moved cautiously and slowly when Galileo faced the Inquisition. He didn't condemn Galileo, but instead cautioned him. In a statement in 1615, he told Galileo and other scientists to treat the Copernican view as a theoretical hypothesis and not as factual truth. In 1616, Galileo did not heed the advice of the Church and openly crossed the line when he publicly advocated the views of Copernicus to be factual. Bellarmine again warned Galileo, but he did not put Galileo on trial.

Nevertheless, Galileo did finally face the Roman Inquisition in 1632, eleven years after the death of Cardinal Robert Bellarmine. This was towards the end of Galileo's scientific career and although he was found guilty of heresy, unlike the braver Bruno, he chose to recant his ideas, so as a result, was not executed but instead imprisoned in the Castel San Angelo dungeon prison for life. He was sentenced in 1633 and died in prison on 8th January 1642.

17

CHARLES VII –
THE MAJESTIC MONARCH

⟶⟨

NE OF THE GREATEST IMPACTS ON THE POLITICAL, ECONOMIC, CULTURAL and social conditions of southern Italy, was its conquest by the French Emperor, Napoleon Bonaparte. He is responsible for the dismantling of much of the ancient feudal regime that had existed there since the time of the Normans in the 11th century, as we have seen. When war had broken out between Austria and Revolutionary France in 1792, the French invaded the Italian peninsula, consolidated many of the Italian states and established them as republics. This was to be short lived because in 1799 the combined Austrian and Russian armies succeeded in evicting the French out of Italy, leading to the demise of the fragile republics.

After Napoleon's rise to power, the Italian peninsula was once again conquered by the French and this time was divided into three distinct spheres of influence. The northern - central region of Italy comprising

Piedmont, Liguria, Parma, Piacenza, Tuscany and Rome was placed (annexed) under the direct control of the French Empire. The newly created Kingdom of Italy which comprised Lombardy, Venice, Reggio, Modena and Romagna, came under the direct rule of Napoleon Bonaparte himself. Finally, the Kingdom of Naples which comprised most of southern Italy, including Molise and Abruzzo, was first ruled by Napoleon's brother, Joseph Bonaparte, and then was passed on to Napoleon's brother-in-law Joachim Murat, who was married to Caroline Bonaparte.

Before we examine the achievements of the Napoleonic Kingdom of Naples, let us look at what had existed there before this conquest. As a result of the War of Spanish Succession which lasted from 1701 to 1714, Naples came under the influence of the Austrian Habsburgs. In 1734 the Spanish prince Don Carlos de Bourbon (later also becoming King Charles III of Spain) conquered Naples, removed the Austrians and established the Kingdom of Naples which then became an independent dynastic state under the control of the Spanish Bourbon rulers. As ruler, Don Carlos crowned himself King Charles VII of Naples. One of the first things that he did after taking power was to visit the remains of the patron saint of Naples, San Gennaro, to seek his blessing.

Charles ruled Naples in the spirit of "enlightened despotism" promoting reforms to modernize the state and to reduce social and political inequalities and injustices. But in his attempt to implement these policies he came into direct conflict with the two most powerful forces in southern Italy, the feudal nobility and the Catholic Church. Similar power struggles were being played out in other parts of Europe, but the combination of the feudal system and influence of the Church was more engrained and extensive in southern Italy than most other regions of Europe. The struggles that Charles was up against with the nobility and feudal barons in his Kingdom of Naples were a direct result of his efforts to restructure the administrative and political institutions of the kingdom and above all to also increase the taxation revenue for his monarchy. Does this sound familiar? This is exactly what King Ferdinand I did when he ruled Naples in the fifteenth century, antagonizing the barons then as well.

(166) *Italy in 1800.*

(167) *King Charles VII of Naples.*

Also looming, was an economic challenge Charles had to contend with which threatened the social fabric of southern Italian communities. There was a growing demand in Europe for a variety of agricultural products which the south was renowned for, including grain, olive oil, citrus fruits and spices; and as a response to this growing demand, the incentive to enclose smaller plots of communal agricultural land into larger privatized farms was very strong.

The expansion of privately owned noble agricultural farms came into direct conflict with two key pillars of the southern agrarian economy; the feudal structure which allowed for peasant farmers to make a living from the land, and the collective forms of farming that centred around the common lands in rural communities.

This struggle between wealthy nobles accumulating larger farm property holdings and paying more taxes to the king as a result; and common peasant farmers having less land to work on and make a living from, as well as the greater centralization of political and economic power away from the regions and into the city of Naples instead, led to ongoing unrest within the kingdom.

In the meantime, with Charles accumulating so much power, the Church felt that its influence within the kingdom had diminished as well. As a result, Charles did not enjoy a good relationship with the Church hierarchy. But there were other areas of interest, where Charles did achieve success. He initiated a number of archaeological excavations which led to the discoveries of Pompeii and Herculaneum. Also, numerous well known artists and writers visited the city during this time including the great German writer Goethe who was quoted as saying: "See Naples and die."

But where King Charles VII particularly excelled was with his building projects. The San Carlo Theatre established Naples as a major European centre of classical music and opera. One of the great architects working for the king was Luigi Vanvitelli who favored the baroque style of building construction. Before he left Rome, he worked on the construction of the Trevi Fountain and stabilized the dome of St. Peter's Basilica. The king personally convinced Vanvitelli to come to Naples where he spent most of his time there on the design and construction of the Royal Palace of Caserta, which rivalled the spectacular Versailles Palace outside of Paris in grandeur, especially with is magnificent beautifully manicured gardens.

King Charles VII also had a passionate vision to eliminate

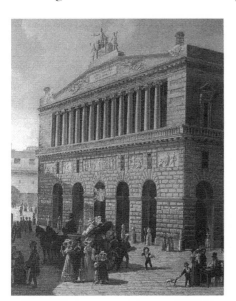

poverty from his kingdom. To this end, he commissioned another well-known architect, Ferdinando Fuga, to build a substantial structure known as "The House of the Poor" in 1751. This project was so significant that work on it continued until 1829 and was little used, because it was under constant renovation.

(168) *Royal Palace of Caserta, outside Naples.*

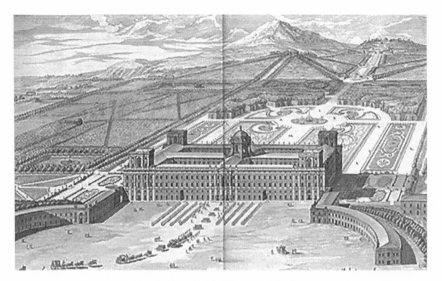

(169) *San Carlo Theatre, Naples.*

This was also a time in Europe when science, art and mysticism became popular. This can be seen by the various works of artists who were commissioned by the king; including the alchemist, scientist and nobleman, Raimondo di Sangro, who completed the stunning mystical fresco paintings in the San Severo Chapel and Giuseppe Sanmartino, who sculpted the "Veiled Christ" in the same chapel, considered to be one of the finest sculptures in Europe.

On 10th August 1759 Charles succeeded his elder brother Ferdinand VI and became King Charles III of Spain. Treaty requirements however prevented him from holding other crowns. So on 6th October Charles abdicated his crown of Naples and left his third son, the eight-year old Ferdinand on the throne. He had to choose his third son because his eldest Philip had been excluded from succession due to illnesses and his second son Charles was his heir to the Spanish throne.

King Ferdinand IV of Naples ended up having one of the longest reigns in European history. Ferdinand was not your typical power-hungry dynastic tyrant and instead grew into a very humble and genuine "man of the people." He was loved for his distinctive Neapolitan dialect and was well known for setting up a small stand in the central market of Naples every evening, so that he could give away to the poor his hunted game or fish that he caught that day.

Amongst his other achievements during his long reign was the establishment of a regular lottery in which the common people could participate and one of the best silk factories in Europe, which focused on producing exquisite hand-crafted silk hangings for royal palaces, of which there were many throughout Europe. Out of this project, a community of highly skilled artisan silk weavers was established, described in 1798 as the "Silk Weavers' Royal Colony."

The Parthenopean Republic in 1799 brought the Spanish Bourbon reign to an ubrupt end, but this Republic failed; bringing Ferdinand back into power, until he was again overthrown after Napoleon's French army entered Naples in 1806. King Ferdinand IV returned to the throne in 1815, after the French rule ended, and he remained as the king until his death in 1825.

The struggle for power in the Kingdom of Naples which led to the formation of the Parthenopean Republic in January 1799 was extremely violent and has been described as an ideological war between the radical educated Jacobins, mainly middle-class intellectuals and noble property owners who were inspired by the French Revolution (which was happening at the same time) and who wanted more economic rights, freedoms and political power; and the monarchists, who supported the divine absolute power of the royal lineage of kings and wanted the Bourbon dynasty led by Ferdinand to remain in power.

After being overthrown from power, King Ferdinand IV fled Naples to seek exile in Sicily, and a new French-backed republican government was formed by the Neapolitan Jacobins. The new government soon found itself in severe financial difficulties, unable to form its own army and thus dependent on French protection and was not successful in its attempts to introduce democratic land reforms within the Campania, Molise, Abruzzo and Calabria provinces which it controlled.

The revolution was to be short-lived, when in June 1799 a counter-revolution was orchestrated by allies of the Bourbon King Ferdinand; the Papal States and the British. A Papal army and an English naval fleet commanded by Admiral Horatio Nelson engaged in fierce brutal battles with the Neapolitan revolutionaries, resulting in the eventual return of King Ferdinand IV to Naples in 1802.

We have seen that the French had been strong supporters of the Jacobin revolutionaries who took control in Naples, so it was no surprise that in 1806 Napoleon Bonaparte took revenge against the Spanish Bourbon dynasty by sending an invasion force to take control of Naples and install his brother Joseph as the new King of Naples.

18

JOACHIM MURAT – NAPOLEON'S MAN

Let us now examine the achievements of the French Napoleonic rule over the Kingdom of Naples. The French control of southern Italy lasted from 1806 to 1815 and began when Napoleon Bonaparte made a declaration from the Schonbrunn Palace in Vienna in December 1805, that the Bourbon dynasty no longer ruled the Kingdom of Naples. In January 1806 the Neapolitan ruler Ferdinand IV and his wife, Maria Carolina, took refuge on British warships and escaped Naples for Sicily, where they remained until the collapse of French rule in 1815.

In February 1806, a French army entered Naples and installed Napoleon's brother Joseph as the king. Joseph had accepted the Neapolitan throne reluctantly and only ruled there for two years before his brother transferred him to the Spanish throne. In March 1808, Joseph was succeeded to the throne of Naples by his brother-in-law, Joachim Murat, the husband of Caroline Bonaparte.

In a book published in 1986, the Italian historian Pasquale Villani said this about the Napoleonic Kingdom of Naples:

(170, above left) *Napoleon Bonaparte.* (171, below left) *Joseph Bonaparte.*
(172, above) *French army in Naples.*

the years between 1806 and 1815, the so-called 'French decade,' were amongst the most dramatic and revolutionary in the entire history of the Kingdom of Naples.

During this period of French rule there was a serious attempt to dismantle the feudal structure in southern Italy, which was largely successful. Within a relatively short time the French laid the foundations of a centralized, bureaucratic and autocratic monarchy with much of the power held in the city of Naples.

In addition to the abolition of feudalism, other reforms included the restructuring of the central and outlying administrative institutions of the state apparatus and the taking of full control of the financial administration and taxation of the kingdom.

The French also had to deal with the huge amount of debt they had inherited from the Bourbon Spanish rulers; debt that had been used for many extravagant building projects. The total debt was over 100 million Ducats compared to an annual crown revenue of 12 million Ducats when the French took over. They sold crown and church lands and increased taxation to pay off a large proportion of this debt. Again, this put the French rulers into direct conflict with the wealthy noble landowners who paid most of the tax and also the Church who had to give up properties for sale.

Although much of the groundwork for the planning of the reform program was laid under the rule of Joseph Bonaparte, it was Joachim Murat who was left with the responsibility of implementing these reforms.

Joachim Murat plays a major role in this story of the history of Molise and Abruzzo; particularly how the feudal system was largely dismantled, directly affecting the lives of my family ancestors. I want to devote some time now to examine his life before he took control of southern Italy and also his major achievements when in power. He was born in 1767 and although originally destined for a career in the Church, he instead ran away from home and joined the army at the age of 20.

In the years that followed, Murat served as one of Napoleon's high ranking officers, serving with distinction on the battlefields of Egypt and Italy, and was recognized as one of Europe's most exceptional cavalry officers.

He married Caroline Bonaparte, Napoleon's ambitious sister, in 1802. Two years later, Joachim Murat was among the elite eighteen men who were designated Marshalls of Napoleon's Empire, his personal entourage. As the French Empire expanded, members of the Bonaparte family received the thrones of newly conquered territories. As we have seen, Joseph, Napoleon's eldest brother was originally placed onto the throne of Naples, however once Spain fell under French rule, Joseph was transferred to that throne which was formerly held by Carlos IV. Napoleon rewarded his brother-in-law Murat by giving him the Kingdom of Naples. Murat and Caroline had expressed interest in this position after they were overlooked for the throne of the Germanic Kingdom of Wesphalia. Murat entered Naples as the king on 6th September 1808, with Caroline arriving two weeks later.

In his first six weeks as king, Murat had succeeded in gaining the respect of many Neapolitans both from the ruling class and also commoners. He also successfully captured the island of Capri from British control. Napoleon Bonaparte hoped that Murat would rule the Kingdom of Naples as a satellite kingdom of France with many key positions held by French officials. However, the new king and queen ruled Naples more like an independent kingdom and placed many Neapolitans in key positions that were based on merit, limiting the control of French officials. This merit based system enabled even the most modest citizens of the kingdom to pursue a career in the government and to advance.

The most important reform that Murat implemented was the abolition of feudalism in the Kingdom of Naples, which was enacted into law on 2nd August 1806. In order to implement this law, Murat restructured the kingdom into fourteen provinces (one of which was Campobasso and its surrounding towns including Montagano, where my parents were born). These provinces were then subdivided into districts. Each province was governed by a provincial council, the members of which were selected by the king. It was the primary responsibility of the members of each provincial council to implement the land reforms which came out of the abolition of feudalism laws. This reform created immediate problems because all of a sudden, the traditional feudal barons and nobles lost much of their power and actively resisted Murat's policies.

Those lands formerly held under the nearly 1,000 years old system of feudal title were instantly transferred into private property. This meant that all of a sudden, peasants throughout southern Italy, including my family, gained legal ownership of their farming plots and residential land which they were previously renting from feudal barons and the Church. This was an incredibly significant reform that marked the beginning of an economically independent working class and middle class in southern Italy.

Murat also opened up the opportunity for Neapolitan citizens to pursue military careers and enroll in the former Bourbon military academy. He cited himself as an example, having risen through the

French military ranks as the son of an inn-keeper. Murat also further expanded the already prestigious University of Naples and commissioned an astronomical observatory, the first in southern Italy.

By 1812 the once powerful Napoleonic Empire was crumbling. In October of 1813 an allied force defeated the French at Leipzig. By this stage, Murat was seeing the writing on the wall for the French Empire and for his Kingdom of Naples. Murat and Caroline began to explore their post-Napoleon survival options by entering into discussions with both the Austrians and the British.

On the 11th January 1814 Murat formally abandoned Napoleon by signing a treaty with Austria. This treaty guaranteed the Kingdom of Naples to Murat in exchange for his pledging of 30,000 troops to support the Austrian campaign in Italy.

Upon hearing the news of Murat's betrayal, Napoleon blamed his sister when he was quoted as saying:"*His wife made him defect, Caroline, my sister, has betrayed me!*"

Napoleon simply refused to believe that his accomplished cavalry officer and close member of his entourage was capable of stabbing him in the back.

In late January 1814 Murat entered Rome with the ambition of uniting Italy and himself becoming the king of Italy. His ambitious plan was not received well by the people of Rome. To further complicate his situation, Murat was reluctant to use his 30,000 troops to fight with the Austrians against the French. Austrian commanders were furious with Murat as he delayed and delayed his decision to deploy the troops. Finally, the embattled Murat finally led his troops to attack France and its Italian allies at Piacenza on 14th April 1814. The treaty with Austria assured Murat for the time being at least, he would remain on the throne in Naples.

With Emperor Napoleon Bonaparte's defeat and exile to the island of Elba in May of 1814, Murat reasoned that he, the ruler of a French client-state, would not remain in power for much longer. In fact, there was already talk circulating about restoring the Spanish Bourbons back to the throne of Naples. Then suddenly, things dramatically changed when Napoleon escaped from Elba and set out for Paris to reclaim his empire, in the "100-day march." Murat now decided to ally himself with his brother-in-law and to wage war against the Austrians. Murat's army fought the Austrians in Italy for the two purposes of saving his own reign in Naples and preventing the Austrians from invading France and attempting to bring down Napoleon. But Murat's efforts were to no avail when his army lost a major battle against the Austrians near the Italian town of Tolentino, within the Kingdom of Naples in May 1815.

With Austrian troops advancing on the city of Naples, Murat fled the city. On 18th May 1815 he issued this proclamation to the people:

"The enemy is still distant, but I shall never expose you to the terrors of warfare within our capital. If destiny must strike, let it strike only me."

Things took a rapid turn for the worse for the French when on 23rd May 1815 Ferdinand IV marched back into the city of Naples and reclaimed his kingdom. Instead of retaining the title, "Ferdinand IV, King of Naples," he assumed the title of Ferdinand I, King of the Two Sicilies, reflecting his control of not only southern Italy but the island of Sicily as well. Ferdinand continued to rule until he died in 1825. After fleeing Italy, Murat went to Paris but Napoleon was so upset with his brother-in-law, he refused to see

(173) *Joachim Murat.*

(174) *Caroline Bonaparte.*

(175) *Execution of Joachim Murat*
(left).
(176) *Giuseppe Mazzini, founder
of "Young Italy"* (above).

him. After the dramatic defeat of Napoleon's forces at Waterloo, Murat's future was sealed. His kingdom was firmly back in the hands of the Spanish Bourbons and there was absolutely nothing he could do about it. Murat was offered the opportunity to retire gracefully and live out his remaining days in peaceful anonymity.

His ego and sense of grandeur got the better of him when instead, he took a handful of his most loyal men and set sail for Pizzo on the coast of Calabria, with some deluded sense that he could use this base as a springboard to raise an army and retake Naples!

Instead, Murat was captured by Spanish Bourbon troops, imprisoned, put on trial and sentenced to death. His appeals to Ferdinand for clemency, were ignored. On 18th October 1815 in a typical display of bravado, Joachim Murat refused to be blindfolded before he was executed by a firing squad.

After the death of her husband, Caroline Bonaparte fled to the then Austrian controlled city of Trieste, where amongst other things, she wrote her memoirs. Whilst in exile, under the protection of the Austrians, she took on the title "Countess of Lipona." Lipona is an anagram of Napoli. In 1830 she married the wealthy Francesco MacDonald, who had been the Minister of War in the Kingdom of Naples in 1814-15. She later moved to Florence where she remained until her death in 1839.

We won't quite leave the story of Murat here though. We can see Murat's level of foresight regarding the events that were going to unfold in Italy, with this proclamation which he issued from the Adriatic coastal town of Rimini, in March 1815: "Italians! The hour has come to engage in your highest destiny. Providence has called you to be an independent nation. From the Alps to the straits of Italy, there is but one cry, Italian independence!"

This was the first time that a formal political proclamation had been made, calling for all foreign forces to be driven out of Italy and for the entire peninsula to be unified into one nation. It is seen as the opening statement of the "Risorgimento," what was to become the Italian word for the drive to unify Italy. Giuseppe Mazzini, who in 1831 founded the "Young Italy" movement, a society devoted to the cause of unifying Italy into a class-free, democratic republic nation, was inspired by the proclamation made by Joachim Murat.

19

UNIFICATION OF
ITALY AND PEASANT
REBELLION

⟶

E HAVE SEEN FROM THE PREVIOUS CHAPTER, THAT IN 1831 GIUSEPPE
Mazzini founded a society of radical nationalist young Italians
who were determined to see the peninsula unified into one democratic
nation. The "Young Italy" movement was focused on producing
propaganda to promote this objective. Mazzini himself said, "Our
problem is, above all things, a problem of national education." He
realized that the people of Italy had to be persuaded of the benefits of
Italy becoming one nation.

I do not intend here to recount in detail, the events which led to
the unification of Italy. My main focus in this chapter will be to look
at how the events leading to unification impacted upon the Molise and
Abruzzo regions of central Italy.

Giuseppe Garibaldi is the hero of Italian unification. He joined
forces with Mazzini in 1833. An Italian patriot, freedom fighter, repub-

lican and true believer of the Risorgimento, the movement to unify Italy; he led his fierce guerilla "Red Shirts" to bring down the Spanish Bourbon Kingdom of Naples and Sicily, and lay the foundation for the liberation of Italy from foreign rule. The struggle was to continue for a number of years.

In September and October 1860, Garibaldi's volunteer army of Red Shirt guerillas, known as the Matese Legion, were instrumental in defeating and overthrowing the Spanish Bourbon Kingdom of Two Sicilies (which ruled over central and southern Italy as well as Sicily) in a series of battles around the Volturno river, between the central Italian towns of Capua and Caserta.

Having achieved this major victory, Garibaldi then surrendered central and southern Italy to King Victor Emmanuel II of Piedmont-Sardinia. Garibaldi believed that Italian unification could only be achieved with the assistance of Victor Emmanuel and his very capable Prime Minister, Camillo Benso, better known as the Count of Cavour. Cavour gave up Nice and Savoy to France, to gain this nation's support for Piedmont-Sardinia control of central and southern Italy. This was crucial because France was very influential in the political affairs of Italy at the time.

If we zoom in on Molise, Abruzzo and other central Italian regions during this time, over ninety percent of the people were barely literate or illiterate peasants living in small villages, in relative poverty, surviving

(177) *Giuseppe Garibaldi.*   (178) *King Victor Emmanuel II.*

mainly from the produce they grew and farmed. During the Kingdom of Two Sicilies, of a total 1,848 villages in southern Italy, 1,621 had no roads. But this Bourbon kingdom successfully kept taxes low and the price of food, cheap. When King Victor Emmanuel II took control, taxes were increased and food prices escalated, creating much resentment and dissent amongst the people.

Also during this time, many villages in Molise, Abruzzo and surrounding regions had to contend with outbreaks of malaria and polio as well as roaming bands of brigands' intent on stealing precious food and anything else of value they could get their hands on.

So in the decade following 1861, as a political revolution was going on to unify Italy into one nation, nothing changed for the peasants of central Italy, except as we have seen, higher taxes and increasing food prices. There was no social revolution to free them from the tyranny of greedy baron landlords and from the political corruption of local municipal administrators, responsible for the running of villages.

On the 17th March 1861, Victor Emmanuel II was proclaimed the King of Italy and the country became a constitutional monarchy. But not all of Italy was unified yet. The Papal States were still operating independently. Civil unrest was escalating and half of the new kingdom's army had to be deployed in central and southern Italy to suppress a series of peasant rebellions protesting the rapid deterioration in their living conditions for the reasons that we have already seen.

On 20th September 1870, the army of King Victor Emmanuelle II took control of the city of Rome and thereby defeated the Papal States under Pope Pius IX, finally ending the long process of the Risorgimento, and unifying all of Italy as a constitutional monarchy with a king, an elected parliament and a government headed by a Prime Minister.

Brigandage created much havoc and distress in central and southern Italy, particularly between 1861-65. "Brigands" is a term to describe groups of disaffected people who roamed the countryside and mountains, seeking food, shelter and other resources to take by force. They came about as a result of the drastic economic policies implemented by the kingdom of Victor Emmanuel II.

(180)
Roaming peasant brigands.

(179) *Camillo Benso "Cavour."*

The bands of brigands were formed by an assort-ment of desperate people, including former Garibaldi Red Shirts, unemployed soldiers of the former Bourbon army and poverty stricken peasants whose traditional ways of life had been uprooted. They were groups of totally alienated outlaws, who would gather in specified locations around a leader. They were fully armed and would attack people and property in order to alleviate their poverty and gain some political power and influence.

The Italian historian Benedetto Croce, provides this description of the life of a brigand:

> He has no bed, no clothes, no man's food, no medicine. He does not know wheat bread or meat course, but only eats an unnamed mixture of farro and rye, when he is not eating with the beasts, the roots given by their step-mother earth to those who love her. The proletarian wants to improve his own conditions as well as we do. This he expected from the so-called revolution; this he expects from the monarchy. Sure, life is a shame, the world unjust and bad, but brigandage is only poverty, utter, desperate poverty.

These people were marginalized and disappointed by the non-ful-filment of Garibaldi's revolution and proposed agrarian reforms which never eventuated. They hated their new masters, who exploited them even more than the previous ones.

The situation became even worse when the government introduced a campaign to take control of Church property and the estates of landowners, and proceeded to sell them by auction. This created severe disruption and destroyed the livelihood of hundreds of thousands of peasants who had worked these lands to grow and farm produce, paying rent to the Church and noble landowners. This centuries-old traditional way of living had now been taken away from them by a new rich class of rural bourgeoisie property owners, who often increased the rent charged to peasants for the use of their land, to the point that many could not survive.

In the summer of 1861 armed bands of brigands not only in Molise, but also in Abruzzo, Calabria, Apulia, Campania and Basilicata, engaged in a frenzy of violent rebellion which involved murder, kidnapping, robbery and arson, mainly directed at the newly rich landowners and representatives of the king and government. They would take refuge in the mountains and were protected and hidden not only by their fellow poverty-stricken peasants, but also the Church and former confiscated landowners.

It was during this peasant uprising that the Italian government responded with the deployment of over 120,000 soldiers under the command of General Enrico Cialdini. The army was faced not with a rebellion, but what really amounted to a peasant revolution involving much of the population. Many innocent people were caught up in the bloody fierce fighting occurring in villages, the countryside and in the mountains where many brigands would seek refuge. Whole villages were destroyed and thousands of peasants were shot dead for being accused of protecting or being loyal to the brigands.

This excerpt is from a letter written by an Italian army officer and has been sourced from Pasquale Villari's book, *Lettere Meridionali*:

To destroy the brigands we let blood flow in rivers, but little thought we gave to more radical measures. In this case, as in many other things, the urgency of repression led us to put aside radical remedies, those only remedies that can stop this evil, which is surely not over, and will last still for a long time. In politics we were good surgeons but very bad doctors.

In 1863 the villages of Pontelandolfo and Casalduni in the province of Benevento became the sites of a massacre of thirteen brigands by the Italian army as a reprisal for the killing of forty-five soldiers by local brigands.

Clearly, the peasant rebellion of the 1860s was a direct result of government policies that neglected and disadvantaged the traditional peoples of central and southern Italy, to the point where their livelihoods were ruined. What else were they to do? They had no political power and were really alienated from the whole unification process. Unfortunately, although the rebellion itself was put down by the time Italy achieved full political unification in 1870; the neglect of Molise, Abruzzo and other regions of central and southern Italy, was to continue unabated by successive Italian governments.

Unification of Italy in 1870.

20

WORLD WAR TWO IN ITALY

⟫

Molise, Abruzzo and the surrounding regions of central Italy played a crucial role in the United States and British led Allied removal of Axis German forces and the liberation of Italy, known as the Italian Campaign, from 10th July 1943 to 2nd May 1945, during World War Two.

The planning of the Italian Campaign started in Casablanca Morocco in January 1943, when the Allied leaders, Churchill, Roosevelt and Stalin, decided to use their massive military resources in North Africa to launch an invasion of Italy, which British Prime Minister Winston Churchill called "the soft underbelly of Europe." The mission was to topple the Mussolini regime, remove Italy from World War Two, secure the Mediterranean Sea and force Germany to divert some of its military resources away from the Russian front and into Italy, therefore taking pressure off Stalin and assisting him with the defense of the German onslaught into Russia.

181) Roosevelt and Churchill at Casablanca in 1943.

182) German Fuhrer, Adolf Hitler.

The Allies also hoped the Italian Campaign would divert German resources away from northern France, where the Allies were secretly planning their massive English Channel crossing, the D-Day invasion of Normandy France, to liberate Europe from German domination and finally push into Berlin, forcing a German surrender and hopefully bring an end to the War in Europe.

Although the invasion of Italy was going to be led by the Americans and British, they were to be joined by armed forces from Algeria, India, Morocco, France, Poland, New Zealand and Canada. On the 10th July 1943, Operation Husky, the code name for the invasion of Sicily, began with a massive series of Allied airborne and amphibious landings on the southern coast of the island. This invasion reverberated shock-

(183) US and British troops landing near Gela, Sicily on July 10th 1943.

ingly within the Italian fascist government, resulting in Prime Minister
Benito Mussolini being removed from power and arrested on 24th July
1943. Replacing Mussolini's regime was a new Allied backed provi-
sional government, under the leadership of Marshal Pietro Badoglio,
who had fiercely opposed Italy's alliance with Nazi Germany. Upon
taking power, he immediately opened up a secret channel of discussions with the Allies about ceasing hostilities and Italian assistance in
removing German forces from Italy.

On the 17th August 1943, Allied forces occupied the Sicilian port
city of Messina, expecting to encounter a strong contingent of German
forces in a large decisive battle. What they soon discovered instead, was
that over 100,000 German troops had managed to escape Sicily and
move into the Italian mainland, causing great concern for the Allies,
who had been expecting a quick, decisive victory in Sicily and not
having to take the battle to the mainland in a significant way.

Determined to defeat the plans of the Allies, German dictator Adolf
Hitler ordered the deployment of 16 additional German divisions to
the Italian mainland and instructed his army group commander in
southern Italy, Field Marshal Albert Kesselring, to defend every inch of
Italian territory to the last man, at all cost.

On the 9th September 1943, American led Allied troops landed
on the Italian coast at Salerno and proceeded to move inland. German
forces entrenched in the high Apennine Mountains at Cassino, halted
the Allied advance in a series of bloody battles that were to last for
four months. Another Allied force landed at Anzio, but was unable to

(184) *Allied forces landing at Salerno.*

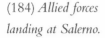

(185) *The Battle of Monte Cassino in 1943.*

advance a great distance because they were bogged down by driving rain and relentless German air raids. The Allied leaders, expecting a rapid push into central Italy, were alarmed at the ferocity of German resistance, prompting Churchill to complain; "I had hoped we were hurling a wildcat onto the shore, but all we got was a stranded whale."

The stalled Allied advance inland gave the Germans enough time to set up several defensive lines across the Apennine Mountains of Abruzzo, Campania and Molise. The southernmost of these was known as the Gustav Line, running just behind Monte Cassino. Despite air superiority in Italy, it took the Allied soldiers four brutal, bloody battles to break through heavily defended Monte Cassino and the Gustav Line.

A Benedictine monk who was an eyewitness to the Monte Cassino battles, wrote:

It was more than the stubble of a beard that told the story; it was the blank, staring eyes. The men were so tired that it was a living death. They had come from such a depth of weariness that I wondered if they would quite be able to make the return to the lives and thoughts they had known.

Things were further complicated for the Allies when American General Mark Clark, ignored supreme command orders and moved his army towards Rome, instead of cutting off and capturing the German soldiers retreating from Cassino. His puzzling decision allowed a large German army to escape further north into the mountains of Italy, eliminating what was a golden opportunity to quickly end the Italian Campaign, after the final victory at Cassino. The American military historian Carlo D'Este called General Clark's decision "*as militarily stupid as it was insubordinate.*"

As General Clark's Fifth US Army marched in to liberate Rome on 4th June 1944, met by hundreds of thousands of grateful, excited Romans who lined the streets, the D-Day invasion of Normandy, scheduled for 6th June, took priority over the Italian Campaign. As a result, six Allied army divisions were removed from Italy and redeployed to southern France to support the Allied landings in Normandy.

Although the remaining depleted Allied forces continued their mountainous village by village raids against the entrenched Germans, who were destroying bridges and roads as they slowly retreated north-wards, it took the capture of Berlin before the German forces in Italy finally surrendered on 2nd May 1945.

(186, left)
US General Mark Clark.

(187, right)
German Field Marshal Kesselring.

The Italian Campaign turned out to be a brutal and drawn out affair, resulting in the death of over 300,000 Allied and 434,000 German troops.

One of the biggest controversies of the Italian Campaign was the Allied bombing and destruction of the sacred and historically significant Monte Cassino monastery which as we have seen, was first established by Benedict in the 6th century. Both the Allies and Germans had committed to the Vatican that the famous monastery would not be attacked. After the war, the Allies insisted the air bombing of the monastery had been justified, claiming they had solid evidence the buildings had been used as part of the German defensive fortifications. A 1949 investigation concluded there was no such evidence. This investigation was kept secret from the public until 1979.

It is worth noting just how valuable the treasures of the Monte Cassino Benedictine monastery were. Prior to the battles at Monte Cassino, an extensive effort was undertaken over several months by the Vatican to remove the priceless monastery collection.

The Benedictine monastery held 800 papal documents, 100,000 original prints, 200 fragile medieval parchment hand-written manuscripts, over 80,000 books from the libraries, 500 incunabula, a

(188)
Allied forces moving into Italy, 1943.

(189) *Abbey of Monte Cassino Allied air attack.*

type of book which was printed and not handwritten, before the 16th century, and pieces of priceless art and precious tapestries. Some of these books and documents had actually originally been transferred from the Keats-Shelly palazzo in Rome to Monte Cassino, for safe keeping in the early stages of the War when there were fears that Rome would be bombed; only then to be sent back, but this time to the Vatican City and its fortress castle on the banks of the Tiber, the Castel San Angelo.

This project was proposed and directed in 1943 by German officer, Captain Maximilian Becker and Austrian officer, Lieutenant Colonel Julius Schlegal. The monastery Abbot Gregorio Diamare approved the plan, understanding the clear and present danger the treasures were under. With the help of Monte Cassino's monks, residents and German soldiers, they frantically scrambled to crate and haul away the priceless collection of artifacts as quickly as possible.

Every night, German army trucks full of treasures and accompanied by two monks, would make their way to Rome. The evacuation project was completed by November 1943, a few months before the bombing and destruction of the monastery in February 1944. Every village in Molise, Abruzzo and the surrounding region will have their unique stories about the events of World War Two and particularly how the Italian Campaign impacted upon the people living there. Later in this book I will talk about how the War impacted my mother as a young child and her family living in Montagano.

(190 and191) *Canadian soldiers in Molise, 1943.*

The recapture of the Molise village of Gambatesa by Canadian Allied forces in October 1943 is typical of what happened during the War, and is a story I would like to tell now. Gambatesa is a mountainous village which had around 4,000 inhabitants in 1943. It is 40 kilometres away from my family village of Montagano. The events which I will be describing here have been sourced from the Valente and DiRenzo family history website.

In early October 1943 the Carleton and York Regiment of the Canadian Army captured the valley of the upper Fortore river below the village of Gambatesa, from the German Army. An attempt on the night of 5-6th October 1943 by a company of the Royal 22e Canadian regiment to establish a foothold across the Fortore river was driven back by heavy and persistent German fire. The German 15th Panzer Grenadier Regiment was heavily fortified on higher ground.

At 7.30am on the 7th October 1943, both of the Canadian assault companies pressed forward along the banks of the Fortore river, but as they did so, were caught out by heavy German machine-gun fire. Nevertheless, the Canadians managed to push away from the river banks, up the long slope and across ploughed fields, even though the firing persisted and driving rain was turning the fields into heavy water-logged mud. Suddenly, in addition to the continuous German machine-gun fire, there was also shelling coming from two self-propelled longer range

(192)

Canadian soldiers with German prisoners.

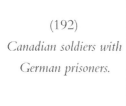

(193)

Canadian soldiers outside Gambatesa.

cannon guns, the exact position of which could not be determined by the Canadians. It was now late afternoon, and for the rest of the day and into the night the Canadian soldiers remained pinned down in their chilly, muddy, rain swept positions, by the relentless gunfire, still with no idea where the cannon fire was coming from. After 24 hours of fighting, 12 Canadian soldiers had been killed and 16 wounded.

Meanwhile, another company of Canadians, known as the West Novas, had made better progress. Their river crossing was only met with scattered small arms fire, which was easily counteracted by the Canadians' rapid machine guns. The West Novas secured their section of the river bank without any casualties and then proceeded to move up the hilly slope. There were German soldiers entrenched in a group of farmhouses midway between the river and the village of Gambatesa, who after continuous and fierce 20 millimetre cannon and machine gun fire were flushed out of their positions by the Canadians.

Throughout the afternoon of the 7th October, the Canadian offensive moved slowly forward and as sunset approached, the Canadians successfully engaged German machine gun posts on top of the ridge. By nightfall, the remaining Germans had abandoned their posts and retreated. The Canadian forces had successfully liberated the village of Gambatesa. This is a typical example of what occurred from village to village during the Italian Campaign as the Allies pushed northwards from Monte Cassino to extract the Germans from entrenched positions throughout mountainous central Italy.

Unfortunately, four Italian civilians were killed during the battle to liberate Gambatesa. This again, tragically, was typical of what happened in so many Molise villages. All four deaths occurred during the fighting. Other civilians died later from land mines and unexploded shells.

While the German and Canadian forces were fighting, many people from Gambatesa would hide in caves. After a pause in shelling, a young local man came out of a cave to see if all was clear. As he did so, shelling resumed and he was killed instantly by an explosion just in front of the cave. There was also the tragedy of an old woman from the village who died when a cannon shell entered her house and exploded inside.

Then there was the unfortunate death of a local shepherd. The Germans had strung telephone wires on the ground for military communication. The shepherd, who was a simple uneducated man, thought he could use the wires, thinking they had been abandoned. Assuming he was a civilian soldier or partisan, the Germans captured and executed him for engaging in what they thought was sabotage.

On another occasion a German sniper was strategically positioned on the roof of the top floor of the Gambatesa municipal building, in the centre of the village square. There was a German soldiers' corpse laying on the road. A local woman walked up to the corpse and removed the dead soldier's shoes. While doing this, the rooftop sniper shot and killed her. Before the War, the peasant people of Molise did not have shoes. They were considered to be a luxury that most families simply could not afford.

On a positive note, after the War, the French sent supplies for the school at Gambatesa. Supplies of used clothing were sent to the town from the United States, these were called "stracci Americani" in the local Molise dialect.

To keep themselves entertained when not engaging the enemy, one Canadian veteran recalled the numerous war songs that soldiers would sing-along together, often in the evenings, around a camp fire, including;

Roll Out the Barrel, You Are My Sunshine, It's a Long Way to Tipperary, The Old Rugged Cross, Onward Christian Soldiers and Dinah Shore's two most popular hits of the time, *I'll Be Seeing You* and *I'll Walk Alone.*

Many decades later, a Canadian veteran visited the Moro River Cemetery in the Abruzzo region where out of a total of 1,615 graves, 1,375 were Canadian. He remembers the many olive trees he slept under or would hang out his underwear and other clothing to dry, during the War. He went on to recount the wonderful friendships that would be formed between the Canadian soldiers and the local peasant farmers who would feed the soldiers with their homemade pasta, cheeses and cold meats and let them sample their red wine.

He goes on to remembering the first battle he fought on 17th January 1944, which was the Battle of Ortona in Abruzzo, to successfully liberate this town from the Germans. A battle in which 500 Canadian soldiers died and 1,800 were wounded. He described himself as just a boy with an overactive imagination and excited about the prospect of battle. When the battle started he said the air shook and the ground beneath him shook his body. He was terrified. Now he knew what fear was really like. His eagerness for battle had evaporated.

He quotes the poem *Into Battle* from the World War One poet, Julian Grenfell, as best describing how this first battle affected him:

> The naked earth is warm with Spring,
> And with green grass and bursting trees
> Leans to the sun's gaze glorying,
> And quivers in the sunny breeze;
> And life is Colour and Warmth and Light,
> And a striving evermore for these;
> And he is dead who will not fight,
> And who dies fighting has increase.
> The fighting man shall from the sun
> Take warmth, and life from glowing earth;
> Speed with the light-foot winds to run
> And with the trees to newer birth;
> And find, when fighting shall be done,

Great rest, and fullness after dearth.
All the bright company of Heaven
Hold him in their bright comradeship,
The Dog star, and the Sisters Seven,
Orion's belt and sworded hip:
The woodland trees that stand together,
They stand to him each one a friend;
They gently speak in the windy weather;
They guide to valley and ridges end.
The kestrel hovering by day,
And the little owls that call by night,
Bid him be swift and keen as they,
As keen of ear, as swift of sight.

The blackbird sings to him: "Brother, brother,
If this be the last song you shall sing,
Sing well, for you may not sing another;
Brother, sing."
In dreary doubtful waiting hours,
Before the brazen frenzy starts,
The horses show him noble powers;
O patient eyes, courageous hearts!
And when the burning moment breaks,
And all things else are out of mind,
And only joy of battle takes
Him by the throat and makes him blind,
Through joy and blindeness he shall know,
Not caring much to know, that still
Nor lead nor steel shall reach him, so
That it be not the Destined Will.
The thundering line of battle stands,
And in the air Death moans and sings;
But day shall clasp him with strong hands,
And night shall fold him in soft wings."

War is the dark stain of humanity and it seems no matter how enlightened our civilization becomes with its most beautiful poetry, literature, music, art, sculpture, architecture, humanism and acts of love as diverse as there are humans on this planet, we are destined to continue to grapple with the sheer horror and long lasting consequences of war.

During the Second World War Italian migrants experienced a harsh backlash and much hatred and resentment from many Australians because of Mussolini's alliance with Adolf Hitler. This is particularly sad because many of the Italians in Australia at the time had left Italy because they did not wish to live in the Mussolini controlled Italian Fascist state.

During the war, Italians in Australia were declared as enemies and were interned in detention camps set up throughout the country.

(194) *Allied forces in Molise.*

(196) *Allies liberating Italy.*

(195) *A war-torn Molise village.*

(197) *An Italian Allied war cemetery.*

Many Italian families were interned with no access to any government support. The Red Cross and Salvation Army did offer emergency food and shelter to families that were living in extreme poverty.

Those Italian women whose husbands were interned and remained at home with their children, barely managed to survive and took whatever work they could find on farms, in small businesses or as seamstresses, among other things. To make things worse, there were numerous instances of internment guards and locals stealing internees' food and clothing packages donated by the Australian-Italian community and charities like the Red Cross and Salvation Army. Some internees even lost their lives in the camps or while engaging in hard labour under the then established Civil Aliens Corps ("CAC").

The Australian government has never publicly acknowledged its harsh treatment of these interned Italians and the abuse of their human rights. They were no threat to Australia's national security. They were racially persecuted.

The closest any government has come to the recognition of this atrocity was in November 2011 when the South Australian parliament unanimously accepted a bi-partisan motion moved by parliamentarian Tony Piccolo, to acknowledge the wrongful internment of Italian civilians living in Australia during the Second World War.

IGNAZIO SILONE – COMMUNISM AND FASCISM

∼

$\mathcal{S}$ECONDINO TRANQUILLI, BETTER KNOWN AS IGNAZIO SILONE, WAS born on 1st May 1900 in the Abruzzo town of Pescina dei Marsi. He was the co-founder of the Italian Communist Party and an internationally renowned novelist for his virulently anti-Fascist novels. Well after his death in 1978, significant controversy arose due to some evidence uncovered in 1996 that Silone may have been a spy for the fascist regime of Benito Mussolini in the 1920s and pre-war 1930s.

Born into a poor, peasant rural family, his life was dramatically altered at age fifteen, when an earthquake killed his parents and four of his five siblings, leaving only himself and one brother as survivors. Managing to finish secondary school, in 1917 Silone began to mix with Socialist groups, became a leading critic of Italy's involvement in the First World War and took on the position of editor of the Rome based Socialist newspaper, Avanguardia ("Avant-garde"). In 1921 he helped found the Italian Communist Party and in 1922 became the editor of the party's newspaper in Trieste, Il Lavoratore ("The Worker"). Following the rise to power of Benito Mussolini, the Fascists forced him into exile and disbanded the Italian Communist Party. Travelling to Moscow, in 1929-30 he was involved in Soviet internal debates, particularly Soviet leader Joseph Stalin's radical plans to push the country towards extreme centrally controlled collectivization, and to purge the Central Communist Committee of any ideological opponents, including the expelling of Leon Trotsky from the Soviet Union, which led to his ultimate assassination in Mexico in 1946 with an icepick driven into the back of his neck. This assassination had been ordered by Stalin in order to remove Trotsky once and for all as a leadership rival.

As a result of his expressed criticism of Stalin, Silone was expelled as an international member of the Central Communist Committee in 1931, by which time he was living in Switzerland. He retired from political life and began to write. Writing under the pseudonym Ignazio Silone to protect his family from Mussolini's Fascist persecution, he published his first novel *Fontamara*, in 1933. Fontamara is a village in Abruzzo, very similar to his place of birth. This novel drew upon his childhood recollections of his beloved Abruzzo and the peasant community which he had left behind. It's hero, he later said, was not

(198) *Benito Mussolini.*

(199) *Joseph Stalin.*

so much an individual as the "*rural proletariat, the eternally suffering peasants*". The novel tells their story through the rebellious eyes of a single peasant, Barbera Viola, who leads a local uprising against the new Mussolini Fascist regime, turning him into a revolutionary. In the novel, Silone describes Mussolini's thugs as "*those men in black shirts, arriving by night and in groups, evil, malicious and treacherous.*" Viola is ultimately arrested, tortured and executed in a fascist jail, symbolic of the fate of all peasant *cafoni* under Mussolini's regime. The book became a huge success and was translated into twenty-seven languages and transformed its author into an international literary celebrity. *Fontamara* could not be published in Silone's native Italy, because of his communist and anti-fascist reputation.

On the back of his international success, Silone published his second novel *Bread and Wine*, in 1936. This book stunned the world with its exposure of the inner-workings of the Italian fascist state and the way in which Mussolini's regime used brute violence to control the bodies of dissenters, and propaganda and lies to control the minds of the masses. Told through the story of the protagonist, Pietro Spina, who returns from fifteen years of exile to organize the peasants of his native Abruzzo into a revolutionary movement; this courageous novel exposed the truth about totalitarianism, a message which is just as relevant in today's world. The book gives a rich, detailed and often humorous portrayal of peasant life in Abruzzo; bringing to life priests, peasants, students, lovers and revolutionaries in a monumental drama of one man's struggle for truth, human rights and goodness in a world that was on the brink of calamitous war. As the writer Irving Howe noted in the introduction to the book, "Bread and Wine *will speak to anyone, of whatever age, who tries sincerely to reflect upon man's fate in our century.*"

The United States Army printed unauthorized copies of *Fontamara* and *Bread and Wine* distributing them to Italians during the liberation of Italy after 1943; in the hope this propaganda effort would permanently turn Italians off any form of totalitarian fascism in the future.

A third novel, *The Seed Beneath the Snow*, was published in 1940, and was the last of what Silone called, his *Abruzzo Trilogy*. It continued the story of Pietro Spina, and his desperate attempts to remove his people from the yoke of fascism; but instead, Spina willingly goes to his death at the hands of the fascists for the sake of personal loyalty to his comrades. The character of Pietro Spina, seems to be a projection of Silone himself; a communist on the run who disguises himself as a priest. He believes himself to be organizing a revolution, but the villagers take him to be a genuinely holy self-denying man of God. "Honor poverty and friendship, and be proud," says Pietro. This is essentially the central moral of the trilogy of books. Silone was by nature, the opposite of the stereotypical gregarious, outgoing and extroverted southern Italian. He was silent, meditative and melancholic. In *The Seed Beneath the Snow* a sympathetic character remarks to Pietro Spina's grandmother (modeled on Silone's own maternal grandmother):

> … there's a kind of sadness, a subtle kind of sadness that must not be confused with the more ordinary kind that's the result of remorse, disappointment or suffering; there's a kind of intimate sadness and hopelessness that attaches itself for preference to chosen souls. That kind of sadness has always been very prevalent among sensitive individuals in this part of the world. Once upon a time, to avoid suicide or madness, they entered monasteries.

(200) *Fontamara.*   (201) *Bread and Wine.*   (202) *The Seed Beneath the Snow*

After the Second World War, and with Mussolini's fascists long gone, Silone returned to a democratic republic Italy and became active in political life as the leader of the newly formed Democratic Socialist Party. His major achievement while in this role was preventing an alliance between the Socialist and Communist parties. His political career didn't last long though, when he retired in 1950 to devote himself to writing. *A Handful of Blackberries* published in 1953 and *The Secret of Luca* published in 1956, both show Silone's continuing concern with the plight of poverty-stricken peasants in southern Italy and the complexities of government social reforms which were not flowing into the south. In his book, *Emergency Exit* published in 1965, Silone vividly describes his ideological shifts from Socialism, to Communism and ultimately in the later years of his life, to devout Christianity. Of particular interest to me is a play he published in 1968, titled *The Story of a Humble Christian* which depicts the life of the hermit pope from Molise, whom I have written about in an earlier chapter; the thirteenth-century Pope Celestine V. The play mainly focuses on the significant inner turmoil Celestine suffered in balancing the demands of the institutional Catholic Church with his own spirituality.

In 1996, documents emerged from Italian state archives that allegedly showed Ignazio Silone had been an informant spy for the Italian Fascist Police in the late 1920s and into the early 1930s. These revelations resulted in a complete reappraisal of the clearly-tormented Silone; and particularly how on the one hand he could be spying for Mussolini by revealing confidential information about Italian communists and socialists operating within Italy; and on the other hand, writing the vehemently anti-fascist Abruzzo trilogy of novels. A major clue to Silone's motivations may lie in the fate of his brother Romolo, who was arrested by the fascists on a charge of having placed the bomb that exploded at the Milan Trade Fair in April 1928, killing eighteen people in an attempted assassination of the Italian King Victor Emmanuel II. To this day, the culprit and the motive remain unknown. Romolo was put on trial for the crime and was found not guilty because of a lack of evidence; but the fascists were clearly intent on pinning him for something, so he was sentenced to a long prison term for going under a false identity and possessing papers that compromised him as a communist. Romolo idolized his brother Ignazio and from a young age, had a romanticized view of Communism. Tortured in prison, Romolo wrote to his brother Ignazio for help, but tragically he was to die in prison soon after. Could this have been the motivation for Silone's spying? To provide the fascists with information in the hope they would free his brother from prison? Although there were a series of letters dated between 1923 and 1927 in the police archives (before the bombing); these were all anonymous letters giving police the where-abouts and movements of Italian communists. But there is no evidence these anonymous letters were written by Silone. Whereas in the months between Romolo's imprisonment and the final letter dated 13th April 1930, there is clear evidence these letters were written by Silone, even though the information he was providing was "generic," in other words, about particular Italian communists, that was already widely available.

As an interesting afterthought, the Italian historian Mimmo Franzinelli mentions an unpublished manuscript titled "Il Dossier," written by Ignazio Silone, which he found in his archives. In this manuscript, a fictional anti-Fascist Minister of the Interior re-reads his own life through the police records of the Fascist period, as if Silone himself, in writing this, knew that one day he would be unmasked. This is a quote from the manuscript:

> In my solitary brooding, that left me not a moment's peace, I passed from fear of punishment to fear of non-punishment. The idea that I was haunted by the wrong I had done only because of the continual risk of being found out began to frighten me. So I began to wonder whether, if better technique enabled one to betray one's friends with the certainty that one would never be found out, that would make it more supportable. So might technique be capable of destroying the distinction between right and wrong, by eliminating the risk of punishment? The idea frightened me.

We will never know whether it was Silone who spied for Mussolini's Fascists between 1923 and 1927, before the imprisonment of his

203) Ignazio Silone.   *204) Leon Trotsky.*

brother in 1928; and if he did, what his true innermost motives really were. There is no doubt that Ignazio Silone became disillusioned with Communism when he observed first hand while in Moscow, Joseph Stalin's brutal conversion of the Soviet Union into a totalitarian state, with the Marxist ideals of Communism discarded in the process. This steered Silone's ideology to Democratic Socialism when he returned to Italy in 1946 and ultimately to his deeply devotional faith in Christianity.

22

THE CULT OF PADRE PIO

*N*O MAN HAS BEEN MORE LOVED AND ADMIRED BY THE PEOPLE OF central and southern Italy in the early twenty-first century, than the humble Capuchin Franciscan monk, Padre Pio, who went on to become a Saint. Literally every house in the region has either framed photographs of him strategically positioned in kitchens, living areas and bedrooms to watch over and protect its inhabitants; and or, a shrine devoted to the revered Padre Pio, usually a statue, accompanied by a constantly lit candle.

Every time I have visited Italy since 2002, his omnipotent presence has been felt everywhere; in homes, in churches, in town squares, in cemeteries. You cannot go into a supermarket, ristorante or retail store and not see a picture of this iconic spiritual man. I can remember going into a nightclub and bar, full of people socializing and dancing while a large candle-lit black and white framed photograph of Padre Pio was watching over them. He has literally gripped the inner souls of the people. How did this cult of Padre Pio come about?

He was born Francesco Forgione on 25th May 1887 in the village of Pietrelcina, thirteen kilometres north of Benevento. His parents, Grazio and Giuseppa, were poor but very devout Catholic peasants who would recite the rosary in prayer every evening before retiring to sleep. As a child, Francesco claimed he received frequent visits from Jesus, Mary and the angels, to protect him from his regular horrible nightmares about the Devil which would awaken him from his troubled sleep, terrified and covered in sweat. He thought these visions were normal so he never told anybody about them.

From a young age, he believed he was destined to devote his life to the Church and prayer, so on 22nd January 1903 at the age of sixteen, he entered a Capuchin Franciscan monastery and took the name of Brother Pio of Pietrelcina. On the 10th August 1910 seven years later, he was ordained as a priest and became Padre (Father) Pio. His dream had always been to become a missionary and to spread the message of Jesus and his devoted Mary to distant lands, but his health was too fragile for him to fulfil that dream.

His constant state of poor health made life very difficult for the young priest and he was constantly sent back to his home town by his superiors, to recuperate. He seemed to have an ongoing lung condition which made breathing difficult for him. Yet in spite of this, he had a phenomenal work ethic, sleeping only 4-5 hours and spending most of his waking hours serving Jesus and Mary in prayer, meditation, confessionals and Mass. His ill-health and the constant presence of the Devil in his soul, tortured his body and tormented his spirit and never left him in peace, according to him. In 1916 his superiors moved him to the monastery of Santa Maria delle Grazie, in the town of San Giovanni Rotondo in the Apulia region, south of Molise. He was never to leave this place. Here, he rapidly developed a following as a miracle worker and a humble apostle of faith. As word of his charismatic charm and total devotion to the people spread, large numbers of men and women not only from the region, but from all parts of Italy and beyond, would make the pilgrimage to San Giovanni Rotondo to attend his Mass and seek confessional from him. Drawing enormous strength from his prayer and the devotion of his followers, he spent up to 16 hours a day leading lost souls back to Jesus and Mary, in spite of the constant pain he was feeling and his inner turmoil driven by the Devil.

Many of his followers saw him as a living saint, flocking to his monastery high above the rocky cliffs of the Gargano peninsula, listening to his charismatic sermons and eager to confess their sins to him. He believed he was following in the footsteps of Jesus. It was common for many people from surrounding regions including Molise to go on group walking pilgrimages to San Giovanni Rotondo, to see Padre Pio conduct his Mass

(205) *Padre Pio.*

(206) *Padre Pio conducting a Mass.*

and to receive his confession. These walking pilgrimages would last for around a week, with the people staying overnight in village inns or with local families, along the way.

In 1950, my mother's father, grandfather Raffaele was part of a group from Montagano who took a bus trip to San Giovanni Rotondo. He had polio so was unable to join the walking groups. He met Padre Pio, attended his Mass and took confession from him. From that day, Raffaele became a devout follower for the remainder of his life.

Something very dramatic happened to Padre Pio. Something that no other priest had ever experienced. On the 20th September 1918 he received the stigmata of the Passion of the Christ, in the form of open bleeding wounds on his hands and feet. This stigmata, was to mysteriously afflict him for the remaining fifty years of his life.

He was visited by many doctors who were unable to come up with any medical explanation for his constant bleeding. He also suffered backlash from non-believers who labelled him a charlatan and fraudster.

(207) *Padre Pio's last Mass*
in 1968.

(208) *The bandages of the stigmata, on*
Padre Pio.

Even the Church became suspicious of him to the extent they suspended him from conducting Mass and confession, for a couple of years. His followers, who believed his stigmata was a direct message to him from his beloved Virgin Mary, were in uproar about the Church's response and after enormous pressure, the Church reversed its decision and allowed Padre Pio to continue his holy mission of Mass and confession.

In the midst of World War Two, when Italy was occupied by the Germans and the Allies had landed to evict them, Padre Pio was so distressed by the suffering of the humble peasant people of central and southern Italy that he started a movement of Prayer Groups, encouraging local communities to gather together and pray for the blessing and protection of the Virgin Mary, through him. Today, these Prayer Groups are continued by his followers all over the world, including by my mother and her devout friends, ensuring the cult of Padre Pio remains very strong amongst the faithful.

His other lasting legacy was the House for the Relief of Suffering, a state of the art hospital in San Giovanni Rotondo, dedicated to looking after devout peasant families from the region, which he was instrumental in establishing. Today, this hospital is one of the largest and well equipped in central and southern Italy, attracting some of the finest doctors.

On the 22nd September 1968 there was a big celebration amongst his faithful followers for the 50th anniversary of his stigmata. At this time, Padre Pio had been very ill, but nevertheless wanted to celebrate Mass, which he did while seated. During the mass he collapsed, the event was captured on film and showed his hands to be free of any stigmata. He died that night at 2am. "*I will make more noise once dead than alive,*" Padre Pio had predicted with his usual satirical wit. How right did he prove to be?

San Giovanni Rotondo has become the second largest pilgrimage site in Europe, after the Vatican, and the second most visited Catholic sanctuary in the world, after our Lady of Guadalupe in Mexico City. An estimated nine million people a year visit San Giovanni Rotondo and view the body of Padre Pio, which was controversially exhumed by the Capuchin Order in 2008, and put on display, fully clothed and his face covered by a lifelike silicon mask; creating an utterly transcendental experience for his worldwide followers.

(209) *New church at San Giovanni Rotondo.*

Throughout his life, Padre Pio believed the Virgin Mary was protecting him in his daily struggle with the temptations of the Devil. On two occasions, in 1911 and 1959, his health had deteriorated to the point of near death. In 1959 in particular, his lung condition was so dire that doctors had given up on him, when suddenly, coinciding with the arrival of the blessed statue of the Pilgrim Virgin Mary from Fatima

(210)

Padre Pio

souvenirs.

Portugal, he made a miraculous recovery to the absolute amazement and joy of his doctors and followers.

He was once asked by a follower if there was a shortcut to Heaven. He replied:

> Yes, Our Lady. She is the sea through which the shores of eternal splendor are reached. I wish I had a voice so strong to invite the sinners of the world to love Our Lady. This prayer is our faith, the support of our hope, the explosion of our charity. Love Our Lady and make her always loved. Always recite the Rosary.

There was an allegedly dark side to Padre Pio. Many, including some Church officials, accused him of creating a personality cult amongst his followers which was more about worshipping him rather than the Virgin Mary. They claim he was constantly seeking attention, fame and power for himself, disobeyed the Church hierarchy, was arrogant and even had a mistress; therefore, according to them, he broke all three of his monastic vows; poverty, chastity and obedience.

Why was there such a deep devotion to Padre Pio? Father Raniero Cantalamessa explained it as follows:

> If the whole world runs after Padre Pio, as one day they were running after Francis of Assisi, it is because people feel that neither technology with all its resources, nor science with all of its promises

will save us, but only holiness. Which is like saying love.

In 1971, speaking to the superiors of the Capuchin Order about Padre Pio, Pope Paul VI told them:

What fame he had. How many followers from around the world. Why? Was it because he was a philosopher, a scholar, or because he had means at his disposal? No, it was because he said Mass humbly, heard confessions from morning until night and was marked representative of the stigmata of Our Lord. He was truly a man of prayer and suffering.

On the 16th June 2002, Pope Paul II canonized Padre Pio as a Saint. During the ceremony Pope Paul II recalled how in 1947 as a young priest, he travelled from his homeland Poland to seek a confession from Padre Pio. "Prayer and charity, this is the most concrete synthesis of Padre Pio's teaching," he said.

I visited San Giovanni Rotondo in 2012 with my mother and a number of relatives, on a bus trip from Montagano. My overriding thought was how commercialized the town had become. On the bright

(211) *Pope Francis visiting the crypt of Padre Pio in 2018.*

sunny day that I was there, the place was teeming with tourists from all over the world. There was a brisk business going on from the myriad of market stalls selling all manner of "Padre Pio" souvenirs. There was perfume, holy water, postcards, plastic statuettes, battery operated candles, large statues, rosary beads, books, calendars, cigarette lighters amongst other things, all badged with the image of Padre Pio. I couldn't help wondering if the tourist business had overwhelmed the spirituality of this place.

As my mother's friends gather at her place for an espresso coffee and biscotti, before they commence their Prayer Group devoted to Saint Padre Pio and kneel together in front of his statue, alongside that of the Virgin Mary on one side and Jesus on the other, I witness firsthand the sheer power the Church and its Popes and Saints have over the people of Molise, to this very day, well into the 21st century.

23

(212)
*The mother is the heart
and soul of Molise and
Abruzzo culture.*

PROVERBS, LEGENDS
AND STORIES

HE LANGUAGE AND DIALECTS OF MOLISE AND ABRUZZO ARE UNIQUE.
So much so that it is difficult for an "outsider" from another
region of Italy, to understand the many Molise and Abruzzo dialects.
I say many, because each of the villages have distinct dialects, even if
only a few kilometres apart. This goes back to the history of the region,
where as we have seen, many different cultural and ethnic groups have
imposed their language, customs and influence on this region, including
Samnites, Romans, Ostrogoths, Lombards, Muslim Saracens, Byzantines,
Franks, Normans, Spanish and French.

Over the centuries, the people of Molise and Abruzzo have developed
a rich tradition of dialectic proverbial sayings and philosophies which
have helped them get through their often harsh lives and have stood the
test of time. By examining many of these traditional proverbs, we will
get an excellent window into their daily lives and their ethics, morals
and what the peasant people of Molise and Abruzzo consider to be the
way to live a good and decent life. I have given the English translation

for each of the proverbs along with the Italian version in brackets. I have also offered my interpretation of what they mean and their importance in Molise and Abruzzo customs and traditions. I should also point out these proverbs were mainly developed and used by the peasant people, not the barons and nobility.

Beauty ends at the door. Goodness ends at death.
La bellezza finisce alla porta. Il bene finisce con la morte.
Men should marry a good woman rather than one who is just beautiful. The spell cast by her beauty will eventually wear away as it fades. But is she kind, selfless and generous? If not, you are stuck with her for the rest of your life.

When the confetti are finished, the defects are born.
Quando I coriandoli sono finiti, nascano I difetti.
Your spouse will not show you their defects before the marriage. They will only emerge after the wedding night.

The one who makes, the one who maintains, and the one who destroys.
Colui che fa, colui che mantiene e l'ini che distrugge.
This is a lesson about intergenerational wealth and was often directed by the peasants against the baronial families who ruled over them. It says, the grandfather makes the wealth, the son conserves it, and the grandson squanders it.

Women. They think about one thing and they add another to it.
Donne. Pensano a una cosa e ne aggiungono un' altra.
Women have the gift to think faster than men, jumping seamlessly from one topic to another; and confusing men in the process.

Where there are church bells, there are prostitutes.
Dove ci sono campane della chiese, ci sono prostitute.
You can find church bells in every village, as with prostitutes. This saying was often used by wives as a warning to their straying husbands.

Forward we go, making clutter and confusion, but always forward."
Avanti andiamo, facendo confusione e confusione, ma sempre avanti.
During times of inevitable hardship, be they famine, cruel barons, disease, natural disaster or war, a peasant family would stoically get on with their lives and survive as a family as best they could.

To prostitute on faith."
Prostituirsi sulla fede.
Beware those who work on the promise of being paid. This saying originated from the many peasants who worked for barons that either did not pay them or underpaid them.

Who lives in hope, dies of despair.
Chi vive nella speranza, muore di disperazione.
There is no replacement for the hard work and toil of the here and now. This is the reality of our life, as harsh as it is. There is no reason to think our hardship is going to go away. We cannot predict the future so we will deal with whatever it throws at us, if and when it happens.

Who is born round does not die square.
Chi nasce intorno non muore quadrato.
Our family are, and always will be peasants. This is our destiny.

The devil does, and the devil undoes.
Il diavolo lo fa, e il diavolo si disfa.
The people were God-fearing and believed in the evil workings of the devil. No matter how good things are looking for us now, a disaster could be awaiting us just around the corner.

What the hell are you going to church for, to bite Jesus Christ?!
Che diavolo stai andando in chiesa, per mordere Gesu Cristo?!
This saying was for the hypocrites who regularly attended mass but were selfish, cruel, miserly and disrespectful to the people around them.

(213) The Devil.   (214) *Saint Peter.*   (215) *Peasant woman.*

If you take and you don't put any in, then in the end you won't find any of it.

Se prendi e non ne inserisci nessuno, alla fine non lo troverai.

This highlighted the importance of thrift in Molise and Abruzzo peasant society. When there is a good harvest, put some money away for the inevitable hard times, otherwise your family will suffer.

Don't call for St. Peter's protection before even seeing any serpents

Non chiamare la protezione di San Pietro prima di aver visto serpenti.

Do not be frightened when there is no reason to be. Be rational, always.

Women have long tongues, long hair and nothing for brains.

Le donne hanno lingue lunghe, capelli lunghi e niente per il cervello.

This saying comes from a time when peasant society was very patriarchal and the father yielded all the power. It was directed by these men at women (often their wives, but not always) who they believed gossiped too much, not thinking before speaking, spreading rumors and causing trouble in the village.

The ox calls the donkey a cuckold.

Il bue chiama l'asino un becco.

The ox has horns on his head, but nevertheless calls the hornless donkey a cuckold. Usually it is the man accusing other men's wives of being unfaithful, who is being cuckolded (that is, to have an unfaithful wife) by his own wife.

It is the worst wheel of the cart that makes the most noise.

E la ruota peggiore del carrello che fa piu rumore.

Every family has a black sheep who dishonors the family's name. We must keep our family secrets (black sheep) away from prying eyes.

To pull the nails from the cross of Christ.

Per togliere I chiodi dalla croce di Cristo.

When somebody is constantly trying to force you to do something you don't want to do and you are running out of patience with them. They are incessantly wearing you down.

"Hurry father," says the wolf to his confessor, "because the sheep are now passing nearby."

"Sbrigati padre," dice il lupo al suo confessore, "perche ora le pecore stanno passando nelle vicinanze."

This was directed at people who constantly did wrong and in spite of promising to correct their wayward behaviour, didn't have the discipline to do it; never really learning from their repeated mistakes.

A mute child is understood by its mother.

Un bambino muto e' compreso da sua madre.

This places the mother at the centre of the family when it comes to nurturing children. Nobody knows and loves a child more than the mother.

At deaths and at weddings you get to know your relatives.

Alla morte e ai matrimoni puoi conoscere I tuoi parenti.

People don't hold back their true feelings and emotions at these events so you will get to see what they are really like. This was often associated with men who would drink too much, saying things to their relatives which they would later regret.

Are you engaged? No, I am playing the field.

Sei fidanzato? No, faccio lo scampa verne.

This was directed at men who never married, were often lazy and afraid of any kind of commitment.

The world is a village."

Il monde e' un villaggio.

Peasants were oblivious to what was going on in the wider world and really didn't care. Their world was enclosed within the boundaries of the village, and what went on there, is all that really mattered to them.

If God wills.

Se Dio vuole.

This was a very common saying for anything planned for the future. It would be considered sacrilege and to bring about misfortune, not to use this phrase. It will only eventuate if God wants it to. My mother often uses this saying.

The one who drinks from his own glass knows what he is drinking."

Chi beve dal proprio bicchiere sa cosa sta bevendo.

When it is time to court a lady, pick one from your own village. That way you will know her family and what you are getting into. This saying was also used when buying livestock. For example, only buy a cow from your village.

When it begins, it never ends.

Quando inizia, non finisce mai.

Misfortune will strike in many successive blows.

You come from a cow's arse.

Tu vieni dal culo di una mucca.

Don't forget your humble origins and don't try and be somebody who you are not. This saying would often be used for people who emigrated from the village and then came back to visit years later, behaving like "fancy Americans," looking down on the locals.

The donkey got crazy.

L'asino impazzi.

This saying was often directed at hopeless romantics who would fall in love and do stupid irrational things.

Only being in a war do you waste time.

Solo essere in guerra ti fa perdere tempo.

This saying became particularly popular after the Second World War. It means that a person is never wasting time, no matter what they are doing, as long as it's not being at war, which is meaningless and never brings a good result.

Money can make a mute sing.

Il denaro puo far cantare un muto.

Money talks! It can buy anything and anybody. This was often directed at corrupt local barons and municipal officials.

America the beautiful, who wants to leave you!

America la bella, che vuole lasciarti!

This was a common saying based on the perception that everybody dreamt of emigrating to America (or similar countries) to seek a better life. It was also directed as a criticism of people who had emigrated and then returned to live in their village.

One father can look after eleven children, but eleven children cannot look after one father.

Un padre puo prendersi cura di undici figli, ma undici bambini non possono prendersi di un padre.

It was not uncommon for peasant families to have eleven children or more. The father was the head of the house, the breadwinner and was irreplaceable; so they needed to listen to, and respect him.

Keep your face clean.

Mantieni il viso pulito.

Stay out of trouble and do not dishonor the family name in any way.

Make me a fool, but make me the oldest.

Fammi uno sciocco, ma rendimi il piu vecchio.

This comes from the time when the eldest son in a family, would inherit everything, regardless of his talent or respect for family.

If you put your foot on every stone, you'll never get there.
Se metti il piede su ogni pietra, non ci arriverai mai.
Don't sweat the small stuff and blow up trivial things out of all proportion
and into a big drama.

To be smart you have to be born early in the morning.
Per essere intelligente, devi nascare la mattina presto.
Never put off anything that you can't get done now. This way, while the
others are procrastinating, you can reap the harvest.

Eat before your husband comes home. That way if he's in a good
mood, you eat again. And it he's not, well then you've already eaten.
*Mangia prima che tuo marito torni a casa. In questo modo se e' di buon
umore, mangi di nuovo. E se non lo e', beh, allora hai gia mangiato.*
This saying was all about not assuming anything, being adaptable to any
situation, and to always hedge your bets in life, whenever you can.

Make your bed in the morning. When you make your bed in the
morning, you honor your face. When you make it at night, you
honor your arse.
*Fai il tuo letto la mattina. Quando fai il letto la mattina, onori il tuo viso.
Quando ce la fai di notte, onori il tuo culo.*
Always keep yourself and your home neat and tidy. Dress well when
going outdoors. Put your best foot forward. By doing this it reflects
well on your family and people will assume that you are orderly and
well organized.

Open your eyes before you marry; close them after you marry.
Apri gli occhi prima di sposarti; chiudili dopo che ti sei sposato.
Make sure you know the person and the family of who you are wanting
to marry. Because if that person turns out to disappoint you in any way
or make your life a living miserable hell, well bad luck for you. You are
stuck with them for the rest of your life or theirs. We must remember
this saying came from a time when it was literally impossible to leave
your husband or wife and there was no concept of divorce.

Story telling was a rich tradition of Molise and Abruzzo culture during a time when without the modern conveniences of radio or television, peasant families would sit together in the evenings after dinner and share stories. These stories have endured over many generations and even to this day, one of the great joys which I have experienced when visiting Molise, is to visit some of my elderly relatives with my parents and listen with great interest as they recount stories from the past, in front of a fireplace while the winter snow or rain is falling. The feeling I get is that this rich historical land is also listening and acknowledging these stories. Here are some examples of this great story telling tradition. As with any legend, it is difficult to ascertain how true they are, but is that relevant, when the power is in the symbolism of the story itself?

The people of Molise and Abruzzo were very afraid and intimidated by the castles which were scattered around the region often in larger towns, because they were a constant reminder of the power of lords and barons who ruled and controlled the lives of peasants with an iron fist, over such a long period of tumultuous history. In medieval times, it was traditional in some parts of Molise and Abruzzo for the baron to sleep with a local woman, on the eve of her marriage, if he chose to. There is one legend which involves a local peasant husband-to-be who dressed up as a woman and went to the castle in the place of his bride, taking with him scissors, hidden under his clothes.

So the legend goes, this man was never seen or heard from again. The story is that in the castle there was a dungeon with a deep well at its centre, where the man was thrown into, for trying to humiliate the baron. If the bride slept with her future husband before sleeping with the baron, the couple would be killed by being thrown into the castle well, according to the legend. Many of these medieval castles had underground escape routes into the countryside, so the baron and his family could escape quickly, in case the town was attacked by invaders.

The message of this legend is for peasants to beware of the lords and barons, who they believed would stop at nothing to abuse and dominate the people at every opportunity.

Another Molise and Abruzzo legend is the old man and the stone. A long time ago there was an old man living with his son's family. It was the custom in those days for one of the male children, usually the oldest, to take care of parents in their old age, particularly after the death of one of the parents. In exchange for doing this, that son would be left with more land in the family will. As the man grew older and older, it was becoming more difficult to look after him.

So one winter day, desperate to inherit his father's property, the favored son decided to get rid of his elderly father. He carried his father on his shoulders and climbed up the nearby mountain with the intention of leaving him there to die. But it was a long distance to the top and his father was heavy, so the son stopped half way up where there was a large boulder on which he could place his father onto, while the son rested. Shortly afterwards he continued his journey up to the freezing summit of the mountain, where he left his father to die, and went back to the village in the valley.

After many years the son grew old and the day came when his own son had to take care of him. As he grew older and older, one day his son put him on his shoulders and began to climb up the same mountain. The old man, not knowing what the purpose of this journey was, asked him a number of times. As they made their way up the mountain, they arrived at the half way point where the big boulder still lay. The son placed his father there and rested. Then, the old man remembered and said to his son: "*I too set my father upon this stone.*" Upon hearing this, it dawned on the son what happened with his father and grandfather all those years ago. Afraid that one day, he himself would be taken and left on this mountain by his son, he picked up his father, put him again on his shoulders and carried him back down the mountain and to his village home. He continued to look after his father until the day he died.

The moral of this legend is that children will observe the way their parents treat grandparents and will then treat their own parents in the same way. What goes around, comes around. Looking after the elderly is a very strong tradition in Molise and Abruzzo. In the larger villages and towns nowadays, many families live in three level apartments, where the grandparents are on the ground floor, the parents on the middle and the married son or daughter with children on the upper floor. They live independent lives except for meal times when all three (or four) generations will eat together as an extended family. Aged care facilities are virtually non-existent in Molise and Abruzzo, for this reason.

Horses and donkeys were critical for peasants living under the feudal system and played a very important role right up to the mid-twentieth century. They were considered to be a prized possession because horses and donkeys were the main means of transport. My great grandfather Luciano had two donkeys which he would use to deliver his fruit and vegetable produce to sell in nearby villages. So those families that owned a number of horses and donkeys were economically better off than those who didn't. The 13th June is set aside for the 'Blessing of the Animals'. This day celebrates Saint Anthony of Padua, the protector of donkeys and horses. Here is an extract from the first chapter of Ignazio Silone's *The Seed Beneath the Snow*, published in 1940, which describes what would happen in a typical central Italian village, during the Blessing of the Animals:

> The old priest, clad in surplice and stole, gave his blessing to the animals when they passed in front of the church. Some of the donkeys were decked with colored ribbons on their heads. But these cheap decorations, borrowed from the hope chests of girls looking forward to marriage, did not conceal the essentially workaday aspect of the poor beasts; the scratches and scars on their backs, their swollen shoulders, their bellies either drooping or enlarged and hanging like those of cows, but without cows' milk, the cracks at their shins and all the other marks of the everyday life they shared with peasants.

During these times, a horse lived and worked for around fifteen years, whereas a donkey, even though not as strong as a horse, would last longer, for up to thirty years. My mother recollects as a girl, that on Blessing of the Animals day, hand woven blankets would be placed on the horses, mules and donkeys, and then they would parade in the town square, with children riding them.

Numerous stories have been passed down generations about marauding brigands and robbers, who would come from outside

(216) *Molise donkey.*   (217) *Horses in Medieval Molise.*

the village and wreak havoc, violence and destruction. When they appeared, the father of a family would shoot at them with an old single-loading rifle. These robbers would come on horseback in small groups and stole whatever they could, often raiding the village markets, bars and taverns, which were easy targets. Another favorite target were the castles and palazzos of barons, although these were usually well defended. The robbers had large knives and long swords. As well as stealing, they would sometimes kidnap a family member of the baron, seeking a ransom.

Stories abound concerning the level of corruption that existed in many Molise and Abruzzo towns and villages within the municipality, particularly when there were mayoral elections. The mayor was very powerful, often given full control of finances provided to the town by the regional government. The peasants just took it for granted that these officials were corrupt. Elections were every five years. People who wanted to run for mayor would try to buy favors and votes. For example, if you vote for me I will make sure the municipality gives your son a job; or I will allow you to extend your farm building; or I will make sure the dispute with your neighbor is resolved in your favor. The person who promised his vote, was expected to also convince his entire extended family to vote for the same candidate. So all of a sudden, for example, he is securing twelve votes. The more votes a person could secure, the more the mayor would look after him and his family, if elected. It was corruption at the grass roots level.

One legend which is popular and comes in many variations, can be traced back to the medieval shepherds, but ultimately I believe, has its roots with the Samnites. My father's family were shepherds and would have heard this story. The shepherds would descend from the mountains playing their bagpipes with the good news that the sheep herds were ready to graze in the valley fields. The peasant farmers would hear the sharp high pitched echoing sounds of the bagpipes as the shepherds came down the side of the mountain. They had colorful pointed hats, from which flowed ribbons. Their long hair would fall onto their short black jackets. The mountain shepherds wore leather sandals. They would come into the fields, singing and sharing food and wine with the peasants as they continued playing their bagpipes.

It may come as a surprise to many readers that bagpipes are part of the Molise tradition. In 1954 an anthropologist, Alberto Cirese, and an ethnomusicologist, Diego Carpitella, while field recording folk music in Molise, came across a medieval ritual which used to take place in the small village of Fossalto near Campobasso, every May. On May Day morning, a shepherd dressed in a cone made of branches, grass and flowers (called "pagliara," a dialect expression for the shepherds' conical cane huts) would walk through the village streets, accompanied by a bagpiper and two singers.

Along the way, from the windows and the balconies, people would throw pails full of water at the bagpiper, while the two singers alternately sang short verses of greetings. After this procession was over, the bagpiper and singers would go to the local church and settle in the priest's garden, where they would ask the villagers for gifts of food and

(218)

Molise bagpipes
originated in
Samnite times.

wine. The pagliara ritual, with its bagpipe playing musicians is fondly remembered and recounted, to this day.

There are a number of legends and superstitions which revolve around birth. Hospital births have only been common in Molise and Abruzzo since the mid twentieth century. Prior to that, as was the case with my parents, there were home births. It was believed that if a pregnant woman's cravings were satisfied, she would not experience labour pains. If on the other hand, her yearnings persisted, they believed the child would be born with a birthmark.

This is why even today, it is not uncommon for a pregnant woman at the markets to be given fruit and vegetables just in case they are tastes she might crave. In the villages of Molise and Abruzzo, relatives and neighbours would bring home-made chicken broth to new mothers. The connection of poultry to feeding a new mother can be traced back to the Renaissance when Florentine nobles would buy a fat pigeon and three fresh eggs for their wives while they were in labour. A Molise and Abruzzo tradition was also to feed a newborn child eggs and salt, the symbols of knowledge and competence; and to give confetti, sugar or spice coated seeds or nuts, on the occasion of the arrival of a new baby.

There is the story of the abandoned southern Italian village, Roscigno Vecchia, in the Apennine mountains overlooking Salerno, which has only one remaining permanent resident, Giuseppe Spagnuolo. This town was founded in the tenth century and has been continuously afflicted by earthquakes and landslides, previously forcing the former residents to relocate and reconstruct their town at least three times. Firstly, in the 1500s, again in the 1700s, and most recently in 1902.

When he was asked why he decided to live alone in a deserted village, Spagnuolo replied, "I don't lack anything. I wouldn't change my two room house with any other. I love to define myself as the only free and special squatter of Roscigno Vecchia. I'm here alone, I don't deny it. But the world rotates around me."

Italian films such as *Cavilli si Nasce* (1989), *Radio West* (2003) and *Noi Credevamo* (2010) have been shot in this desolate village.

(219) *Giuseppe Spagnuolo, the sole resident of Roscigno Vecchia.*

I will conclude with a legend about a baron and his raven, which originates from the village of Roccascalegna, 150 kilometres north of Montagano. Baron Corvo de Corvis, lived in the local castle in the sixteenth century, during the time of Spanish rule in this region within the Kingdom of Naples. Baron de Corvis relentlessly levied the peasants with high taxes for his coffers and also insisted his subjects kneel before a black raven.

The raven was placed in a cage outside the front entrance of the baron's castle high up on a mountain, where it could see all the activities of the people in the village below. Anybody entering or leaving the village had to pass the castle and raven because there was only one road winding down the side of the mountain to the village. Those who refused to pay homage to the baron, by kneeling before the black raven, were arrested and sometimes put to death, to frighten the villagers.

Many years of terror passed, and the baron who was approaching his forty-fifth birthday, decided to introduce a vile and disgusting medieval custom, one similar to the story at the beginning of this chapter, the "Jus primae noctis," which obligated every newly-wed bride to spend her first night of marriage with the baron. This unjust and cruel baronial law, deeply angered and offended the village priest, who protested publicly. As a result, the baron ordered his guards to arrest and execute the priest.

A number of months after this horrific execution, on one winter's night, while the baron was preparing to lay alongside a young bride, she took out a sharp hidden dagger and stabbed him directly into his heart; fleeing and panicking as the baron lay on the floor shouting horrible curses at her, while dying. Just as he was nearing death, the baron placed his bloody hand on the wall on top of his bed, where it is said, the bloodstained hand print remained until the 27th January 1940, when the castle tower collapsed during World War Two, destroying the bedroom. It is also said that over the centuries, whenever somebody tried to wipe away the blood soaked hand print, it would reappear, redder than before.

The people of Roccascalegna believe to this day, that on stormy nights, when the chilly northern winds hit the castle, and the main entrance door creaks, the ghost of the baron reappears again, and endlessly goes through the agony of his death, accompanied by the ghost of the black raven.

220) Roccascalenga Castle.

24

ROBERT DE NIRO – YOU TALKIN' TO ME?

*W*HAT IS IT ABOUT ROBERT DE NIRO AND MY RAWEST INNER emotional reactions? Sure, part of it is to do with us sharing a similar Molise ancestry. But it goes much deeper than that. I have always considered De Niro to be the most outstanding actor I have ever seen on the silver screen. He immerses himself into characters like no other actor. There are seven of his films in particular, which have evoked strong emotional responses from me, tapping into a wide variety of my feelings. I will explore each of these films briefly.

The first time I saw Robert De Niro was 1975, in "The Godfather Part II," when he played the role of young mob boss Vito Corleone, who of course had also been played by Marlon Brando in the first movie. He went on to win an Academy Award for his performance, as did Brando; the only time two people playing the same character both won the award. This is definitely the film which made De Niro into a superstar actor of great distinction. He prepared for this role by devoting four months learning to speak the Sicilian dialect and living

(221) *De Niro as Vito Corleone.* (222) *Godfather Part II.*
(223) *De Niro and Al Pacino.*

in Sicily for three months. Director Francis Ford Coppola considered bringing Marlon Brando back to play the younger Vito Corleone, convinced that with the right makeover he could play the part. He was so impressed with De Niro's audition performance however, that he gave him the part without ever offering it to Brando. Robert De Niro's mastering of the Sicilian dialect, the intensity he brought into the Corleone character and the scene in which he is seen running over the rooftops of Little Italy New York, during the annual Feast of San Rocco festival, particularly mesmerized me.

1900 was a generation spanning historical drama released in 1976 about two childhood friends, beginning in 1900, through early 20th century Italy, before the rise of Mussolini, and then continuing into the Fascist years until the collapse of the Mussolini regime during the Second World War. De Niro's character, Alfredo, is the son of a baronial landowning family and his best friend Olmo, played by Gerard Depardieu, is from a peasant family. These two characters symbolize the power struggle unfolding in Italy during that time, in the dying days of the residual feudal system, which I have talked about. Alfredo understands he is from a privileged class, yet he refuses to give up his lifelong friendship with Olmo, at great cost to himself. Nevertheless, there are periods of intense conflict in their friendship; one of the most dramatic scenes in the movie is when Olmo is wrongly accused of killing a child at a baronial family wedding party and Alfredo allows black shirted fascist thugs, hired as bodyguards for his family, led by Attila, played

(224) *De Niro and Gerard Depardieu* (225) 1900 *movie poster.*

by Donald Sutherland, to beat up Olmo into a bloody mess. It is so frustratingly agonizing to watch because Olmo didn't do it!

Also released in 1976 was the disturbing *Taxi Driver*, about a New York taxi driver Travis Bickle, played by De Niro, who suffers from insomnia and instead of sleeping, roams the streets picking up a variety of societal outcasts in the early hours of the morning. He becomes increasingly detached from reality and mentally unhinged as he dreams about becoming a vigilante, determined to clean up the city from its filth. What disturbed me greatly about this film was the way we see Travis gradually descending into a state of insanity, right in front of our eyes, one night after the next. His state of mind deteriorates sharply when he picks up and becomes infatuated with Betsy, played by Cybill Shepherd, who is a campaign volunteer for Senator and presidential candidate Charles Palantine. At the same time, Travis is disgusted by the sleaze, dysfunction, random violence, drug-taking, pornography and prostitution, that he sees every night. This is brought home to him dramatically when he picks up Iris, an under-aged prostitute, played by Jodi Foster. She is escaping from her pimp, Sport. The movie comes to a dramatic crescendo when Travis Bickle decides to take it upon himself to purge the city of dirty politics and crime by intending to assassinate Palantine and kill Sport, deluding himself in the hope of winning the love of Betsy in the process. This movie has left a dark cloud for Robert De Niro who rarely talks about it. When John Hinckley tried to

(226) *Robert De Niro as Travis Bickle in* Taxi Driver. (227) Taxi Driver *poster.*

assassinate President Ronald Reagan in March 1981, the FBI revealed that Hinckley had been inspired by De Niro's portrayal of the crazed loner Travis Bickle in *Taxi Driver*. Eventually the movie was screened as evidence for the jury during the Hinckley trial. De Niro was horrified by the controversial worldwide publicity the movie received. "*Can a film drive someone to murder?*" he asked. "*Don't they realize I'm not that guy?*", De Niro would repeatedly say. After the attempted assassination, the movie's director Martin Scorsese said, "*I refused to comment for six months. I didn't feel like making another film for a while, and I'd never felt that way before.*" He added, "*I do not regret I made Taxi Driver. It was not an irresponsible act - it was a responsible one. Bob (De Niro) and I both thought so at the time. We both thought, this is something we're attracted to — let's go for it! Movies don't kill people. People kill people.*"

Then in 1979 I saw De Niro in *The Deer Hunter*, about three young factory workers from Pennsylvania; Michael, Steven and Nicky, who enjoy deer hunting and enlist into the Army to fight in Vietnam. Before they go, Steven marries his pregnant girlfriend Angela and their wedding party also serves as a farewell for the three men. After some time experiencing many horrors in Vietnam, the three young soldiers fall into the enemy hands of the Vietcong and are brought to a prison camp in which they are forced to play Russian roulette with a loaded pistol, against each other. This Russian roulette scene is gut-wrenching to watch at the deepest visceral level and is full of unbearable suspense.

(228) The Deer Hunter. (229) *Scene from* Raging Bull. (230) Raging Bull.

It literally had me at the edge of my seat, but it also drew me deeply into the bond that these three young men clearly had. Michael, played by Robert De Niro, makes it possible for them to escape. When he returns home, Michael realizes his carefree deer hunting days with his buddies are over, because of the trauma he suffered in Vietnam. He is further distressed when he finds out Steven is severely handicapped and Nicky has not returned home. So Michael goes back to Vietnam to rescue him.

In 1980 I saw *Raging Bull*, about Jack La Motta, played by De Niro, an Italian-American boxer who stops at nothing to achieve his dream of winning the middleweight title. The movie, filmed very effectively in gritty textures of black and white, is really a study of male violence and the pointless destruction it leads to. Although a brilliant, fierce, aggressive and ambitious boxer who literally obliterates his opponents with brutal violence, as depicted in the boxing scenes which are as confronting and as realistic as you will ever see on film. Jack is unable to control his violence and rage outside the ring in his personal life. He is a ticking time bomb, ready to go off at any time. This is what sticks in my mind, Robert De Niro's brilliant character portrayal of a deeply flawed and helpless man, consumed by his need to express himself through violence and unable to communicate his inner feelings and emotions, without outbursts of rage. La Motta desperately wants his family's love and their recognition for his boxing achievements, but his unpredictable bouts of paranoia and jealousy seem to come between them. It's this kind of rage which made him into a champion, but in real life, he ends up a sad and lonely misunderstood man.

The most terrifying De Niro character portrayal for me, was in the 1991 remake of the film, *Cape Fear*. Max Cady, played by De Niro, is a psychopath just released from prison for rape. He is seeking revenge from his lawyer Sam Bowden, played by Nick Nolte, who he believes deliberately withheld important evidence about his case during the trial, which if presented, could have kept him out of jail. When released, Cady comes to a small town to terrorize Bowden, his wife and fifteen years old daughter. Robert De Niro perfectly portrays Max Cady as purely evil, and we see this in his menacing eyes, his veiled threatening language, street cunning intelligence, love of violence and in the way the movie constantly heightens the tension from one scene to the next, culminating in a dramatic climax on a boat in a swamp in the middle of the night.

(231) *De Niro in* Cape Fear. (232) Cape Fear *poster.* (233) *De Niro as Max Cady.*

I must say when I first saw Robert De Niro in comedy roles I was surprised how effortlessly he mastered the timing and delivery of humour! His standout comedy role for me was in *Meet The Fockers* which I saw in 2004. This was a sequel to *Meet The Parents*, made in 2000. In the first movie, Ben Stiller had to win the trust of Robert De Niro, the father of his girlfriend. In *Meet The Fockers*, the whole family goes to Florida where Stiller's parents, the ageing wild hippie Fockers played by Dustin Hoffman and Barbara Streisand, have a luxurious mansion and estate; against the tastes of the stoic and conservative ex-CIA agent De Niro. This clash of personalities forms the basis for the non-stop humour in the movie. De Niro has an impeccable sense

 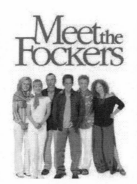 

(234) *De Niro and Dustin Hoffman.* (235) Meet the Fockers.
(236) *De Niro and Mr. Jinx.*

of comic timing, relying very much on his facial gestures, which had me in stitches of laughter. One of the most memorable scenes in the movie for me is when De Niro's beloved cat, "Mr. Jinx" terrorizes the Focker family dog, to De Niro's great joy.

Born in Greenwich Village Manhattan, New York on 17th August 1943, Robert De Niro was the only child of Virginia Admiral and Robert De Niro senior. On his father's side he is of Molise descent. His father was a painter, sculptor and poet who was part of a loosely knit artistic community which had begun to flourish in Greenwich Village during the Second World War. His grandfather was born in the town of Ferrazzano, which is 19.5 kilometres from my parent's town of Montagano. Although his parents divorced when Robert was two, he had a very close relationship with both of them, who lived within a short walking distance of each other.

He is a very private man, who does not get caught up in celebrity fame and party culture and rarely gives interviews, believing his perfor-mances speak for themselves and that there's nothing further which is relevant for him to add. When asked whether he enjoyed watching his own movies, his reply was; *"No! I fall asleep when I'm watching my own movies."* His privacy applies to his friends as well. *"Bobby never answers his own phone,"* says a friend. *"He calls you – you never call him."* Even on the rare occasion he gives interviews, he categorically refuses to talk about his private life.

De Niro had an early start in show business, when at ten he played the Lion in a local production of The Wizard of Oz. He did not continue with acting though, instead he joined an Italian gang, roaming the streets, sleazy bars and pool halls of Little Italy in New York. The gang members gave him the nickname "Bobby Milk" because he was pale and strange as milk. Not enjoying school, he dropped out at 16 to study acting in 1960. When asked in an interview why he decided to take up acting, he replied, "Because then I can express myself; acting is a cheap way to do things that you would never dare to do yourself." He began going to watch lots of movies with his father at this time. He enrolled at the Stella Adler Studio of Acting. Adler was a strong believer in the 'Stranislavski' method of acting which involved the deep psychological immersion and investigation of a character. She was an intense teacher who made a great impression on the young De Niro; and was once described by *The New York Times* as someone who would "*curse, cajole, rage, roar and, from time to time, even compliment her students.*" Adler immediately recognized De Niro's innate talent and later commented that he was one of her best students. After completing his training with Stella Adler, De Niro studied briefly with Lee Strasberg at the Actor's Studio in New York, attending auditions at the same time.

De Niro would show up to auditions with a portfolio of 25 pictures of himself in various disguises to prove that he wasn't just an ethnic Italian actor. After a brief cameo in the 1965 French film *Three Rooms in Manhattan*, his real debut came in the 1968 film, *Greetings*. He had to wait another five years to achieve critical acclaim when he performed in two 1973 films; *Bang the Drum Slowly*, in which he played a terminally ill baseball player, and *Mean Streets*, his first of many collaborations with director Martin Scorsese, who coincidentally, grew up in the same Greenwich Village neighbourhood as De Niro. In *Mean Streets*, he played a street thug opposite Harvey Keitel who became a lifelong close friend. As we have seen, Robert De Niro established himself as a great actor in his 1974 portrayal of a young Vito Corleone in *The Godfather Part II*. The rest, as they say, is history.

There are so many interesting aspects to De Niro, who has never been a conformist and instead very much does things his way. "You talkin' to me?" is the famous line from "Taxi Driver" which really established De Niro's reputation as a "tough guy" actor; yet we have seen that in reality he has taken on a wide variety of character roles in his long and distinguished career, including taking to comedy like a duck to water! Not many actors have been able to transition into so many other genres of acting as successfully as he has. Loyalty is a strong character trait of his. Grateful for the big break Martin Scorsese gave him in *Mean Streets*, the two have not only become close friends but have collaborated in other films such as *Taxi Driver, Cape Fear* and *The Irishman*. Leonardo Di Caprio can thank De Niro for some of his career success. After working with Di Caprio in the 1993 film *This Boy's Life*, De Niro recognized his immense talent and promoted him to Scorsese.

Another close friendship De Niro developed was with the late comedic actor John Belushi, of *Blues Brothers* fame. After Belushi died of a cocaine and heroin overdose in March 1982, De Niro broke down and cried. He had been with Belushi on the night of his death, but left early, feeling that the woman Belushi was with was interested only in his fame and behaving in a "trashy" fashion. John Belushi was unable to cope with his sudden fame and tragically he paid the ultimate price.

Another close friend was the late actress Shelley Winters. She was instrumental in casting him in the film *Bloody Mama*, about the legendary criminal Ma Barker and her four psychopathic sons, who terrorized the American South during the 1930s. De Niro played Lloyd Barker, a sadistic, morphine-addicted killer who eventually dies of an

(237) John Belushi. (238) Shelley Winters. (239) Harvey Kietel.

overdose. Winters said that De Niro prepared for the role by refusing to eat and drinking only water so he could shed thirty pounds and look like an addict. He was like a son to her and she gave him much advice on all manner of subjects including his personal relationships. Every Thanksgiving Shelley Winters would put on a dinner for Robert De Niro and Al Pacino, whenever they were free. I would have given anything to be at those dinners. Al Pacino is a close second to De Niro as my most favoured actors.

Some movie roles have required De Niro to not only psychologically immerse himself into a character but also to perform severe physical transformations. For his academy award winning role in "Raging Bull," he had to put on over 60 pounds of weight by gorging on pasta and ice cream, earning him the world record at the time for the most weight put on by an actor in a movie. De Niro also spent a year training to be a boxer and competing in the ring. He has been an avid follower of the 'Stranislavski' method of acting throughout his career. He prepared for "Taxi Driver" by getting a taxi driving license and spending many weekends driving a taxi in New York, working twelve hour shifts in the evenings and early hours of the morning, in order to capture the mood and atmosphere of that environment. To prepare for "Cape Fear" he paid a dentist $5,000 to deform his teeth. De Niro soaks up every aspect of his character from appearance to mannerisms to dialect to facial expressions to clothing to investigating the history of that character from every aspect. He is very much there, in the moment, delving into new characters, new situations, always watching, observing, listening. Liza Minelli said she would never forget De Niro's intensive work ethic on the music for *New York, New York*. "I'd leave the studio around midnight, and I could hear the wail of a saxophone. As a musician he was fabulous. That's the way he found the character, through the music. That's the way he put it together." "He never breaks character," said June Guterman, his assistant on *Raging Bull*, "even when filming stops." Comedian Sandra Bernhand, who improvised with him so brilliantly in the film *King of Comedy* said, "He is totally concentrated, totally absorbed in the role." When asked what the secret to her son's success was, his mother replied, "Will. Force of will."

In his early years, Robert De Niro was obsessed with discovering his family roots. One summer he hitchhiked from Ireland, where his mother's family had originated, to Italy, trying to locate relatives on his father's side. He finally found the De Niro clan in the small Molise village of Ferrazzano, not far from the city of Campobasso. I visited Ferrazzano in 2012 and can remember how proud the villagers were of the De Niro family connection. Relatives of his still live there and I was told De Niro has visited on a number of occasions. When Donald Trump was elected President in 2016 he swore that he would leave America and take up residence in his family village! De Niro has been an avid supporter of Trump's opposing Democratic Party, his whole life. He lobbied against the impeachment of President Bill Clinton and strongly supported Democratic Party presidential candidates Al Gore in 2000 and John Kerry in 2004; and of course, Barack Obama, who won the 2008 presidential election.

Outside of his acting career, Robert De Niro has been a big supporter of his native New York, becoming a co-founder of the Tribeca Film Festival, showcasing independent films, which went a long way towards lifting the morale of New Yorkers after the September 11, 2001 terrorist attacks; helping rebuild lower Manhattan, the place he grew up in. The first festival was held in 2002 and drew an audience of over 150,000 visitors from outside the city. De Niro has also used his money and influence to invest in restaurants. He has co-owned the Rubicon restaurant in San Francisco with residents, movie director Francis Ford Coppola and the late, great comedian Robin Williams. He also co-founded the Nobu worldwide chain of fine dining Japanese restaurants, with 32 across five continents, including one in my home city of Perth in Western Australia.

One controversial aspect of Robert De Niro's acting career has been the criticism he has received from some Italians for his "glorifi-cation" of the Mafia in many roles he has played, giving Italians a "bad name" so they claim. This issue came to a head in 2004 when the Italian government announced it was granting honorary Italian citizenship to Robert De Niro and Martin Scorsese. When this announcement was made, many Italians like me, thought the honorary Italian citizenships

(240) *The De Niro family village of Ferrazzano in Molise.*

were well deserved. These men are creative artists who are fearless in bringing alive to the screen the real gritty world of organized crime, amongst many other controversial issues in American life and culture in particular.

So I was disappointed when I learnt that one of the largest Italian-American organizations in America, the "Order of Sons of Italy in America," ("OSIA") with over 600,000 members, sent a letter to the then Italian Prime Minister Silvio Berlusconi, requesting that he cancel the honorary citizenships. "De Niro has made a career of playing gangsters of Italian descent," they said. They went on to say; "He has done nothing to promote Italian culture in the United States. Instead OSIA and its members hold him and his movies responsible for considerably damaging the collective reputations of both Italians and Italian Americans."

Giovanni Gianfelice, the mayor of De Niro's ancestral Molise village of Ferrazzano, strongly disagreed, stating that De Niro is a great actor who has helped make Italy known all over the world. I agree. Robert De Niro is a unique artist who has given us captivating windows into so many aspects of life and the human condition; not just the Mafia.

25

DON DELILLO – THE JFK ASSASSINATION

*on DeLillo is a very influential and prolific American novelist whose parents, just like mine, were born in Montagano Molise. Many of his relatives still living in our family village are known to my parents. Don was born on 20th November 1936, growing up in an Italian-American neighbourhood in the Bronx, New York. When reflecting on his early years, he said: "I was always out on the street. As a little boy I whiled away most of my time pretending to be a baseball announcer on the radio. I could think up games for hours at a time. There were eleven of us in a small house, but the close quarters were never a problem. I didn't know things any other way. We always spoke English and Italian all mixed up together. My grandmother, who lived in America for fifty years, never learned English."

As a teenager, DeLillo was not interested in writing until he developed a habit of reading to alleviate his boredom whilst doing a summer job as a public park attendant. He said: "I had a personal golden age of reading in my twenties and my early thirties, and then my writing began to take up so much time." A number of writers had a major influence on his early writing, including James Joyce, William Faulkner and Ernest Hemmingway. DeLillo's writing was also influenced by European cinema. He developed a love of cinema: "European and Asian cinemas of the 1960s shaped the way I think and feel about things. At that time, I was living in New York, I didn't have much money, didn't have much work, I was living in one room; I was a man in a small room. And I went to the movies a lot, watching Bergman, Antonioni, Godard. When I was little, in the Bronx, I didn't go to the cinema, and I didn't think of the American films I saw as a work of art. Perhaps, in an indirect way, cinema allowed me to become a writer."

DeLillo also praises his parents for his career as a writer: "They ultimately trusted me to follow the course I'd chosen. This is something that happens if you're the eldest son in an Italian family. You get a certain leeway, and it worked in my case."

Much of DeLillo's writing has focused on eccentric, ostracized, outcast or misunderstood characters living in the shadows or on the fringes of mainstream American society. There is the emotionally damaged and traumatized David Bell in his novel, "Americana," the mentally ill Bill Gray in "Mao II," the lone assassin Lee Harvey Oswald in "Libra," the suicidal Eric Packer in "Cosmopolis," and Jack Gladney, a professor who has made his name by pioneering the field of Hitler studies and who fantasizes about mass murder in "White Noise."

(241) *"Americana" book cover.* (242) *"Mao II" book cover.* (243) *"Libra" book cover.*

DeLillo views himself as something of an outsider in American society, preferring his own family privacy to socializing in large groups. This has enabled him to take on the perspective of a dispassionate observer, when writing. "When I work," he says, "I'm just translating the world around me in what seems to be straightforward terms. For my readers, this is sometimes a vision that's not familiar. But I'm not trying to manipulate reality. This is just what I see and hear."

DeLillo lives with his wife Barbara, a landscape designer, in a comfortable estate in Westchester County in New York State; but he has not completely left his childhood neighborhood. Every year, he goes back to meet his old school friends he grew up with on the streets. "We meet on a major street and have a meal together and laugh," he says. They mainly talk about baseball which Don refers to as their second language. Baseball, he says, "was just so natural, because we all grew up with it. We played it; we listened to it on the radio, and then we went to Yankee stadium. It was taken-for-granted pleasure."

He equates writing with "living and breathing" and calls working on his novels "a life and death struggle." He gets great pleasure from what he says is "the construction of sentences and the juxtaposition of words, not just how they sound or what they mean, but even what they look like." He still does all his writing on a manual typewriter, which he says lends itself to a sculptural feeling of pressing new words into blank paper, a process which enhances his creativity. About the writing process he says: "I am a sentence maker. Like a donut maker, only slower. Every sentence has a truth waiting at the end of it and the writer learns how to know it when he finally gets there. On one level this truth is the swing of the sentence, the beat and poise, but down deeper it's the integrity of the writer as he matches the language. I've always seen myself in sentences. I begin to recognize myself, word by word, as I work through a sentence. The language of my books has shaped me as a man. There's a moral force in a sentence when it comes out right. It speaks the writer's will to live."

Of all the novels that Don DeLillo has written, I am particularly fascinated by "Libra," his 1988 story about the Kennedy assassination from the perspective of Lee Harvey Oswald. Since my teenage years,

(244) *President John F. Kennedy.*   (245) *Lee Harvey Oswald.*

I have had a deep interest in the events leading up to the JFK assassination. I have read widely on the subject and conduct an annual "Lee Harvey Oswald mock trial" when I am teaching Civics to my high school students. Although we will never know exactly what happened on that fateful day in Dealey Plaza Dallas at midday on 22nd November 1963; I believe the assassination was carried out by three gunmen, one on the sixth floor of the Texas School Book Depository building, one behind the picket fence on the grassy knoll, and a third on the freeway overpass bridge, directly ahead of the motorcade. Although the third gunman was only there as a backup in case the other two failed, which they didn't. It's quite likely to me, Lee Harvey Oswald was the assassin on the sixth floor, but in any event, the ballistics evidence and the Zapruder film clearly show the shots from the sixth floor, behind the motorcade, were not those that killed the president. The fatal bullet which struck JFK in the head came from the front of the motorcade, almost certainly from the picket fence on the grassy knoll. I believe it was a conspiracy, more than likely organized by rogue elements within the CIA and Pentagon, concerned about Kennedy's policies of not wanting to escalate the Vietnam conflict, reluctance to remove the Communist leader Fidel Castro by invading Cuba; and his seeking of a peaceful détente agreement with the Soviet Union to de-escalate the Cold War.

DeLillo's "Libra" takes the reader from Oswald's childhood to his adolescent years in the US Marine Corps and then on to his brief defection to the Soviet Union and marriage to Marina, a Russian. Then the book traces Oswald's return to the USA with Marina and his role in the JFK assassination. Oswald is portrayed as a loner and outcast, whose pro-Cuba communist ideological views make him a misfit in capitalist American society. He is not portrayed with sympathy but nor is he demonized. He loves his wife and dotes on his children, yet he regularly humiliates and beats Marina. He is well-read and intelligent and not a crazy man. DeLillo writes about Oswald's dyslexia and the intense ongoing frustration it caused him because of the great difficulty he experienced when writing letters and reading books.

In DeLillo's version of events, the assassination attempt on Kennedy is in fact intended to fail. The conspiracy is initiated by disgruntled die-hard, anti-Communist and anti-Castro former CIA operatives who intend to "scare" Kennedy into thinking that Castro is behind the attempted killing, hoping the president will respond by taking America into a war with Cuba. The novel juxtaposes historical fact with fictional imaginings. Real life characters are interwoven with characters created by DeLillo. In his author's note at the end of the book, DeLillo writes that he has made no attempt to furnish actual answers to any questions raised by the assassination. It is merely his interpretation, saying this about "Libra": "I thought I would be haunted by this story and these characters for some time to come, and that turned out to be true. But it didn't affect the search for new material, the sense that it was time to start thinking about a new book. Libra will have a lingering effect on me partly because I became so deeply involved in the story and partly because the story doesn't have an end out here in the world beyond the book. New theories, new suspects and new documents keep turning up. It will never end. And there's no reason it should end. At the time of the twenty-fifth anniversary one newspaper titled its story about the assassination 'The Day America Went Crazy.' About the same time, I became aware of three rock groups, or maybe two rock groups and a folk group, touring at the same time, the Oswalds, the Jack Rubies, and the Dead Kennedys."

246) "Zero K" book cover. 247) Don DeLillo.

When asked what motivated him to write "Libra," Don DeLillo said this in a November 1988 interview: "I didn't start thinking about it as a major subject until the early part of this decade. When I did the 1983 piece (about the JFK assassination) in Rolling Stone, I began to realize how enormously wide reaching the material was and how much more deeply I would have to search before I could begin to do justice to it. Possibly a motivating element was the fact that Oswald and I lived within six or seven blocks of each other in the Bronx. I didn't know this until I did the research for the Rolling Stone piece. He and his mother, Marguerite, traveled to New York in 52 or early 53, because her oldest son was stationed at Ellis Island with the Coast Guard. They got in the car and drove all the way to New York and eventually settled in the Bronx. Oswald lived very near the Bronx Zoo. I guess he was thirteen and I was sixteen at the time."

26

FAMOUS PEOPLE
AND CELEBRITIES

◆

N THIS CHAPTER I WILL BE RECOUNTING THE STORIES OF MANY FAMOUS
people who were either born in Molise or adjoining Abruzzo, or
can trace their family ancestry to these Italian regions, influencing their
culture. I have decided to use these stories as case studies of how sons
or daughters of central Italy have broken away from their traditional
peasant family roots and created something of cultural, scientific or
historical significance to the wider world; similar to Robert De Niro
and Don DeLillo, who I have featured in the previous chapter.

Dean Martin was born Dino Paul Crocetti, on 7th June 1917, in the
town of Steubenville Ohio, USA. His father Gaetano, who was a barber,
was born in the Abruzzo village of Montesilvano on the Adriatic coast
and around 175 kilometres north of my family village of Montagano.
Dean's language of birth was Abruzzi Italian and he did not speak
English until he started school at the age of five; the same as me, except
my first language was the slightly different dialectical Molise Italian.
This was typical of the sons and daughters of Italian immigrants. He was

not an attentive student and so for all of his life he felt self-conscious about not being well educated and ashamed of his limited vocabulary and social skills.

He was an actor, singer and comedian and was one of the most popular American entertainers of the mid-20th century. Martin was nicknamed "the king of cool" because of his naturally seamless easy charm, charisma and self-confidence. He really established a name for himself when he teamed up with comedian Jerry Lewis in a series of MGM and Paramount movies and live comedy-musical performances over a ten-year period from 1946 until 1956, when they acrimoniously parted ways, after Martin told Lewis, he meant nothing to him other than a dollar sign.

Dean Martin then went on to greater fame in a solo career which included more movies, the most popular being "Ocean's 11" and "Robin and the 7 Hoods," in which he co-starred with his good friend, Frank Sinatra. He was also a member of the iconic and super-cool Rat Pack, which also included Frank Sinatra, Sammy Davis junior, Peter Lawford and Joey Bishop. The Rat Pack were legendary for their always sold out Las Vegas live shows at the Sands Hotel. Martin and Sinatra were both great supporters of African American civil rights, often standing up for Sammy if he was racially discriminated in any way. They were also good friends with President Kennedy as a result of Peter Lawford, who was JFK's brother-in-law. Dean always felt inadequate when mixing with Kennedy and his political friends because he didn't have much knowledge of political matters. Unlike Sinatra, who had close connections with the Mafia, Dean knew a lot of underworld figures through his love of gambling, but wasn't impressed with keeping company with them. Sinatra loved being around Dean and their friendship was so strong that Dean was the only person who could say "no" to Frank and get away with it, without Frank flying off the handle into a rage.

Although Dean Martin cultivated an image as a suave ladies' man and serial seducer of women, this couldn't be further from the truth. In reality he was a family man who spent a lot of time at home, doting on his children. His second wife Jeanne put it succinctly when she said; "He was home every night for dinner."

Later on in his career, starting in 1965, Dean went on to star in his own weekly television show, "The Dean Martin Show," which ran for 264 episodes until 1974. I have fond memories of watching this show with my Dad, who was a big fan. We would often argue about who had the better singing voice, Martin or Sinatra. I believed Sinatra did; my Dad strongly disagreed. Dean would

(248) Dean Martin.

always appear intoxicated, drink in one hand, cigarette in the other, exploiting his image as a carefree drunkard crooner and womanizer, while chatting quick-wittedly on the show with his many celebrity guests, and singing many of his signature songs as well as his interpretations of other artist's songs. The program gained much notoriety, not only for his apparent heavy drinking, put-downs of women and slurred speech, but also for the numerous "spontaneous" obscene Italian

(249) Dean Martin and Jerry Lewis.

words he would blurt out, offending many Italian viewers, who understood exactly what he was saying. He seemed to delight in doing this, grinning like a cheeky child. The reality was that even though he enjoyed drinking regularly, his alcohol consumption was contained and disciplined and he rarely was intoxicated. Nevertheless, the heavy drinking was just as much a part of his carefully cultivated celebrity image as the cool crooning and womanizing.

In 1976 Dean Martin publicly reconciled with Jerry Lewis, when Frank Sinatra, who had orchestrated the meeting, brought Lewis onto the stage at a charity event. As Martin and Lewis shed tears and emotionally embraced, the audience gave them a standing ovation. They resumed their friendship, but only performed one more time together in 1989, when Martin was celebrating his 72nd birthday.

Undoubtedly the most tragic event of Dean Martin's life happened on 21st March 1987 when his son, actor and pilot, Dean Paul, died at age 35 after his F-4 Phantom jet fighter crashed while he was flying with the California Air National Guard. He was part of a formation of three Phantoms, flying in the middle. Ten minutes into the flight, Dean Paul's aircraft disappeared from radar screens in a mountainous area, covered in thick clouds. The plane had vanished from radar screens shortly after the pilots had been told to turn left in order to avoid the 11,500-foot high Mount San Gorgonio, the highest peak in southern California. For four long agonizing days, search helicopters and planes scoured the rugged mountainside, but found no sign of the missing plane. Dean was hopeful his son may have survived. Then finally, the tragic news came through that Dean Paul's plane had been found. His plane had disintegrated when it crashed into the side of the mountain at a speed of 550 miles per hour during a freak blizzard storm. The death of his son absolutely shattered Dean, leaving him depressed, demoralized and devoid of any further ambition, for the remainder of his life.

Dean Martin was a heavy smoker, and it was this addiction which finally took his life, when he died of acute respiratory failure associated with his lung cancer, at his Beverly Hills home on Christmas day 1995 at the age of 78. His crypt features the epitaph, *Everybody Loves Somebody Sometime* along with *That's Amore*, one of his biggest hit songs.

Dean was renowned for his many off the cuff quips and quotes about many aspects of life. Here are some of them.

About his fame, he said; "In a tuxedo, I'm a star. In regular clothes, I'm a nobody." "If this is just the beginning, my life's gonna be beautiful." "I don't mind being a legend." "I want to be remembered as a damn good entertainer, nothing spectacular. A good entertainer who made people enjoy themselves and made them laugh a little. I want them to think: He was a nice guy. He did pretty good and we loved him." "To those who felt I joked my way through songs during concerts and nightclub appearances. You wanna hear it straight, buy the album." "Motivation is a lotta crap." "I can't stand an actor or actress who tells me acting is hard work. It's easy work. Anyone who says it isn't never had to stand on his feet all day dealing blackjack."

About his drinking and gambling, he said: "I feel sorry for people who don't drink. When they wake up in the morning, that's as good as they're going to feel all day." "If you drink don't drive. Don't even putt." "You're not drunk if you can lie on the floor without holding on." "When the world seems to shine like you've had too much wine, that's amore." "If people want to think I get drunk and stay out all night, let 'em. That's how I got here, you know." "I was so drunk last night I fell down and missed the floor." "I don't drink anymore. I freeze it and eat it like a popsicle." "I drink because my body craves, needs alcohol. I don't drink, my body's a drunk." "When your opponent's sittin' there holdin' all the aces, there's only one thing to do: kick over the table."

About love, marriage and family, he said: "Love is a flower that blooms so tender, each kiss a dew drop of sweet surrender. Love is a moment of life enchanting, let's take that moment that tonight is granting." "I've got seven kids. The three words you hear most around my house are 'hello,' 'goodbye,' and 'I'm pregnant.'" "I know it's the gentlemanly thing to let the wife file for divorce. But then, everybody knows I'm no gentleman."

Mario Lanza, born Alfredo Arnold Cocozza, on 31st January 1921, in Philadelphia, was an Italian-American tenor and Hollywood film star of the late 1940s and 1950s. His mother Maria Lanza, was from the village of Tocco da Casauria, in the province of Pescara in the region of Abruzzo. His father Antonio Cocozza, was from the village of Filignano, in the province of Isernia in the region of Molise.

Lanza began studying to be a professional singer at the age of 16. His developing operatic career was interrupted by World War Two when he was assigned to the Special Services of the US Army Air Corps as an entertainer. After seeing him perform at the Hollywood Bowl in 1947, the legendary head of MGM, Louis B. Mayer, signed Lanza to a seven-year film contract. Lanza had a reputation for being rebellious, stubbornly tough-minded and fiercely ambitious. For most of his acting career he suffered from addictions to alcohol and overeating which had a serious impact on his health and relationships with directors and fellow cast members. His biggest screen role came in 1951 when he played the part of the famed tenor Enrico Caruso in the movie, "The Great Caruso," which was one of the biggest hit movies for that year.

While at MGM, Lanza worked closely with the Academy Award-winning conductor, composer and arranger Johnny Green. In a 1977 interview, Green said: "Had Lanza been already a leading tenor, if not the leading tenor at the Metropolitan Opera House, and come to Hollywood in between seasons to make a picture, he would have had the security of having the Met as his home." Regarding Lanza's voice, Green said: "He had an unusual, very unusual quality, a tenor with a baritone color in the middle and lower registers, and a great feeling for the making of music. A great musicality. I found it fascinating, musically, to work with him."

In May 1957 Lanza moved to Rome and was cast in the film, "Seven Hills of Rome," and in November of that year, performed for Queen Elizabeth II at the Royal Variety Show at the London Palladium. From January to April 1958 Lanza did a concert tour of the United Kingdom, Belgium, Netherlands, France and Germany. In September 1958 he made a number of operatic recordings at the Rome Opera House for the soundtrack of what would become his final role, in the film, "For the First Time." Tragically, his renowned fame was to be cut short when in April 1959 Lanza became ill with heart problems and pneumonia. Not fully recovering, on 25th September 1959 he was admitted to the Valle Giulia Clinic in Rome to lose weight for an upcoming film. He had fallen into a vicious cycle of overeating and crash dieting, whilst continuing to drink heavily, which resulted in very high blood pressure. While he was in the clinic, he underwent a controversial weight loss program, known as "the twilight sleep treatment," which required patents to be kept immobile and sedated for extended periods of time. On 7th October, Lanza died of a pulmonary embolism, triggering a massive heart attack at the age of 38.

The story doesn't end there. Rumours have persisted that Lanza was the victim of a Mafia vendetta against him for canceling a planned performance for Mafia godfather Lucky Luciano at a concert in Naples. With four children and a lavish lifestyle to support, Lanza accumulated a large amount of debt. One day, his friend and fellow Abruzzo-Molise Italian, the heavyweight champion boxer Rocky Marciano, visited Lanza with Mafia boss Tomaso Lucchese, who proposed to settle Lanza's debts in return for a series of performances for Mafia organized events.

 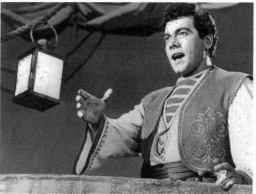

(250) Mario Lanza.   (251) Mario Lanza was a trained opera singer.

Lanza was horrified by the suggestion, and threw them both out of his home. When he and his family moved to Rome and lived luxuriously in the former royal Villa Badoglio, Lucky Luciano visited him from time to time. Lanza had been scheduled to do the Mafia performance in Naples in September 1959, but instead as we have seen, he ended up in the Valle Giulia Clinic. After Lanza's death, his wife Betty immediately expressed suspicions that her husband had been murdered in the clinic by the Mafia. No evidence has emerged confirming these suspicions.

For the remainder of this chapter, I will proceed to tell the brief stories of other famous people from Molise and Abruzzo, in chronological order; starting with Saint Adamo Abate, who was born in 990CE in the village of Petacciato Molise. He was an influential medieval Benedictine abbot who promoted the unification of southern Italy under the Norman ruler, Roger II of Sicily.

Jacopo Caldora was born in the village of Castel del Giudice Molise, then part of the Kingdom of Naples, into a noble feudal family in 1369. His mother Rita Cantelmo, was a noblewoman from a powerful French family. He began his military career as a leader of mercenary soldiers, whom he recruited from the surrounding mountain villages and proceeded to accumulate large landholdings through conquest. He ultimately became the feudal Lord of Bari, Vasto and surrounding areas. Caldora's achievements gained the attention of the French Anjou Queen Joan II of Naples, who enlisted his services as a military advisor to her court. During the political intrigue and turmoil that was occurring in Naples at this time,

Caldora offered his services as a mercenary general to the Spanish Alfonso V of Aragon, in his attempt to take control of the Kingdom of Naples. When the Aragon army was left under siege in Naples, Caldora again changed sides by serving for Queen Joan, helping her retain control of Naples. He was rewarded by being given the role of assistant to the Kingdom's Commander in Chief, Muzio Attendolo Sforza. During the Battle of L'Aquila in 1424, Sforza drowned and Caldora took control of Queen Joan's army, defeating the Spanish. He ultimately returned to his baronial lands when his attempt to secure more power by arranging for his daughter to marry Francesco Sforza of Milan, failed when Pope Martin V annulled the marriage for political reasons.

Antonio Giordano, also known as Antonio da Venafro, was born in the Molise village of Venafro in 1459. As a young man, he moved to Siena to study law at the university there. In 1488 Venafro was elected professor of law at the University of Siena, and in November 1493 was elected a judge in the Siena court. As a highly accomplished lawyer and judge, Venafro was able to work himself up to the position of trusted advisor and private secretary to the Lord of Siena, Pandolfo Petrucci. Venafro became a close confidante of the Lord of Siena and was ultimately appointed Prime Minister of Siena. Venafro was a political statesman of the highest calibre, playing a key role in negotiating a peace settlement with Cesare Borgia, who had attempted to militarily conquer the Duchy of Siena on behalf of his father, Pope Alexander VI. In chapter 22 of Nicolo Macchiavelli's highly acclaimed book, "The Prince," Venafro is described as an excellent minister.

(252) Saint Adamo Abate. (253) Jacopo Caldora.(254) Antonio Giordano.

Paolo Gamba was a painter of the Baroque period and was born on the 29th October 1712, in the village of Ripabottoni in the province of Campobasso Molise. His family were poor peasants with his father barely making a living as a decorative painter. Paolo had developed artistic painting skills from a young age and after meeting the Bishop of Larino in 1731, he was given the opportunity to study under the patronage of the highly accomplished painter, Francesco Solimena, in Naples. He developed a passion for painting religious frescoes and sacred subjects, particularly featuring the Virgin Mary, in numerous churches throughout the region. Many of his famous frescoes have survived in Molise to this day.

Vincenzo Cuoco was a historian and writer, born into a middle class family in the town of Civitacampomarano, near Campobasso Molise on 1st October 1770. He is mainly remembered for his book, "Historical Essay on the Neapolitan Revolution of 1799." He is considered to be one of the founders of the Italian liberalism political ideology and its associated realist school. Cuoco criticized the shortcomings of the political liberal rationalism of Edmund Burke and Joseph de Maistre and developed their philosophies further, using the Neapolitan Revolution as his case study. Cuoco was forced into exile for his involvement in the failed Neapolitan Revolution of 1799. Living in Milan, he wrote what became one of the nineteenth century's most important treatise on political revolutions. In this treatise, Cuoco offered an explanation for why and how revolutions succeed or fail. A major influence on political thought during the unification of Italy, the "Historical Essay" was also an inspiration to twentieth century Italian thinkers such as Benedetto Croce and Antonio Gramsci. Vincenzo Cuoco strongly supported the new liberal Republican government installed in Naples in 1799 in place of the Monarchy of King Ferdinand I of the Two Sicilies. In 1810, Cuoco returned to his native region and was made Chief of the Provincial Council of Molise. In 1812 he wrote "Journey Through Molise," one of the first works of literature about the natural and historical attractions of Molise.

Gabriele Pepe was born on 7th December 1779, in the village of Civitacampomarano in Molise. He was a soldier who fought in the defense of the Neapolitan Republic in 1799. He entered the Neapolitan army at a young age and during the revolution in Naples he was captured by royalist troops and exiled to France, where he fought in the Napoleonic armies when they conquered the Kingdom of Naples, firstly under Joseph Bonaparte and then Joachim Murat. He took part in the Neapolitan Revolution of 1820, and was once again sent into exile, this time to Florence. On the 19th February 1826, while still in exile in Florence, he dueled with the French poet Alphonse de Lamartine, who had compared Italians to "human dust" in one of his poems. He wounded the French poet in the right arm. In 1836, he returned to Naples and even though he was aged 57, he participated in the 1848 riots which had been initiated by Italian nationalists who were seeking to overthrow the Austrian monarchy in Naples and replace it with a liberal republican government.

Pietro Ramaglia was a physician and surgeon who was born on the 31st March 1802, in the village of Ripabottoni Molise, from a peasant family of humble origins. His father Francesco, was a tailor and his mother Veneranda, was a farmer. Pietro was one of the leading figures in the history of medicine in Molise and the wider Kingdom of Naples. He served as the personal physician to Bourbon King Ferdinand II of the Two Sicilies. In medicine he was one of the proponents of the experimental anatomic-clinical method and the founder of the Neapolitan positive-naturalistic school of medicine. In 1839 he married a noblewoman Marianna Tambelli, whose family were the barons of the towns and surrounding regions of San Martino and San Anzino. In 1857 he co-founded a medical journal named "Il Morgagni," after the famous

(255) Vincenzo Cuoco. (256) Gabriele Pepe. (257) Pietro Ramaglia.

anatomist Giovanni Battista Morgagni, which under his direction, became one of the most prestigious publications in its field, throughout Europe. Ramaglia studied tuberculous meningitis for 40 years, significantly enhancing the body of knowledge and understanding of that disease.

Arturo Giovannitti was an Italian-American union leader, socialist political activist and poet, born on 7th January 1884, in the village of Ripabottoni, near Campobasso Molise. He immigrated to Canada in 1900 and worked in a coal mine and a railroad crew. Soon after, he moved to the USA where he ran rescue missions for exploited Italian workers in Brooklyn and Pittsburgh. He also began writing a weekly article for the newspaper of the Italian Socialist Federation, becoming its editor in 1911. He is best remembered as one of the principal organizers of the 1912 Lawrence textile workers strike and as a defendant in a celebrated trial arising from that event; being wrongly charged with inciting a riot that led to a police crackdown on the striking workers, resulting in a worker being shot dead by the police. Giovannitti was three miles away from the scene when the incident happened. The imprisonment of Giovannitti and co-defendant Ettor, created much publicity in the USA and Europe, inspiring many activists to protest about the erosion of freedoms and workers' rights in the USA. He was acquitted of all charges at the end of the trial in November 1912. In 1914, he published his first book of poems, "Arrows in the Gale." In an introduction to the book, the acclaimed author and political activist Helen Keller, wrote: "Giovannitti is, like Shelley, a poet of revolt against the cruelty, the poverty, the ignorance which too many of us accept."

Carlo Montuori was a cinematographer and cameraman born on 3rd August 1885, in the village of Casacalenda, near Campobasso Molise. At age twelve he moved to Milan to live with his uncle, a photographer and painter. He started working as a cameraman in 1907 thanks to contacts his uncle had. He also started working in a photo studio where he learnt the basics in the newly emerging field of artificial lighting. Starting from 1911 Montuori was amongst the first in Italy to test the application of artificial lighting techniques in cinematic film. After working with many directors from the silent film era, he collaborated

(258)
Arturo Giovannatti.
(259)
Carlo Montuori.

in the making of the 1925 blockbuster film, "Ben-Hur."

Mario Tanassi was a politician who served on several occasions as a minister in the Italian Republic. He was born on 17th March 1916, in the village of Ururi, near Campobasso Molise. He entered politics as a member of the Italian Democratic Socialist Party, serving as minister of defense for the first time in 1970 and then again in 1972, when he was also vice-prime minister to Giulio Andreotti. A number of years later he was involved in a corruption scandal when he was accused of accepting financial bribes from the American weapons manufacturer Lockheed, whilst he was defense minister. In 1979 the Constitutional Court of Italy found him guilty of bribery and he spent four months in jail. He was the first former Italian minister to be imprisoned.

Benito Jacovitti was born on 19th March 1923, in the city of Termoli Molise. He was a comic artist who had a love of drawing from a young age, when as a kid, he would draw on the pavement of his neighborhood streets. At age sixteen, Jacovitti graduated from the Firenze Art Institute. While studying there, he was given his nickname "fishbone," because he was so thin. This nickname stayed with him throughout his career. In 1939, he started doing comics for the Florentine satirical magizine, "Il Brivido," and a year later he began an almost 30-year collaboration as a cartoonist with "Il Vittorioso," a Catholic comic magazine targeting teenagers and young adults. In 1956, he began working for the national daily, "Il Giorno," where he gained national prominence. Jacovitti's unique style is immediately appealing to children and adults alike. His characters have huge noses and feet, his pages are full of minute details. During his career he produced more than 60 characters and produced around 150 books.

Carmine Pecorelli was an investigative journalist who was shot dead in Rome, a year after former prime minister Aldo Moro's kidnapping and killing. He was born on 14th September 1928, in the village of Sessano del Molise, near the city of Isernia. He was described as a maverick journalist with excellent Italian secret service contacts. According to Pecorelli, Aldo Moro's kidnapping had been organized by a "lucid superpower" (code for the USA) and was inspired by what he said was the "logic of Yalta" referring to the February 1945 conference in which the three allied leaders, Roosevelt, Churchill and Stalin, laid down plans for the post-war reorganization of Germany and Europe, leading directly to the Communist Warsaw Pact Eastern Europe and Democratic NATO Western Europe. It is believed Pecorelli was a member of the ultra-secretive Italian masonic lodge, the P2, which had close ties to the Vatican Bank. After Aldo Moro's 1978 assassination, Pecorelli published some confidential documents, including Moro's letters to his family which he wrote while he was being held hostage by his kidnappers, the Red Brigades. In a cryptic article he published in May 1978, Pecorelli drew a connection between Operation Gladio, NATO's US backed, Italian based anti-communist organization, and Moro's death. Pecorelli was killed in Rome's Prati district on 20th March, 1979, when he was shot four times at close range. In 2002, former prime minister Giulio Andreotti and Mafia boss Gaetano Badalamenti, were sentenced for 24 years for Pecorelli's murder; but the sentence was appealed and overturned by the Italian Supreme Court in 2003.

Ruggero Santilli is an Italian-American nuclear physicist, born on the 8th September 1935, in the village of Capracotta Molise. He held various academic positions in Italy until 1967, when he took a position at the University of Miami, residing in the USA ever since. He is best known for his controversial research in testing the validity of quantum mechanics within nuclear and hadronic structures. In 1985 he published a book, "Il Grande Grido: Ethical Probe on Einstein's Followers in the USA, an Insider's View." In this book he claims there is an effective conspiracy to suppress or not investigate new theories in physics which may conflict with established theories, such as Einstein's theory of relativity. According to Santilli, institutions receive funding and have established entire

(260) Benito Jacovitti (far left).
(261) Carmine Pecorelli (left).
(262) Ruggero Santilli (above).

departments dedicated to long-standing theories, so he argues, it would be against their own financial interests to explore alternative theories. Santilli also claims that a number of prominent scientists, including Nobel laureates Sheldon Glashow and Steven Weinberg have conspired to stop him from conducting his own original research because it contradicts part of Einstein's theory of relativity.

Emilio Gentile is a historian who was born on 31st August 1946, in the Molise village of Bojano. His specialty is the ideology and culture of fascism. Gentile is considered one of Italy's foremost cultural historians of fascist ideology and its application in the Mussolini years in Italy. He considers fascism to be a form of political religion, creating the same degree of fanatical following and controlling the masses in the same manner as organized religion, while dampening the ability of its subjects to criticize a fascist regime rationally. Gentile created controversy when he applied his theory of political religion to the Bush presidency and its declared "War on Terror" in the aftermath of the September 11, 2001 attacks on the USA.

Gilda Giuliani is a singer who achieved national prominence in Italy in the 1970s. She was born on 19th June 1954, in the Molise city of Termoli. After some experience singing in various choirs, Giuliani won the "Due Voci Per San Remo" competition in 1972 which gave her the chance to compete in the 23rd San Remo Music Festival. The song which she performed, "Serena" was a big hit and launched her career, with her unique vocal style receiving widespread critical acclaim. In December of 1972 she also competed at the World Popular Song Festival in Tokyo, winning both the Grand Prix and Most Outstanding

Performance Award with the song, "Parigi a Volte Cosa Fa." From the mid-1970s she slowed down her activities in Italy, instead focusing her career on international performances. After a period of silence, Giuliani reappeared on Italian television in the 1990s as a regular in the RAI musical programs.

In addition to the people mentioned above, there are a number of celebrities who can also trace their ancestral roots to Molise or Abruzzo. The singer Madonna, whose birth name is Louise Veronica Ciccone, was born to Madonna Fortin, a French Canadian and Silvio Ciccone, a first generation Italian American; but she can trace her paternal grandparents, Gaetano and Michelina, to the village of Pacentro in Abruzzo. The singer Ariana Grande claims Italian heritage on both sides. Her father, Frank Butera is Sicilian and her mother is originally from Molise.

Garry Marshall, whose birth name was Garry Masciarelli, was a producer of the popular 1970s television sitcoms, "Happy Days," "The Odd Couple" and "Laverne and Shirley." He also produced the successful Hollywood movies, "Pretty Woman" and "The Princess Diaries." Garry's father Anthony Masciarelli who was born in Molise, changed his surname to Marshall in the 1940s when he began his career as an industrial filmmaker.

World heavyweight boxing champion Rocky Marciano, can trace his family ancestry to the city of Chieti, the capital of Abruzzo. Originally born Rocco Francis Marchegiano, he became Rocky Marciano after a ring announcer in Rhode Island couldn't pronounce his surname. Marciano started out playing professional baseball, but he was cut from the team for joining a church group. His first boxing match was in July 1948 and he went on to become World Heavyweight Champion in 1952. He won an unrivalled 49 straight fights.

Perry (Pierino) Como's ancestry can be traced to the Abruzzo town of Palena, where the famous De Cecco and Delverde pastas are made. Pierino was the seventh of thirteen children born to Pietro Como and Lucia Travaglini, and the first to be born in America. His first big hit, "Til the End of Time," was the biggest hit of the year in the USA in 1945. He would go on to become a legendary Las Vegas performer, winning numerous Emmy Awards for his crooning ballads.

French Canadian singer-songwriter Michael Buble has been an Italian citizen since his birth under "jure sanguinis," an Italian rule that grants Italian citizenship if either of your parents at the time of your birth, were Italian citizens. Buble's maternal grandparents were from Abruzzo. His Italian grandfather was responsible for his very first singing engagements. Demetrio Santaga ended up swapping his professional plumbing services business in exchange for managing his grandson Michael's blossoming music career. Today Michael Buble has an international audience and has won many Grammy, American Music, BRIT and Juno awards. After a pause in his career when his son was fighting cancer, Buble made an emotional return to the stage to accept the Canadian National Arts Center Award.

263) Gilda Giuliani. (264) Rocky Marciano. (265) Perry Como.

Actor Bradley Cooper has an Abruzzo ancestry, on the side of his mother, Gloria Campano's family. Cooper's maternal grandmother, Assunta de Francesca, was born in the Abruzzo village of Ripa Teatina. Bradley credits her with his passion for cooking.

Formula One champion driver, Juan Manuel Fangio (aka El Maestro) can trace his ancestral roots to the city of Chieti, the capital of Abruzzo. He is acknowledged as one of the greatest racing car drivers of all time, having won the World Driver's Championships five times. This is a record he had for 47 years until he was overtaken by Michael Schumacher. Fangio dominated the first decade of Formula One racing. His father emigrated to Argentina from Chieti, where he worked in the building and construction trade.

Henry Mancini (aka Enrico Nicola) whose ancestry is from the

(266) Michael Buble. (267) Bradley Cooper. (268) Juan Fangio.

(269) Henry Mancini. (270) Madonna. (271) Ariana Grande.

town of Scanno Abruzzo, was a celebrated Hollywood music writer and producer. Amongst his most famous music scores were "The Pink Panther" and "Breakfast at Tiffany's." He went on to become the "house arranger" for numerous Hollywood studios, working on over 100 films during the course of his career.

John Fante was an Italian-American novelist whose most famous work was the gritty American classic, "Ask the Dust," a semi-autobiographical novel that features his alter-ego Arturo Bandini. Although Fante was born in Colorado in 1909, his father Nicola Fante was born in the village of Torricella Peligna in Abruzzo.

Finally, there was the last surviving veteran of the First World War, and at the time of his death, the oldest medical doctor in Italy and one of the oldest people in the country, Annibale Ciarniello, who died in his home village of Bagnoli del Trigno Molise, just six days before his 107th birthday. He was remembered as the grandfather of Molise and for having been one of the most well-known doctors in the rural province surrounding the city of Isernia where he lived and practiced medicine.

PART TWO

CARMELINA'S STORY

27

MY FAMILY AND THE
TWO WORLD WARS

⟋⟍

HEN MY MOTHER'S GRANDFATHER LUCIANO CATERINA WAS ENGAGED, the doctor did not want him to get married because he said he had a weak heart and probably didn't have much longer to live. Luciano was a proud hardened but loving family man who refused to believe this. He had a stubborn streak about him which would often involve him ignoring the advice of others, no matter how sensible it may seem to be. Sometimes I wonder if I have inherited my stubbornness from my great grandfather!

The young Luciano felt as fit as a lion. He and his sweetheart, Maria Giuseppa were so determined to get married that they eloped on a donkey in the open fertile fields of the Molise countryside outside the town of Montagano. Many people in the village assumed that Luciano was sick because he had a constant cough which never seemed to go away. But if he was sick, his body wasn't sharing this knowledge with him. He was a vegetable farmer. Every morning at 2am he would awaken, load his fresh vegetables onto his donkeys, and travel to nearby towns, selling his produce. Luciano was a kind hearted man who treated everybody with gentleness and respect, but he particularly was fond of his granddaughter Carmelina, my mother.

Every time my grandmother Assunta would make a new dress for my mother as a young child, Luciano would call her over and ask her if a new dress had been made for his baby doll. "Baby doll" is what he called young Carmelina. He would then put money in the pockets of her dress, for her to buy sweets. He was always very kind to her for the entire time right up until she left Montagano for her long voyage to Australia. But I am jumping ahead of myself now. More about that later on. Five years before he died, Luciano had a stroke which prevented him from traveling from town to town selling his produce.

During the years of the Second World War, with a wife, five daughters and a son, Luciano was actively supporting his family by maintaining a vegetable farm and selling his fresh produce in other towns. He had a difficult life. He had witnessed the death, shortly after birth, of two of his daughters and a son, so his family would have been even bigger. Large families of seven to ten children were not uncommon in the Molise region of central Italy in the 1930s and 40s. The family was to suffer further hardship when his daughter Lina died from heart failure at the age of fifteen. When this tragic death occurred in 1935, his daughter Assunta, my grandmother, was married and was expecting a daughter, whom she named Lina. Tragically, the baby Lina died at nine months of age. My mother Carmelina was never going to have the sister she had yearned for as a child.

One afternoon during the Second World War in early 1943, Luciano was walking along the road from Montagano to Pitrella with his two donkeys fully packed with fresh produce, when a convoy of German soldiers on motorcycles approached. During that stage in the war, the Italians under the fracturing leadership of Benito Mussolini were still allied to the Germans. Molise was occupied by German soldiers. They accused my great grandfather Luciano of being a spy. He denied this, saying he was just trying to make a living to feed his family. They insisted he was a member of a local spy ring which had been passing on German troop movement information to American intelligence. At

(272 and 273) *German soldiers in Molise during World War Two.*

this stage in the war, the Americans had not yet begun their liberation of Italy.

American and other allied forces did not land in mainland Italy to commence the campaign to eradicate the Germans until later in that year, in September 1943. The German soldiers handed my great grandfather a shovel and demanded that he dig his own grave. Luckily, as he began to dig his grave, a local municipal official was passing by and managed to convince the Germans not to shoot Luciano. They didn't release him until twenty-four hours later, after they had interrogated him using a translator and were finally satisfied that he wasn't a spy for the Americans after all. This did not faze him. He continued his daily routine of delivering fresh vegetables to nearby towns every morning and then in the afternoon tending to his vegetable farm.

Luciano's eldest daughter Antonietta who was born in 1910, was married before the war years and already had two children, a son who went on to become a prison guard and a daughter my mother's age,

LUCIANO CATERINA

(274) *My great-grandfather.*

MARIA GIUSEPPA MUCCINO

(275) *My great-grandmother.*

who ended up migrating to Toronto Canada. The first bombs that struck our family village of Montagano smashed the front entrance of Antonietta's house on the outskirts of the village. She was so traumatized by this bombing that she suffered severe shellshock and paralysis, which tragically cut her life short when she died in 1957.

The Germans were positioned in the nearby village of Sant Angelo, which was higher up in the mountains and therefore gave them an excellent vantage point to conduct their bombings of surrounding villages. Antonietta's husband remarried after her death. The lady he married had a daughter who he treated as if she was his own child. Antonietta's daughter, Maria, became engaged to a young man from a nearby village called Guadiaferre. The marriage was arranged by the local matchmaker. Each village had a matchmaker who served a very important role in bringing together couples from different villages in the region.

Luciano was a humble and simple man whose greatest joy was doing whatever he could for the wellbeing of his family. If his family was lacking in anything, he felt it personally. He enjoyed making mozzarella and provolone cheese from the cows which he owned. The money he made from selling his vegetables and cheeses would be placed in a container he kept in a cupboard in his kitchen. This money was freely available for everybody in the family to use for whatever purpose they required. He was an incredibly generous man.

The romance of Luciano and Maria Giuseppa started when they were a young age, living close to each other in in the fields near the Biferno river, on the outskirts of Montagano. Maria Giuseppa's mother, Francesca, would walk the 12 kilometres daily to the most exclusive hotel in the region, The Grand, situated in the nearby city of Campobasso; collect the dirty linen, carrying it in a basket on her head, walk back to the village and wash the linen at the nearby spring water fountain. This was a daily activity she did for many years in the early 1900s, bringing in much needed income to supplement their living off the land.

(276) *The Grand Hotel, Campobasso.*   (277) *Grand Hotel coat of arms.*

My mother Carmelina was a young girl when her great grand-mother Francesca died. She remembers the colourful floral dress that her mother Assunta had made for her at around the same time of Francesca's death. Francesca's husband, my great-great grandfather Domenico died tragically from malaria while on a sea voyage from Italy to the USA, seeking to find work opportunities. They threw his body overboard to avoid a contagion of the disease on the ship.

Luciano and Maria Giuseppa were heartbroken when their eldest son, also called Domenico migrated to Canada with his young family. Not long after this, Maria Giuseppa died from pneumonia and two weeks later, Luciano also died. My grandmother Assunta would wash her father Luciano daily after his wife died, because he was so distraught by the death of his loving wife. Assunta would sometimes call Luciano's brother Rocco, to help her in bathing her father, but it was clear to her Rocco was not comfortable with this, so Assunta took this chore upon herself reassuring Luciano not to be embarrassed because she felt it her duty as his daughter to bathe him and keep him clean. The death of his wife had destroyed his will to live on.

After the death of Luciano, my mother's youngest brother Mario, had wanted to migrate to Australia, so not long after, my grandparents and their sons, Antonio and Mario left Italy to join my mother Carmelina and her brother Nicoa, in Australia. My grandmother told Carmelina that the reason she decided to come to Australia was the cross that my mother had borne, particularly with the responsibility of looking after her brother Nicola, had placed enormous stress onto her daughter and she was now determined to assist her. But I'm jumping ahead of myself now. I'll talk more about my mother's voyage to Australia, later in this book.

(278) *Antonietta, Carmelina's grandmother.*

(279) *Luciano and Maria Giuseppa.*

Luciano and Maria Giuseppa's parents and grandparents had also been born in Montagano. Their family history had always been as peasant farmers growing their own produce, living off the land, selling any surplus to nearby villages.

After the death of her husband at sea, Francesca met a man in Campobasso while there for her Grand Hotel linen collection. They married. She had three more sons from this marriage; Giovanni, Vincenzo and Domenico. One of the sons remained in Montagano, marrying a local woman, the other two migrated to the USA.

My great grandfather Luciano and his brother Rocco had travelled to Brooklyn New York often, around six months each time, doing a variety of jobs to bring in income for their families. The work would mainly be unskilled manual labour in industries such as railways and construction. Rocco would use his extra money to buy more property in the village, but unbeknownst to him, his wife Maria registered the properties in her name only. So when he died, he didn't have any property in his name. Maria's relatives were the exclusive inheritors of the properties.

Luciano had a cassino (farmhouse) in the fields outside the village which had large donkey stables, wine cellar, a kitchen and upstairs bedrooms. During 1943 when Montagano was being regularly bombed by the Germans, many of the children, including my four-year old mother, would stay at this cassino for safety. One morning while staying there, Carmelina and her mother went into the village to make a large corn pizza for all the children staying at the cassino. Corn pizza is a local delicacy which can be cut in half and filled with olive oil, sausages, anchovies, cold meats or cheeses.

Whilst returning from the village to the cassino in the fields alongside the road, they heard the sounds of motorcycles in the distance. They hid in a ditch near the road as an entourage of German soldiers sped by, two on each motorcycle, one riding and another in a side carriage. After the Germans had passed, they continued their journey to the cassino to feed the hungry children. Carmelina and her father Raffaele were lucky to escape a German bombing another day, when they were walking in the village square, after visiting my mother's grandmother (Raffaele's mother) Antonietta and quickly raced to safety when the bombs started hitting. Many buildings in the village were heavily damaged that day. The home of the village magistrate was destroyed. Another bomb entered through a window of another house and whizzed outside the back door landing in the garden and did not explode. My mother's friend Assunta was a four-year old girl living in that house at the time. Some fragments from the interior wall hit her on the face and she has carried those physical and emotional scars with her, ever since. She now lives in Perth Australia. Her husband Agostino went on to create Uncle Domenic's Italian restaurant which was very popular in Perth in the 1970s and 80s.

My mother Carmelina recalls that during the war years a contingent of Polish soldiers were encamped near the centre of our village. These soldiers were from the Polish Second Corps, transferred from Egypt to Italy in 1944 to become part of the British Eighth- Army which was in Italy to remove the Germans, under the command of General Oliver Leese. There were numerous soldiers living in a very large tent just outside the village. Carmelina and many other young children would go to the tent in the mornings and the soldiers would treat them well, giving them chocolates and candy. One of the Polish soldiers came to inspect the cantina (basement) of Luciano's house near the centre of the village and told our family it was a very safe place to stay when the German bombs struck, because of its very thick walls. One young woman in the village who lived near my family, had a relationship with a Polish soldier which resulted in a child. She remained a single mother and was ostracized as a result. Not long after the Polish soldiers left, a contingent of equally friendly American soldiers arrived in the village along with jeeps and tanks. The entire town was so excited to see the Americans arrive, because it meant the hated Germans had retreated further north.

In those days, people in the village would get most of their news from billboards that were posted on walls. Carmelina remembers the children being frightened by Italian Communist Party posters. They were told the communists would send all the children to Siberia if they misbehaved! The end of the war was announced in 1945 by a series of

(280, 281and 282) *Italian Communist Party posters.*

billboard posters all over the region. The people were ecstatic! The war years had caused much destruction and hardship in the Molise region.

My grandfather Raffaele had seen action in the Second World War. He wasn't supposed to be enlisted because he was the son of a deceased First World War soldier. His father Nicola, had fought in northern Italy and died in the town of Radipuglia, where he was buried. His belongings, including his military uniform, assorted medallions and documents were sent to his family in Montagano. My uncle Nicola took possession of these medallions and gave them to his daughter, my cousin Sandra, who has preserved and restored them.

At the time, Italian men whose fathers had died in the First World War were exempted from enlisting in the Second World War. Nicola had also traveled to the USA on numerous occasions, seeking to support his family with extra income from work. This was typical of many Molise men in the late 19th and early 20th centuries because poverty was

(283) *Staten Island Immigration Building and Statue of Liberty, New York City.*

rampant in the villages of Molise during this time. Men needed to travel abroad to supplement their incomes.

Maria Giuseppa, Luciano's wife and my great grandmother, was a very fine proud woman. My mother has fond memories of regularly visiting her. Whenever there was an upcoming festival, she would ensure that her grand-daughter Carmelina had enough money to buy a nice dress for the occasion. Both of my mother's grandparents doted on her, always incredibly generous and selfless.

In order of oldest to youngest, Luciano and Maria Giuseppa's children were Antonietta, a dark haired beautiful woman with two children who suffered paralysis and trauma from the war and died in 1957 as we have seen. In her later years she had a pet lamb she doted on. Her sisters including my grandmother Assunta would do all of her washing for her. Second oldest was my grandmother Assunta. Third was Ida who lived a long healthy life and died in her nineties in Montagano. Next was Maria, the mother of Pina, who has written an excellent history of Montagano. Then there was Yolanda and the youngest, a son, Domenico born in 1928, who migrated to Montreal Canada.

On my father Filippo's side, his grandfather on his father's side was also Filippo and grandmother was Stella. My father's family originated from Naples. The first Ferrone arrived in Montagano in the early 1800s. Filippo was the son of this man, whose name is unknown. Filippo and Stella had four sons, from eldest to youngest they were Domenico, Giovanni, Francesco, who died in 1963 and whom my brother, born in 1963, was named after. The youngest was my grandfather Giuseppe, whom I am named after.

The Ferrone family had always worked as farm labourers in the fields outside of Montagano. Being the youngest, my father Filippo worked as a shepherd as a young man, tending to the family's sheep. His only sister Maria looked after him because his mother Teresa would leave home early every day to work in the fields. Maria was unable to work because she had polio which affected the mobility in her legs and ability to work outdoors. She cared for my father, often spoiling him and letting him get away with many things and favouring him ahead of the three older brothers, Domenico, Roberto and Antonio.

Polio was widespread in Molise during the 19th and early to mid-20th century, with a vaccine not discovered until 1955. Unfortunately, the vaccine was of no help to those who had already contracted polio. My grandfather Raffaele had this affliction too. Antonio was definitely the "wild boy" amongst the Ferrone brothers. He would always ask his mother for money to spend when he was regularly going out as a teenager. Although she didn't have much money because times were difficult, he would cause such a commotion, including throwing tantrums, that she would give him what little she had. The other two older brothers resented this, receiving very little from their mother. Antonio was Teresa's favoured son. Maria would do part time dressmaking to supplement her income and would generously look after my father, caring for him like a son.

Maria was kind-hearted and caring for her entire life. When she moved to Australia she lived with and looked after her parents, Giuseppe and Teresa. Although she married, unfortunately they weren't together long because her husband Barney died from an asbestos related disease; a legacy of the many years he worked at the Wittenoon asbestos mine in Western Australia.

(284) *My grandfather Giuseppe.*

(285) *My father Filippo.*

The Ferrone family had a farm with sheep, using the wool to make their own clothing, including trousers, skirts, jumpers and socks, which they would colour with dyes and sell at the local markets and also provide for themselves. The period immediately after the First World War was particularly harsh for the villages of the Molise region. Families had to be self-sufficient, money was very tight, the economy was in a very bad way. This was aggravated because the Italian government neglected the Molise region, with very little investment committed to this area. My grandfather Giuseppe fought at the border between Austria and Italy between 1915-1918 during the First World War. He was lucky not to sustain any injuries. He fought in a series of battles there. Italy had hoped to rapidly gain the territories of present-day Trentino and South Tyrol from the Austria-Hungarians, but instead the front soon bogged down into trench warfare, similar to the Western Front that was fought in France, but at much higher altitudes and extreme cold, particularly in the winter months.

The fighting along this front displaced much of the surrounding civilian population. Several thousand civilians died from malnutrition and illness in Italian and Austrian refugee camps. The Allies eventually prevailed, resulting in the disintegration and ultimate destruction of the Austria-Hungarian empire and the Italian capture of the cities of Trento, Bolzano and Trieste. These cities came back to Italy. This is why the Italians refer to this conflict as the Fourth War of Independence and the completion of the last stage of the unification of Italy, which had commenced in 1870. In spite of getting these cities back, did Italy receive what it deserved in the aftermath of the First World War?

By the end of the First World War in 1918, 600,000 Italians were dead, 950,000 were wounded and 250,000 were crippled for life. The Great War cost more than the Italian government had spent in the previous 50 years. By 1918, Italy was stricken by very high inflation and substantial unemployment. There was optimism that Italy would be duly rewarded for its efforts and sacrifices in Versailles Paris in 1919.

This was not to be the case. Many Italians believed the nation was humiliated by the "Big Three" victorious allies; President Woodrow Wilson of America, Prime Minister Lloyd George of Britain and

Prime Minister Georges Clemenceau of France; who literally ignored the Italian delegation led by Prime Minister Vittorio Orlando. In the Treaty of Versailles, the Italians did not get what they believed had been promised to them at the Treaty of London. This caused great resentment in Italy.

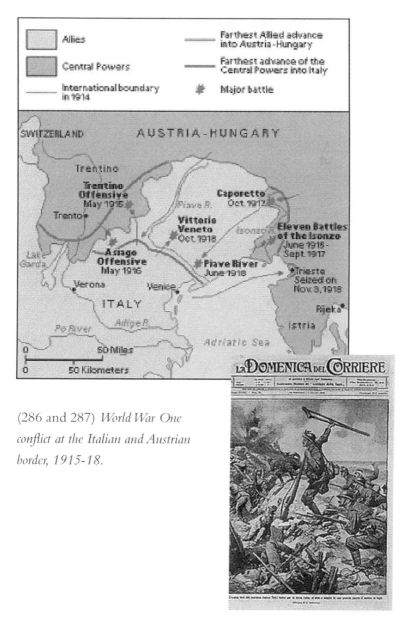

(286 and 287) *World War One conflict at the Italian and Austrian border, 1915-18.*

28

CARMELINA'S EARLY YEARS

～～

In the early years of the twentieth century one of the most popular traditional foods in Molise was corn pizza with a variety of fillings, the most common of which was sausages. The pizza would be cooked on tiles above wood-fired natural fireplaces, which were common to all kitchens at the time. There was no electricity or gas available at the time. Polenta was also a very popular dish as well as gnocchi made from potatoes; pasta and fasciole; and home-made pasta, using their own tomato sauce. In fact, Montagano had a reputation for the best tomatoes in the Molise region. The Naples based Cirio sauce company would buy up all the tomatoes that the village could produce, sending a large truck to the town every week, providing a much needed income to many families at the time, including ours. Montagano also had a reputation for excellent large yellow table grapes.

My mother Carmelina has fond memories of making home-made pasta as a five-year old girl, standing up on a chair in the kitchen, ready for when her mother arrived home from the fields in the late afternoon.

(288 and 289) *CIRIO*
Tomatoes Naples.

One day she made the pasta too soft. As her mother was coming down the path, she rushed out to greet her, telling her that she had made a mess of the pasta that day, and nobody was going to want to eat it. "What have you done, my child!" her mother Assunta said in an agitated voice. When Carmelina told her what had happened, her response was, "Is that all? Don't worry my child, we can fix that problem together." She was relieved that's all it was because her biggest concern was not wanting her kids to do anything embarrassing that may dishonour the family name within the village. Assunta did not want it to be thought that she was unable to control and look after her own children. This was a very real concern for all the families living in small villages in Molise at the time. Bringing dishonour to your family by not conforming to the customs of the time, was the worst thing that could happen to a family.

Assunta would leave for the fields at 8.30 every morning, returning around 6.30 in the summer evenings, earlier in the winter. The fields were just on the outskirts of Montagano, a relatively short distance. The vineyards were further afield, so it would be a longer trip when tending to these. Not long after this occurred, Assunta gave Carmelina the sole responsibility of preparing the evening meals, including deciding what to cook each day, causing her much anxiety as a little girl! To this day, Carmelina is anxious about what to cook for the family, not wanting any disapproval.

Carmelina's daily routine as a young girl would start with her awakening at 2.00am to go and get the water from the mountain spring well, along with two other girls who lived nearby. At the time, there was only one fountain outside the village with drinking water. This was a five kilometre walk for her. If they left on time, they would not encounter too many others, but if they left a little late, they would be confronted with a long line, hundreds of metres long of other villagers, including many children, waiting to fill their containers with fresh drinking water. If Carmelina did go late, and had to line up, arriving home later than usual, she would often be punished by her mother Assunta with slaps to her bottom and legs. Carmelina was enterprising! When she was around twelve years of age, in addition to the family bronze container, she would also fill the village dressmaker's container each day, receiving 600 lire per month, and she also would hire out a third container to another family for a further 600 lire per month; using the 1,200 lire per month to buy shoes for her long walks. These shoes would not last more than a month, because of the amount of walking she was doing.

As a teenage girl Carmelina would go to the fields to work at the vineyards picking grapes and packing them into wooden crates to earn some extra money. All through her childhood and teenage years Carmelina was able to maintain a degree of financial independence by doing odd casual work. She always used her own initiative in securing this casual work.

Montagano's economy would be at its best during the tomato and grape season because people had more spending money at this time. Virtually all tomatoes and grapes produced in the fields had a ready-made customer, often from outside companies. It was during this season that many people would buy their clothes and shoes, and festivities would occur, including baptisms, confirmations, engagements, weddings and the religious celebrations dedicated to the saints of the region. At no time does Carmelina recollect her family going through very hard times, even though money was always tight.

(290) *Traditional wine-making in Molise.*

(291) *Peasant girls fetching water.*

Their financial situation was helped by the fact that my grandfather Raffaele received a war pension resulting from the death of his father Nicola in the First World War. But unfortunately, he was caught up in a financial scandal. There was a businessman in Montagano representing an Italian bank. He would take savings deposits from many villagers, including Raffaele's war pension money. My grandfather had also sold some land, placing the proceeds in the bank until he was ready to buy a larger family house in Montagano. The bank went into liquidation and my grandfather Raffaele lost all of his savings! This was a big blow to the family. Raffaele was a proud man who always dressed elegantly. He put on a stoic brave face after this major financial setback urging the family to just get on with their lives and continue to work hard.

Assunta and Raffaele had met as neighbours. Everybody in the village considered Assunta to be the most beautiful of Luciano's daughters. She was a petite vivacious girl with light curly auburn hair. As a young woman she had many courtiers. Assunta was reluctant to marry Raffaele at first, even though they had known each other since childhood. She enjoyed the attention from all the eligible men. Like many other girls, Assunta only had four years of education, but she had basic literacy and numeracy skills which were honed by the daily life of a vibrant village, with no shortage of salacious gossip!

At the time that Assunta was a seventeen-year old teenager in 1927, sheer panty hose stockings were available for the first time. During a San Alessandro religious festival, she put on the panty hose stockings. As she

(292) *My grandmother Assunta.*   (293) *My grandfather Raffaele.*

stepped into the kitchen she saw her father Luciano and mother Maria Giuseppa look at her in a very bewildered manner. Her mother told her not to leave the house like that and put socks on instead. Assunta held firm and said she was going to keep the panty hose stockings on. She then stormed into the bedroom and jumped out of the window!

My grandmother Assunta and her older sister Antonietta were engaged at the same time. It was a custom in the village at the time that during Easter and Christmas engaged women had to prepare a wooden chest full of gifts to present to their fiances. The gifts would include shirts, ties, socks and trousers. My great grandmother Maria Giuseppa only prepared a chest for her eldest daughter Antonietta, not one for Assunta. To add further insult to that humiliation, she demanded that Assunta deliver the chest of gifts to Antonietta's fiance! "Where is my chest of gifts mother?" Assunta asked. "We cannot afford one for you" was her mother's reply. "We will do one for you another time" she added. When her mother and sister had left the house, Assunta took the chest, brought it to the donkey stables below the house, and angrily destroyed all of its contents! "If I can't have a chest, neither will my sister!" she said. Assunta was grounded for a week for this outburst.

Luciano and Maria Giuseppa loved entertaining family and friends. Luciano maintained the traditional belief that his children must always come to visit him and not vice versa. And so they did, which pleased him endlessly. Every night one of the sons or daughters would visit the parents for dinner and to catch up on the day's gossip around the village. My mother Carmelina has many fond memories of these visits, as a child.

My grandfather Raffaele's mother was Antonietta. She was born in the nearby village of Petrella and was considered to be an excellent host so her house was always full of family and friends who would drop in at all hours of the day and evening. It was a custom in Molise at the time for people to call in on each other unannounced, particularly in the summer months when many families would go for their late afternoon and evening "passeggiata's" or long walks and then drop in to see relatives and friends. Every family always had food, sweets and drink ready for these spontaneous visits. Antonietta had a reputation for

(294) *Molise village donkey.*

(295) *Molise elderly women.*

making her own delicious goat cheese and ricotta. Carmelina remembers often visiting her as a young girl and seeing the cheese and ricotta. Yet when she would ask for some to take back to the family, Antonietta would say that it wasn't ready yet. Carmelina would not leave her house until she got what she came there for.

Nevertheless, Carmelina does have fond memories of sleep-overs at her grandmother Antonietta's house in Petrella. She was a strong willed and opinionated woman who hated parting with her cheese and ricotta delicacies. She died in 1974. Antonietta had two sisters, Nicola, who migrated to Pittsburgh USA and Filomena, who along with her two sons accumulated a substantial property portfolio in and around Petrella. One son Giuseppe, migrated to Pittsburgh as well and the other Domenico, remained in Petrella. Filomena also had a daughter, calling her Antonietta.

It was a hot summer day in July 1946, seven-year old Carmelina was at home washing the floor, when suddenly her five-year old brother Nicola arrived home, covered in grimy grease, oil and dirt, rushed into the house and immediately threw himself onto my grandmother Assunta's bed, making a mess on the floor and her hand embroidered bed cover. Although it was a Sunday, the parents were not home, instead they had been visiting their parents. Carmelina knew that her mother Assunta was going to be very angry if she saw this big mess. Carmelina sent her young brother Nicola to the local store to buy some dirt removing liquid, but it wouldn't remove the grease and oil stains on the bed.

They then heard the chatter of their parents as they were approaching the house. Panicking, they fled through the back door, terrified of the punishment they were going to receive from my grandmother Assunta. They went to an elderly neighbor whom Assunta admired, telling her what had happened and pleading with her to calm Assunta down so she wouldn't punish them. Carmelina doesn't know what the conversation between the elderly lady and Assunta was about, but when she returned home shortly after, Assunta grabbed them both and hugged and kissed them. Just the threat of punishment from my grandmother was enough to terrify Carmelina and her brothers! On another occasion, seven-year old Carmelina was again at home washing the kitchen floor and her brother Nicola kept stepping on the wet floor. He would race up and down sliding onto the floor after she had washed it. She warned him many times to stop doing that and go outside to play. Having had enough, Carmelina told Nicola that there were some sweets in the small pantry room adjoining the kitchen. Curious, he opened the door and stepped inside. Carmelina immediately locked him inside where he remained for the entire day while she went about cleaning the rest of the house, in spite of his screams and banging on the door. She made sure he was released before her parents arrived from the fields. He had learnt his lesson to never get in the way of my mother when she was cleaning the house; a lesson that I have also learnt to this day!

Christmas and Easter in Montagano were wonderful times for Carmelina and her brothers when they were children. Assunta, like all of the other mothers would cook the village delicacy, pasta in forno, which was cooked from their wood-fired oven. The pasta sheets were hand made. They would use their own home made tomato sauce. The pasta in forno would include a variety of cheeses, sausages, eggs, tiny meat balls and an assortment of vegetables. There would be many varieties

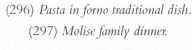

(296) *Pasta in forno traditional dish.*
(297) *Molise family dinner.*

and shapes of home-made pasta that were used. The other delicacies during the festive seasons were sponge cakes filled with ricotta and home-made almond biscuits.

At Christmas time there was always a large amount of pasta cooked so that the leftovers would last into New Year's Eve and the "Befana" witches celebration on the 6th January. Every village in Molise had an elderly wise woman who was the "good witch." Her role was to ward off "malocchio" evil spirits that they believed would afflict the people from time to time. She would do this with specific plant based potions and with unrecognizable chants. Being the winter time, the pasta could be preserved and recooked well into January so it was an opportunity to cook in bulk for the family.

The family would awaken very early in the morning on a festive day, Assunta doing the cooking, assisted by her daughter Carmelina. The family would all go to the twelve noon mass, which in those days would be performed in Latin. Upon their return, the family would sit down

(298, 299 and 300) *Claudio Villa, Mario Lanza and Giorgio Consolini.*

for a long and joyous lunch, filled with laughter and storytelling. Later in the afternoon when lunch was over and the dishes were washed, the tradition was that relatives and friends would freely and spontaneously drop in, and the wine would be flowing.

Every family in Montagano made their own wine of the highest quality because of the superb grapes grown in the fertile soil of the region. No chemical preservatives were added to the wine, so it was one hundred percent natural, resulting in no early morning headaches and hangovers if too much of it was drank! The house was full of people and the celebrations, games, stories, laughter, great food and wine, would flow well into the evening. My mother's auntie Concetta would start singing traditional Molise songs accompanied by uncle Domenico playing the piano accordion, with everybody including Carmelina as a child, joining in. Everybody would then be dancing into the early hours of the morning, often finishing at around 2am.

Carmelina has always loved music. As a child growing up in the 1940s she recalls many popular performers of the time including Claudio Villa, Mario Lanza, Luciano Paoli and Giorgio Consolilo. She recalls a gramophone that they owned and vinyl single records which they would play, featuring these artists in particular. From an early age, Carmelina enjoyed singing along to music. In the summer, when my mother was a teenager, she would often go with a group of friends to the pine forest surrounding Montagano where they would play and sing along to recorded music well into the balmy evenings.

I have many fond memories waking up on a Sunday morning to the sweet sound of my mother's voice singing while Italian music was playing on the record player. It wasn't just Tom Jones as I alluded to at the start of this book! My great grandmother Antonietta's (Raffaele's mother) home was the place of many enjoyable gatherings for her grandchildren, and likewise my mother would carry on the family tradition by saying to her grandchildren, particularly my daughters and nieces, that her home was also a place of enjoyment, surrounded by music.

As a child growing up Carmelina does not recall receiving any Christmas or Easter presents, other than sweets, biscuits and small amounts of money from her grandparents. This is because the times were hard in Molise and money needed to be saved to get through the difficult winter months when not much could be grown in the fields. In 1940s Molise, there was no concept of Father Christmas and presents. Instead, when celebrating "La Befana" on the 6th January the tradition was to fill a stocking with sweets, biscuits and fruit, for the children to eat on that day.

The children believed the Befana witch would come down the chimneys to fill the empty stockings which were left near the chimney by each family. From the Befana tradition then came the tradition of Father Christmas and the stocking in the late 1950s. As a child my mother recalls sitting near the chimney with her brothers on the eve of the Befana, waiting for the good witch to fill their stockings. They would fall asleep and on the morning of the 6th, Assunta would tell the

(301 and 302) *La Befana Italian Witch celebration on 6th January.*

children that they missed the visit of the Befana because they fell fast asleep. The Befana was very useful for disciplining children too. Many times Assunta would say to her children, "behave yourselves, otherwise the Befana will fill your stocking with charcoal and dirt!" If the children were naughty Assunta would see to it that the stocking would include some charcoal and dirt alongside the food to reinforce her point about the consequences of bad behaviour.

The children of Molise had mixed feelings about the Befana. On the one hand they were very excited by her arrival because of the sweets and food but they were also fearful of her, thinking she would cast an evil spell on the family if they had misbehaved. Carmelina recalls a kind neighbour called Michele who would make wooden dolls for her and soldiers for her brothers, which he would give to them on the day of the Befana. Later, when he married the village dressmaker, she would make clothes for Carmelina's wooden dolls.

At dinner time as children, Nicola would always sit opposite his sister Carmelina and would constantly kick her shins under the table, my mother giving right back to him as much as she got. Assunta, finally having enough of these antics, would say, "children, you better stop this right now, or I will get the wooden paddle and smack you both across your legs." But they would just carry on, ignoring her. "You started this," Carmelina would say to her younger brother. "No I didn't!" Nicola would reply. Suffice to say that the outcome of these antics was both children getting the wooden paddle and being sent off to bed early. There was only two years of age difference between Carmelina and her brother, my uncle Nicola. The two other brothers, Antonio and Mario were a number of years younger, so they were infants during this time.

An exciting time when Carmelina was a child was when a package would arrive from a cousin living in Brooklyn New York. These packages would often include clothing for the children. On one occasion, when Antonio was just born, a package arrived. There was seven years of age difference between Carmelina and her youngest brother. "Is this all there is in the package?" my mother Carmelina said. "Open the window and let's toss it out," she went on to say. She was upset because it only contained baby clothes and nothing for her and her older brothers. Carmelina was nine years old when her brother Mario was born, so she was given the prime responsibility of looking after him. Whereas Antonio was looked after by a baby sitter who was called "Zia Maria from the fountain" because of the location where she lived in the village. She had five daughters and a son. My mother would call her "nonna" and loved going over there to play with those children, often staying overnight to be with her youngest brother Mario too. The two eldest daughters were excellent dressmakers and would often make lovely clothes for Carmelina.

It was these two sisters who taught my mother how to sew. As a nine-year old girl she would pass many hours observing them and practicing with the left over offcuts of cloth. All of the sewing in 1940s Molise was done manually with metal knitting needles. Carmelina remembers knitting a multicoloured sweater which was her pride and joy as a child. All through my childhood I have many memories of my mother sewing for the family, using metal knitting needles and a peddle powered sewing machine, including making a blue and white striped sweater for me when I was in early primary school. To this day, she is still doing alterations for her sons and grandchildren at a very high standard.

Playtime was a particularly fun time for children growing up in Molise in the 1940s. Carmelina and Nicola would meet up with a group of other children in the village and they would tie a skipping rope to two trees in the nearby pine forest, passing away many hours.

At the time, Montagano had two professional cyclists, Coppo and Bartoli, who had competed in the Gira Italia and Gira France events. The children would sit in a row, on the side of the main road leading into the village, watching them do practice trial races, whizzing by at great speed. Board games made from buttons and cardboard were also popular, particularly in the winter months.

A form of baseball would be played in the village square, using a piece of wood as the bat and cloth filled yellow sand as the ball. This was initiated by the villagers who had been to America. Soccer would be played, again using a large circular cloth filled ball because nobody could afford a soccer ball at the time.

Carmelina started going to school at age five. She only had four years of schooling which was typical of the children in Molise in the immediate post war years. She loved her school experience. History was her favorite subject. To this day she remembers learning a legend "Mucchio Schevele," where the hero has his hand cut off by vengeful gods, leaving a deep impression on my mother. She loved to read, requesting all the books that the teacher could lend her. She remembers a particular book one of her uncles bought her, called the "Il Ponte dei Sespiri," which translates to The Bridge of Sighs in Venice. She read this book over two nights and then recounted the story to her friends.

With every family having an average of four to seven children in Molise at the time, the very busy elementary school in Montagano was in a four level building situated close to the centre of the town. Classes were full, often with over thirty children in each class.

Carmelina's teacher was Mr Cannavino, a passionate and dedicated educator who inspired her to learn at her full potential. Originally from the nearby town of Petrella, he and his wife had developed excellent reputations as engaging and popular teachers, winning the respect of the townspeople. He was so impressed with the learning potential of young Carmelina that he would often visit the family home and try to convince Raffaele and Assunta to allow her to continue beyond the compulsory four years of education.

(303) *Molise Flower festival.*

(304) *Molise village classroom.*

(305) *My mother, Carmelina in 1955.*

With three young brothers and a busy farm to look after, this was going to be out of the question. The family needed her hard work ethic. In fact, with the birth of Mario, Carmelina did not even get a chance to complete her fourth year, having to pull out in October 1947 shortly after the birth of her brother. Her primary responsibility was to look after her two youngest brothers while Assunta worked on the farm in the fields. This would also involve ensuring that there was enough milk powder for their feeding. In those days, milk powder was dispensed by the town doctor whom Carmelina would often visit. At the time the elderly doctor was in the process of retiring and was training a young doctor to take over. One day when my mother turned up as she often did, to collect more milk powder, the young doctor asked, "Carmelina, tell me, who is drinking this milk, you or the babies?" "We drink it together" replied my mother with a mischievous grin.

29

PEASANT SOCIETY IN MONTAGANO

As we have seen, Montagano is the village of my parent's birth. It rises on one side of the Biferno river, where once was the ancient Samnite settlement of Fagifulae, which in the 4th century BCE sided with Hannibal against the Romans, and later became a Roman "municipium" or small settlement. The village of Montagano is mainly built in white stone, and the surrounding fields are neat and intensively farmed. The village tradition states that a parish priest by the name of Damiano Petrone (1659-1710) listened to the confessions of many peasants at that time, and as penance for their sins, asked them to plant as many trees and vines as they could. He also offered them some Church money to buy tools. Hence the reputation of Montagano being an excellent fertile area for peasant farming, began. Montagano is high up in the Apennine mountains, fifteen minutes by car away from Campobasso and forty minutes away from Termoli, on the Adriatic coast.

The peasant society within Molise in general and Montagano in particular could be divided into three categories. There were those at the lowest rung of the ladder, who owned no land and survived by providing ad-hoc itinerant labor on the farming fields. This group lived a life of poverty, often short of food, particularly in the winter months when they could not work. The middle rung which included my family, owned small farming plots and were able to survive from the produce they grew and the animals they herded. Yet they also experienced hardship in the winter months. The upper rung were owners of larger farms, small business owners or artisans who lived what today would be considered a middle class life. My grandmother Assunta was a very generous woman who would often prepare enough food to ensure that neighbouring poverty stricken families were fed before her family sat down for dinner in the difficult war years and winter months.

There was Natalina who lived nearby, a widow with two young sons, whose husband died of cancer in 1940. One of her sons came from a brief relationship that she had with an American soldier based in the town during the war in 1944. Natalina lived in poverty, shunned by many people in the town for having an illegitimate son. She survived by going to the fields and pleading with families to give her some produce. Assunta would often cook for her and invite her and her two sons to the family home for dinner. The sons were slightly younger than Carmelina and Nicola and became good friends, often playing together. Assunta did not judge Natalina, she looked after her as best she could, with compassion and an open heart. These were traits which the young Carmelina possessed too, and would result in her caring for her family in a way in which she would selflessly sacrifice her self-interests to those of her family. There were some families who suffered severe poverty and hardship. The townspeople would rally together and take turns to ensure that these unfortunate people were fed and clothed. With a farm that produced many varieties of cheeses, olives, tomatoes, chickens and goats, Assunta and Raffaele were fortunate that they could provide for their family.

My mother tells me at the time that she was a young girl in the early 1950s there was a street in Montagano which was dedicated to the artisans and merchants. Along this street could be found merchants for cotton and wool, cardigans, socks, embroidery, dressmakers, food

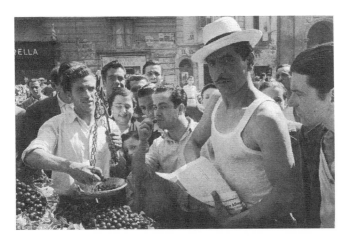

(306)
*Molise village
market.*

products and general merchandise. There were also artisans specializing as blacksmiths, carpenters and barbers. At the time there were also two doctors, two lawyers and a pharmacy. The village also had two bars and two specialist clubs, one catering for the "artigianti" (artisans) and another catering for the "contadini" (peasants).

There were some family tragedies that the family had to deal with. One in particular involved my Carmelina's brother, Nicola. He had grown into a handsome and popular young man. At age seventeen in 1958 he worked as a farm labourer on his grandfather Luciano's farm. He was good at negotiating an adequate income from his grandfather in exchange for hard work, saving his hard earned money by hiding it in a cloth sack in the cellar, always dreaming of a better life for himself and migrating to a faraway country like USA, Canada, Argentina or possibly even Australia. These were the destinations that most Italians from Molise were migrating to at the time.

One day, his uncle, also Nicola, who had recently returned from working in Belgium, asked his nephew Nicola to assist him with a construction job which he was working on alongside the Biferno river outside Montagano. Uncle Nicola worked as a coal miner in Belgium. Like many men from Molise, he was forced to seek work in northern Europe because of the post war dire economic situation in Italy in the 1950s. He needed to support his family. In 1957 whilst working at the Belgian coal mine, it collapsed, resulting in the deaths of many miners. Uncle Nicola survived and was physically unscathed but emotionally traumatized by the accident. He considered himself to be a very lucky and blessed man. For the entire time that he worked at the coal mine in Belgium, he would return home every six months to visit his family. Shaken by the disaster, he vowed that he would never work in a coal mine again, so this time he was to remain permanently in Montagano and try to secure work, hopefully in construction.

The Molise regional government initiated a project to construct additional roads and dykes along the Biferno river to channel the water to irrigate many inland farms in the region. One of these dykes was being constructed at the river, outside Montagano. Representatives from the contractor visited the towns in the area in June 1958, seeking to recruit men to work on the dyke irrigation project. When they visited Montagano, uncle Nicola eagerly enrolled for the project. It was going to give him guaranteed work for at least twelve months. Telling his nephew Nicola about this project, he too enrolled. His father Raffaele liked the idea of his son working on a construction project because it would give him additional skills which would hold him in good stead for his future employment prospects, particularly when the family migrated overseas to start a new life, as they were planning during this time.

My mother Carmelina vividly remembers the bright sunny morning in June 1958 when uncle Nicola came to the house to collect her teenage brother Nicola to commence working on the Biferno river project. Over thirty men from Montagano had been secured to work on the project and the contractors had arranged for a bus which was waiting in the town piazza to take them to the site. My mother remembers how excited her brother was to be working on a construction project with many of the town men whom he respected and admired.

Gionnina kissed her husband Nicola on the cheek and wished him the very best for his first day of work at the construction site. The bus was to travel to the nearby town of Roccomandolfo to collect more men, before making its way to the construction site. Gionnina had recounted that the night before, Nicola had awoken in the middle of the night in a panicked state after having had a bad dream. He had dreamt of a funeral and said he vividly saw a coffin draped with red

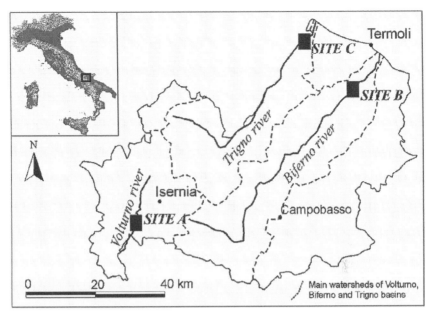

(307) *The Volturno, Biferno and Trigno Rivers, in Molise.*

roses. That morning just before he left, he said to his wife, "Gionnina, please look after the children extra carefully today, because I had a bad dream last night." They had two young sons and a daughter; Adriano, Gino and Emma.

Within two hours of the men leaving town on the bus, a number of distressed men who had been working at the site arrived in Montagano and went straight to Gionnina's home to let her know there had been a tragic accident at the construction site and her husband Nicola was badly injured. A group of men including Nicola were required to lift a heavy sheet of steel to place onto a tray-top truck. Nicola was a hard diligent worker and applied all of his strength when lifting and carrying the sheet of steel. Unfortunately, there were some men who did not have the right grip and did not exert sufficient strength, so as a result two of them lost their grip and balance resulting in the very heavy steel falling onto the chest and neck of Nicola after he too had stumbled as a result of the commotion and panic. He was rushed to Campobasso Hospital but tragically died from his injuries that afternoon on 3rd June 1958. His death devastated not only his immediate family but the entire town. He was a very popular man and everybody knew him.

My uncle, young Nicola had witnessed the accident and was severely traumatized by the sight of his uncle, covered in blood, laying in agony on the road. To this day, he suffers from post- traumatic stress disorder and constantly has terrible nightmares about what he witnessed that day. This event shook Carmelina to the core. Uncle Nicola was always very kind to her and would bring her gifts every time he returned from Belgium. In his earlier years, he often came rushing from his home to assist the polio afflicted Raffaele and his wife Assunta when they were returning from their farm in the fields carrying fresh produce, two donkeys in tow.

In the lead up to Christmas 1957 an eighteen-year old Carmelina, who had a very close and deep connection with her father Raffaele, asked him if she could buy a new bright colourful woolen pullover to keep herself warm during what was a particularly harsh cold winter that year. This style of pullover was fashionable in the Molise region at the time and she knew that many of her girlfriends had convinced their parents to buy them one, even though they were expensive. They were a fashion statement amongst Molise teenage girls and my mother did not want to miss out.

She knew it was a particularly tough time for the family and money was short, but nevertheless she made her plea to her father. Raffaele knew he didn't have enough money. He asked his daughter to visit auntie Angelina, who was very close to the family and had money set aside for a rainy day; and told his daughter to ask her for a loan of 3,000 lire which Raffaele would repay to Angelina in February from his war pension. Just as father and daughter were having that conversation, in walked uncle Nicola. He insisted he would take Carmelina to Campobasso with him the following day to buy the pullover using the money from auntie Angelina. He was a very generous man. Not only did he accompany her to buy her pullover, but he bought her a woollen skirt to go with it, as a Christmas gift. That afternoon there was a snow storm in Campobasso so the bus service back to Montagano had been delayed. So Nicola and his niece Carmelina enjoyed hot pasta and fascioli at a trattoria in Campobasso before taking the later bus back to Montagano.

My mother's uncle Nicola had a heart of gold and Carmelina was definitely his favourite amongst his nieces and nephews. His sons, Gino and Adriano have both taken after their father, always extremely hospitable to us whenever we visit Montagano. When uncle Nicola and Carmelina returned home she told her father she didn't have enough money to buy the skirt as well as the pullover and that uncle Nicola had generously given her the money for the skirt. Raffaele replied, "That's fine dear, my brother and I have an understanding about these things and will sort it out between ourselves."

Raffaele had three brothers, Nicola, Domenico and Antonio. All three of the brothers acknowledged that Raffaele made the best wine in the family, so when the time came to make the wine, they would allow Raffaele to use his special recipes and techniques. The result was always the same; a selection of white and red wines which were the envy of Montagano's townspeople. Winemaking in Molise was a tradition that went back many centuries to ancient times. The grapes were hand-picked from the fertile vineyards of the region and then crushed by stomping men, as tradition dictated. Enough wine was produced to last the entire year and the best vintages were exchanged amongst many families in the village. The wine was stored in the underground cantina cellars which each house had; also used to accommodate their donkeys. At the time most families had two donkeys for transporting produce from the farm fields to the town. It was a tradition for the men to gather together in each other's cantinas, alternating from one to another on Friday evenings, sampling and enjoying the family wines, cheeses and sausages while playing the card games of briscola and scoppa, late into the evening.

The biggest religious festivals in Montagano were Santa Croccie on the 3rd May, Santo Antonio on 15th June, and Santo Alessandro on 10th July. Santo Alessandro is the patron saint of Montagano, so this festival was always the biggest celebration of the year. Much of the money raised to enable these festivals to proceed would come from money collected from Montagano emigrants who were living overseas including other parts of Europe. The municipal local government would write directly to these emigrants on behalf of the local church, requesting that they contribute to the festivals. My grandfathers, Raffaele and Giuseppe,

(308)
*Santo Alessandro festival
in Montagano.*

(309)
*Santo Antonio festival
in Montagano.*

contributed $300 annually each for the entire time they lived in Australia. During the mass on the day of the festivities, the priest would read out the names of all ex-Montagano people who had donated money, where they were now living and how much they had donated.

The disclosure of amounts donated always created inter-family conflicts, jealousies and rivalries, which was always a sensitive issue in these Molise towns. At the end of each festival, the local priest posted a notice outside the entrance to the church disclosing the total funds raised and spent on the festival. This was done to give the people confidence that the church was actually spending all money donated on the religious festival and not squandering any of the money. Confidence in the ability of the church to manage money responsibly was important for their ongoing money raising and credibility within the community.

There were a number of scandals in other Molise towns in the 1940s and 1950s where money donated had been embezzled by priests who were then forced out of the church. As a child Carmelina was always excited on the day of a religious festival. Large amounts of food were prepared in the morning, including the traditional corn pizzas and pasta in forno. Carmelina's family attended the church service at midday. Then immediately after, would be the procession through the streets of Montagano, with the saint hoisted high up on a pedestal carried by a number of strong able-bodied men at the front of the procession, alongside the town priest. Immediately behind would be a brass band, many of the musicians whom came from Campobasso and adjoining Molise towns. Behind the band would be the mayor and members of the municipal council, followed by the townspeople, entire families of men,

(310)

Dancing at a Molise festival.

(311)

Traditional Molise costumes and dancing.

women and children. After the procession the people gathered at the picnic areas in the pine forest and enjoyed food, wine, card games, music, dancing and continuous chatter well into the evening when the festival culminated in a fireworks display. All of the families openly shared their food and wine with each other. Then for the remainder of the evening most of the people continued to congregate in the village square piazza where numerous food stalls and performers were established.

The atmosphere was one of great joyful celebration, to give thanks and count their good fortune and blessings. It was an opportunity for the entire village to happily get together, this is why all the festivities were communal, not in the homes. One of the longstanding traditions of these religious festivals was for a tall wooden pole to be erected alongside the church in the centre of the village and at the top of this pole a large prosciutto was tied with rope. A competition was then conducted in the evening to see who could successfully climb to the top of the pole and take the prosciutto for them to keep. Carmelina remembers this being an intensely competitive affair with families trying to get the honour of the sacred prosciutto.

In Molise towns and villages, the priest was highly respected. Not only did he conduct all of the church services, including baptisms, communions, confirmations, weddings, confessions and funerals, and lead the religious processions; he was also a trusted confidante and counsellor, giving the people guidance and advice on a wide range of family and personal issues and problems. Families would regularly invite the priest to dinner and family celebrations.

It was common knowledge that often the priests were in intimate relationships with women, sometimes more than one, and occasionally they fathered children. This was never spoken about openly. As long as the priest was discrete, it was tolerated, but there were instances when scandals developed to the point where the priests suddenly were transferred to other towns by the church, a fair distance away, and the new priests started afresh with a clean slate, nobody knowing what scandals they had left behind in other towns.

When Carmelina was a child, Montagano had a population of around 4,000, compared to today when it is just under 1,000. At that time there were three priests, typically all of them were born in Montagano. My mother remembers one of them was called Padre Don Cosimo. He was the arch priest of the town, the most senior priest. He was the priest the people would speak to, in order to organize their religious services, from baptisms, to weddings to funerals. Don Cosimo was a priest in the town for over fifty years. He was ably assisted by Don Luigi. In those days there were three functioning churches in the village, each priest responsible for delivering all of the sermons and services from one of the churches. Don Luigi was a younger priest who got along very well with the youth of the town, often organizing sporting and social activities for them. These priests held positions of enormous influence and power in the village because they knew many of the secrets of the families that would confide in them. It was sacrosanct that the priests maintained confidentiality. If they breached this just once, their power and respect in the town would evaporate and they were then forced to relocate.

Funerals were particularly intensely emotional events in Molise villages. When a person died, the body remained at home for a full day, to enable family, relatives and friends to grieve and pray for the soul and its journey to heaven. Upon death, billboards were placed at various locations around the village to inform the people of the death, where the body was and the date and time of the funeral service. Children could view the bodies as well. My mother recalls attending grieving wakes at homes many times. The body was cleaned and dressed formally, then laid out on a bed. People came to the home, filing into the bedroom, three or four at a time, viewing the body and praying. Then they would adjourn to the kitchen and share food and wine whilst reminiscing fondly about the life of the deceased.

These gatherings typically lasted from mid-morning until late into the evening and were always held on the day before the funeral. It gave loved ones an opportunity for emotional closure before the body was buried. On the day of the funeral, the body was placed in a simple wooden coffin, and carried by the closest relatives from the home to the church with the priest leading the entourage. After completion of the funeral service, the entourage would make its way to the cemetery.

It was not unusual for most of the town's population to be in this entourage. In Montagano the cemetery is five kilometres outside the village, so the procession takes around thirty minutes to get there. At the cemetery hundreds of people would gather, many screaming and wailing with uncontrollable raw emotion as prayers were recited and the coffin was lowered into the earth, or placed into a crypt.

Carmelina recalls the tragic death of her friend Emma, from cancer at twelve years of age. Her mother was beside herself with grief, screaming and wailing for the entire day before the funeral, never leaving her daughter's body. When it came time to place her daughter Emma in the coffin the next morning, her mother lay on the bed alongside Emma and refused to allow the body to be removed. She had to be restrained by relatives. "Take the keys to my house!" she screamed. "This house is closed and dead, as is my heart!" she shrieked and wailed. A number of times during the day of the funeral, the poor woman fainted, on the way to the church, in the church and at the cemetery, where again she refused to allow the coffin to be lowered.

Carmelina was also twelve at the time. Emma's funeral was the first she attended. She remembers often waking up in the middle of the night after having nightmares where she would see Emma crying out to her from her deathbed. At around the same time, Carmelina also remembers a horrible incident involving a thirteen-year old boy who was getting off a bus after having visited Campobasso. As he stepped off the rear exit of the bus, his foot was caught on the steps and he stumbled under the bus. Not realizing this, the driver took off and the boy was dragged a number of metres along the road. At the exact time this was happening, Carmelina was visiting her aunt who lived nearby. She heard the boy screaming desperately and as she raced outside the house she saw that he was caught underneath the bus, and was being dragged. Miraculously, as the bus drove past the metal cross just before the village entrance, the boy was able to free himself, surviving the accident. The people of Montagano were very religious and believed the boy had been saved by Christ and the Madonna.

A third tragedy she remembers also at around the same time, was one of the town bakers getting his hand caught and severed in a pasta-making

(312) *Traditional Molise wedding* (right).

(313) *Modern Molise wedding* (above).

machine when she was in the general store next door. Carmelina remembers him racing out of the bakery with blood gushing from his severed wrist. Reflecting upon these events today, she wonders whether these were omens designed to strengthen her resolve to guide her through the next phase in her life, which was her emigration to Australia.

Weddings were a joyous occasion in Montagano. After at least six months of courting, it was expected that the suitor would ask the father of the girl for his permission to marry her. He had to let the father know at least three days in advance and then they would schedule a time for the suitor to come to the family home and sit with the father and mother. The mother would not say a word, only listen and act as a witness to the event. The young man would formally request to marry the daughter. The father had to provide an immediate reply. If he said yes, he would then proceed to counsel the suitor on how he should treat his daughter. Then a wedding date would be set. This date had to be within one month of the father giving approval. On the day of the wedding, the bride's family prepared her for the church ceremony, which was usually conducted at 10am. Anybody was free to attend the church service. Then during the afternoon, the townspeople could visit the bride's family home and give their best wishes and provide gifts.

The wedding function was held in the evening at the bride's family home and would be attended by invited guests only. It involved a large traditional meal, with wine flowing freely. The children were seated at a separate table. Music and singing was typically performed by two men hired for the occasion, one a singer and the other playing a piano-accordion. The celebration was usually completed by midnight. It was not uncommon in Molise for cousins to marry each other. This was a necessity when towns were so sparsely populated and families were large. It was inevitable that relatives would get together and marry. Even in those times, there was an unspoken stigma associated with cousins who married. Often a direct anecdotal connection could be made between the children of these couplings and some form of intellectual, behavioural or developmental disability. Of course in the Molise of the 1940s and 50s, mental illness and psychological disorders were largely undiagnosed.

It was assumed that everybody was responsible for and could control their behaviour except those who had the misfortune of being possessed by demons. In these cases, the remedy was considered to be a visit to the wise elderly befana witch. An example that my mother cites is of her good childhood friend Maria, who now lives in Sydney. Her late husband Angelo's parents, the Muccino's, were first cousins. When they expressed a desire to marry, both sets of parents were hostile to the idea, urging their respective son and daughter not to keep seeing each other and to forget the idea of marriage. They were married by eloping and the end result was out of a total of seven children, four were born blind.

Angelo was not one of the blind children. Shortly after marrying Maria, they migrated to Sydney where Angelo's first job was working on the construction of the Opera House. Angelo's oldest sister Rosa, was also born healthy. The next child Maria, was born blind as was their first born son Giuseppe and the following two siblings. Later on Giuseppe married and had a son called Franco. He was born with a severe intellectual disability.

My mother remembers that when she, my father and youngest

(314)

*Sydney Opera House
under construction.*

brother Luciano travelled to Italy in 1972, they visited Giuseppe's family in Rome. Their eldest son Franco had a bright red toy fire truck which my brother was keen to play with. The young boy Franco, threw a violent tantrum, refusing to allow my brother to play with the truck. One day in 1978, at age seventeen he mysteriously left his home, telling his parents he was going to stay with a friend who lived on the outskirts of Rome, for a few months. He never returned and ceased all contact with his family.

In 1980 when the Red Brigades terrorist group were at the height of their anarchical violence, including the blowing up of the Bologna railway station which resulted in the deaths of 76 people, a carabenieri police officer knocked on the door of the Muccino household. When Giuseppe answered, he was informed his son Franco had been killed in a police shoot out on the outskirts of Rome, when they raided a Red Brigades underground cell. It turns out that Franco had been a member of this notorious terrorist group and had been involved in the planning and execution of the Bologna attack.

The Red Brigades was an extreme left wing terrorist organization and urban guerilla group responsible for

(315)

*Red Brigades bombing
in Bologna, 1980.*

many violent incidents in Italy during the 1970s and early 1980s, including the assassination of former Italian Prime Minister Aldo Moro in 1978, numerous kidnappings and robberies and major bombings such as the Bologna railway station incident.

Formed in 1970, the organization wanted to create a Communist State by using violence to destabilize Italy to the brink of anarchy, which they hoped would then incite the workers to start a revolution, similar to that which occurred in Russia in 1917 under the Bolshevik leadership of Vladimir Lenin.

Part of their mission was to remove the influence of the United States in the political, economic and military affairs of Italy, and to this end, they agitated for the removal of Italy from membership of the North Atlantic Treaty Organization ("NATO").

Ultimately, the Italian government succeeded in breaking up the Red Brigades with a series of successful raids and arrests in the 1980s.

On a more positive note to end this chapter, Italian Australians comprise the sixth largest ethnic group in Australia, which is 4.6% of the total population, according to the 2016 census. This is just over

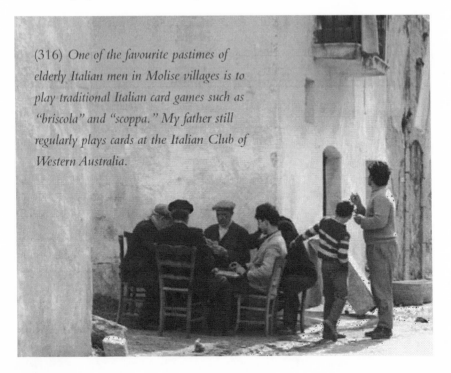

(316) *One of the favourite pastimes of elderly Italian men in Molise villages is to play traditional Italian card games such as "briscola" and "scoppa." My father still regularly plays cards at the Italian Club of Western Australia.*

1,000,000 people either born in Italy or descendants of Italians born in Australia, like me.

In the two decades after the end of World War Two, there was a significant wave of Italian migration to Australia, which included my parents, who arrived in the 1950s. These Italians made a substantial contribution to Australia's economic development including such large scale projects as the Snowy Mountain Hydro Electricity Scheme and the construction of the Sydney Opera House.

Berardino Forlano is just one example of an Italian immigrant who came to Australia for a better life. Born in the medieval Abruzzo village of Guardiagrele, he migrated to Australia in the 1950s and worked on the construction of major infrastructure projects in the eastern and central states of Australia including power generation, television communication masts and high-rise buildings in Melbourne.

He died in 2012, at age 83, surrounded by his family at his home in Melbourne.

30

COURTING RITUALS

⟪⟫

*I*N THE MOLISE REGION THERE WERE STRICT COURTING RITUALS THAT all young couples followed. These rituals can be traced back to medieval times. When a young man had a romantic interest in a girl, he would approach her when she was on a passegiata walk with her girlfriends. Unlike the very restrictive traditions in Calabria and Sicily, young girls in Molise were free to go on walks in their villages as long as they were accompanied by an adult or their girlfriends. The young man, often accompanied by his friends who would encourage him and give him confidence, would walk behind the group of girls which included his romantic interest. He would then call out the name of the girl he liked but not actually have a conversation with her.

This was the first step in the process. It made clear that the boy had an interest in courting a particular girl. If the girl acknowledged his calling of her name, smiled at him whilst making eye contact, and didn't ignore him, then he knew she was interested in him which meant he could proceed to stage two. The second stage required that the young man serenade his love interest. Shortly after sunset, he would arrive outside the girl's home and sing a love song to her, sometimes even accompanied by a friend playing the piano-accordion or guitar. This serenade served three purposes. Firstly, it clearly indicated to the girl that the boy was interested in her. Secondly, it delivered the same message to her parents and family in an acceptable manner. Thirdly, the singing was consciously designed to get the attention of neighbours who could then spread the word around the village that the boy and girl were a newly formative couple. This is how my father courted my mother.

Although my parents' families knew of each other, living in the same village, they didn't have much contact. In 1956 when my mother Carmelina was sixteen and my father Filippo was twenty-one, he showed interest in her by following her with his friends while she was walking in the piazza centre of the village with her friends one evening; calling out her name and gently tugging at her hair, which was also an acceptable part of the courting tradition. She turned her head and smiled at him. He knew she was interested. He then serenaded her the following night, not wanting to waste time because he knew of at least two other young men who had expressed an interest in Carmelina.

My father's serenade was unique; he had recently bought a battery operated record player and proceeded to sing along to a popular 1954 Claudio Villa song called "Luna Rossa" ("Red Moon") while standing outside Carmelina's family home. He had chosen this song because he knew my mother Carmelina loved the music of Claudio Villa. She had met one of the other suitors as a fifteen-year old when she was on her way delivering sausages to her grandmother. As Carmelina left her home accompanied by two of her girlfriends a young man named Roberto began to walk behind them and started calling out "Carmelina! Carmelina! Carmelina!" She knew his family and knew that the following morning he was going to be leaving town for military training in northern Italy. My grandmother Assunta had witnessed Roberto calling out her daughter's name and immediately called her to come back home. She did not approve of him, firstly because he had a reputation of having serenaded a number of other girls and secondly because he was going to be away for at least eighteen months. Sure enough Roberto appeared that night to begin serenading Carmelina, wearing his full military uniform, singing Giacamo Rondinella's 1953

(317 and 318) *Giacomo Rondinella was a very popular singer and actor in 1950s Italy.*

hit song *Surdato Nnammurato* ("Soldier in Love"). After he left the next morning, she didn't hear from him again, eliminating him as a suitor, to my father's great pleasure.

Before my father Filippo made it obvious he was interested in Carmelina, he often conveniently would show up in various places around the village where my mother was. One day Carmelina was sitting on a bench in the pine forest on the outskirts of the village with her girlfriends after snow had fallen when suddenly Filippo appeared with his friends and proceeded to throw snowballs at the girls. Another time, after her part time job of washing wine bottles for the village landowning baron at his palazzo, Filippo would often be sitting nearby, greeting Carmelina as she left the palazzo for home. Carmelina did not realize Filippo was interested in her though, until he followed her and called out her name, around three months later. My mother should have realized Filippo's interest sooner because her friend Anna would often point out to her that he really liked her, but Carmelina didn't see the signs which appeared very evident to her friends. She thought he was a very handsome man and just didn't think he would be interested in her.

Before he began courting Carmelina, Filippo enlisted in the Italian navy in 1954. He had long wanted to leave Montagano and see the world before he settled down in marriage, not wanting to spend the rest of his life on the family farm as a shepherd. The navy was the perfect opportunity for him. At the time, the Italian government wanted to expand their navy so there was an active recruitment program across the country. It was when he returned from the navy in 1956 that he began courting Carmelina.

Music was an important part of the lives of teenagers and young adults in Molise of the 1950s. With the availability of inexpensive portable record players everybody was listening to the most popular Italian performers of that day. Carmelina's favorite was Claudio Villa. Born in Rome in 1926, he recorded over 3,000 songs, appeared in 25 musical films and sold over 45 million records. Villa died in 1987. On his gravestone are the words " *Vita sei bella, morte fai schifo.*" ("Life, you are fine, death you stink.") Filippo's favorite was Giacamo Rondinella who was the son of actors from Naples. Born in 1923 he started his career as a singer after World War Two, following failed attempts to pursue a military career and a career as a boxer. As well as his music he had a successful career as an actor.

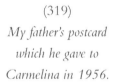

(319)

My father's postcard which he gave to Carmelina in 1956.

My father Filippo left Montagano in 1954 and was assigned to a naval ship which left for Messina Sicily from the northern Italian port of Genoa. In the two years that he was in the navy, the ship was mostly berthed at Messina. This was a great adventure for Filippo. He was assigned the role of a typist for a ship's officer. The training was minimal. He hadn't even learned to swim; instead he underwent a four week typing course in Genoa before the ship sailed. When Filippo returned to Montagano in 1956 he started his relationship with Carmelina. For

(320) *My father Filippo is in the front row, viewer's far right. Taken in 1954.*

nine months they were able to get to know each other well, including the respective families. During this time that they were engaged, Filippo began to discuss with Carmelina, his plan for them to emigrate overseas and start a new life and family together.

At the time, four countries were actively seeking Italian migrants; the United States, Canada, Argentina and Australia. My father's decision to migrate to Australia in late 1956 was simple. Most of his relatives and friends in Montagano had migrated to the other three countries, but very few to Australia. He wanted to start a new life, in a country he knew very little about. He chose Australia for this reason as well as the fact that this was a young country with what he considered to be a bright future. When he looked into it further, he found out that he would be undertaking his voyage on the Lloyd Triestino passenger ship "Neptunia" which would stop first at Fremantle Western Australia, near the city of Perth and then continue on to Adelaide, Melbourne and Sydney.

He decided that he was going to make his life in Perth. During the voyage, Filippo wrote to Carmelina's parents and formally expressed his desire to marry her by proxy. This was a common marriage practice in Italy at the time. Between 1945 and 1976 over 12,000 Italian women

(321) *My father sailed to Australia on the Lloyd Triestino ship,* Neptunia *in 1956.*

were married by proxy and then emigrated to Australia, in many cases for the first time, just like Carmelina, to start a new life with their husbands. Marriage by proxy is the celebration of the union of two people in which one of the two spouses is absent at the time of the ceremony, and is symbolically replaced by a "proxy."

(322 and 323) *My mother Carmelina in the mid 1950s.*

Many Italian men who were living in Australia at the time were looking for a wife and turned to their Italian based families to help them find an Italian lifelong partner. Very often, the young woman would make the long voyage to Australia, after being married by proxy, and then saw her husband for the first time. There were many instances when the husband looked nothing like the photos he had sent, being much older than he stated. This created great family distress because it was considered a significant shame on the bride's family if she did not go ahead with the marriage and remain in Australia, even though in many instances these young Italian women were so horrified with their predicament that all they wanted to do was board the next ship and head back to Italy.

At least Carmelina and Filippo already knew each other, so for them, marriage by proxy was done for convenience. Carmelina could arrive in Australia as a married woman. The marriage ceremony was conducted in Montagano with Filippo's brother, my uncle Roberto standing in on his behalf as the "proxy husband."

A Spell is Cast

➤

In 1958 after settling down working on a sheep and wheat farm near the town of Moora Western Australia, my father completed the formal paperwork with the Australian government to arrange for Carmelina to come to Australia. Carmelina's uncle Mario accompanied her to Naples on the day that she had to complete her Italian government emigration documents. Arriving in Naples was a real adventure for my mother. It was the first time she had seen the ocean. Carmelina was going to be undertaking her voyage with a Lloyd Triestino passenger ship, just like Filippo had. This was a major shipping company with a fleet of 85 passenger vessels and 17 services to Africa, Asia and Australia. The Lloyd Triestino ships which voyaged to Australia at the time were the *Australia, Oceania* and *Neptunia.* Carmelina was excited when she found out on that day that she was going to be voyaging on the *Australia.* The *Australia* was launched on May 21 1950 and departed on her maiden voyage to Australia on April 19 1951.

After completing the necessary paperwork, Carmelina and her uncle Mario returned to Montagano. Three days later, Carmelina awoke one morning feeling aches and pains all over her body, very dizzy, confused and drained of all energy. She also had a high fever, shook uncontrollably and had difficulty talking. Her mother Assunta recognized the symptoms very well. She immediately believed that a spell had been cast on Carmelina. It seemed the spell had been cast on her by either a scorned woman who had wanted to marry Filippo or a disgruntled man who had wanted to marry Carmelina.

Carmelina went to see the town doctor Petrone in the first instance but he was unable to accurately pinpoint what was wrong with her. She felt helpless, often sitting on the front steps of her house, crying with distress. She had lost her interest to go to Australia. As the weeks dragged on, Carmelina wasn't feeling any better. In the meantime, Filippo wrote her letters asking her what date she was coming to Australia. Not telling my father how sick she was and that she suspected a spell had been cast on her, she instead told him she wasn't ready to make the voyage yet because the necessary documents had not been completed.

My grandmother Assunta took Carmelina to see the local elderly good witch, Angelina. In the Molise culture, every town and village had a good witch or *maggara befana*. Upon seeing the condition that she was in, she said that Carmelina had been inflicted with a very heavy evil spell. The only maggara witch that could remedy her spell was living in the nearby village of San Biase, she said.

The next morning the three of them boarded a bus for the town of San Biase. When they arrived in the town, they had to be discreet

(324) *The village of San Biase in Molise.*

because the maggara befana did not want it to be widely known that she was a witch. They knew they had to ask for the elderly auntie (zia) Giovanna. They went directed to her home but were told she was in the fields and would not return until midday. When Giovanna arrived and examined Carmelina, she gasped with horror. "Somebody hates you because they have put a very bad evil spell on you. They want you dead!" When they entered her old stone house, she took out a very large old book, in the form of a manuscript.

She gave Carmelina a long piece of white woollen string and asked her to tie as many knots on it as she could. Giovanna then placed the knotted string in between two specific pages and closed the book for an hour. She said, "When I open the book, if the knots are undone and the colour of the string remains white, the evil spell will be removed and you will recover. But if the knots are still there and the string turns black, nobody will be able to help you and you will die." During the time that the book was closed she proceeded to chant in a strange unfamiliar tongue, her arms outstretched while she looked directly at the book for the entire hour. When she opened the book, the knots had all come undone but the string was partially black. "You are very lucky. Your spell will be cast aside but the string has changed colour, so you must come and visit me every day for the next five days, then you will make a full recovery. If you had left this one day longer, there would have been nothing that I could have done for you and you would have died," Giovanna explained to Carmelina while holding her hands. My mother was in a state of incredulous shock.

Carmelina visited Giovanna every morning as requested, accompanied by her aunt Yolanda. During each visit, the good witch Giovanna would perform exactly the same ritual, and each time, the string became lighter and lighter in colour, until on the final day, the string became pure white again. Carmelina had been cured. The evil spell had been broken. She made a full recovery. Her energy, excitement and determination to make the trip to Australia was restored. It was forever going to be a mystery as to who had cast that terrible spell. Whoever it was did not succeed in bringing down Carmelina.

Before she left the good witch on that fifth day, Giovanna gave her a hand embroidered handkerchief which she asked Carmelina to keep with her for her remaining days in Montagano, so that if whomever had cast the spell did it again to her, the handkerchief would save her. Carmelina urged Giovanna to tell her who had cast the spell. She was duty bound not to tell Carmelina who it was because disclosing this information could bring the spell back, but she did say it was somebody who lived in Montagano and that the spell had been cast on her while she was walking in the centre of town. She also confirmed that the motive was the jealousy of her marriage to Filippo.

There were two lingering after effects from this drama that afflicted my mother. Firstly, she continues to suffer neck and back pains to this day which she believes can be traced back to that fateful day when the evil spell was cast on her. Secondly, she was disappointed in her fiancé's parents (my grandparents) Giuseppe and Teresa for not believing that she had been cast with an evil spell and for thinking instead that she had second thoughts about joining their son Filippo in Australia.

To this day, my mother has no idea who cast the spell and why. Shortly after this episode, the day finally arrived when my fully

(325) *Italians in Australia greeting newly arriving migrants from Italy.*

recovered mother was to depart for her sea voyage to Australia. That morning, her mother, father and brothers saw her for the last time in Italy. While her mother Assunta embraced her, Carmelina said, "Mama, I will be fine. We will see each other again in Australia." She remembers being very excited about her trip to Australia and not shedding any tears that morning.

One of the best classic Australian films which succeeded in capturing the Italian immigration experience was the 1966 film, *They're a Weird Mob*. It tells the story of Nino Culotta, a newly arrived Italian immigrant to Australia. He arrives expecting to work for his cousin as a sports writer for an Italian language magazine, but instead, upon his arrival in Sydney, Nino discovers that his cousin has closed down the magazine, leaving an unpaid debt owing to Kay Kelly. Nino declares he will help his cousin by getting a job and paying back the debt.

The film then traces the adventures and experiences of Nino, working as a labourer; making new friends (mates); battling with Australian racism, slang and culture, and developing a romantic relationship with the Aussie girl, Kay Kelly. This is complicated for him because his cousin owes her the money, she's not getting repaid and her conservative Irish father has an intense dislike of Italians.

The film is tinged with racism towards Italians at the time, coming from the predominately Anglo-Saxon and Anglo-Irish Australians. Italians were given slang names like "ding," "dago" and "garlic-muncher." As a boy growing up in the 1960s I experienced much of this racism directly, particularly in the school yard.

This racism towards non-Anglo foreigners was embedded into Australia at the time. We need to remember that during this time the "White Australia Policy" was still in place; not disbanded until Gough Whitlam came to power in 1972.

32

MONTAGANO
AND FAIFOLI

HE ORIGIN OF MONTAGANO, THE VILLAGE OF MY PARENTS' BIRTH, CAN be dated back to 1039 when the Lombard dukes of Benevento proclaimed the independence of the municipality and recognised it as a free village.

Since its formation, Montagano has been reknown throughout Molise for its excellent quality tomatoes, its muscat wine extracted from an ancient grape called "muscatello," and for its cheeses produced from sheep's milk. The feudal castle of Montagano was built by the Normans in the 12th century high on a hill in order to control and defend the village and its surrounding countryside. The castle was extended and further fortified during the rule of the King of Naples, Ferdinand I of Aragon in 1459. The castle was sold to the Ianigro baronial family in 1700. This family were a major influence on Montagano throughout the 18th, 19th and first half of the 20th century, including during the time my mother Carmelina was a young girl.

Near Montagano, is the ancient settlement of Faifoli. The two villages closest to Faifoli are Montagano and Limosano, located on either side of the Biferno river in Molise. Faifoli was a major Samnite settlement and sanctuary known as "Fagifulae." When the Romans subjugated the Samnites, Faifoli continued as a Roman town. In the 11th century, the Benedictines constructed the Abbey of Santa Maria di Faifoli, which remains there to this day.

The first historical records of the abbey date back to 1134, when it was a sanctuary for Benedictine monks. In 1232 at age seventeen, the future Pope Celestine V, Pietro Angelerio, commenced his period of education and meditation there. Pietro returned to Faifoli in 1276 as an abbot at the request of Archbishop Capoferro of Benevento, who sought his assistance to mediate a dispute between Simone Santangelo, the feudal lord of Montagano and King Charles I of Naples. Apparently the feudal lord Santangelo was abusing the local peasants and taxing them excessively, which greatly displeased the king, who wrote a letter to the regional executioner, demanding Simone Santangelo be executed. Pietro Angelerio played a crucial role in preventing the execution and gaining a sworn oath from the fuedal lord promising he would stop his abuse of the local peasants and reduce their taxes.

The Abbey of Santa Maria remained Benedictine until 1808, when the Napoleonic French represented by the ruler Joachim Murat, based in Naples, banned the Benedictine Order. The last monks who owned the abbey belonged to the Celestine Order of Benevento and ultimately it came first under the ownership of a local baron, Quintiliano Petrone and later the Ianigro baronial family. The abbey remained in the Ianigro family until 28th February 1998, when the municipality of Montagano took it over. The municipality have been maintaining and restoring the abbey ever since, with the assistance of funds raised from the local surrouding communities.

All that was left of this place in the 1950s was the old abbey church and the baron's palazzo which was used as a holiday retreat by descendants of the Ianigro barons. The palazzo building was surrounded by immaculate gardens and fountains. At the time, the Ianigro family were responsible for maintaining its surrounding gardens and the church. On the last Sunday of April, there was a big religious festival, "La Festa di Faifoli." It celebrated the madonna, Santa Maria di Faifoli.

When my mother Carmelina was a child she remembers that the festival was the highlight of Montagano's calendar of festivities. At the time, the gardens were being maintained in an immaculate condition. The people from surrounding towns would follow the tradition of walking the approximate five to ten kilometres (depending on the town of origin) to Faifoli. They knew when they were close to their destination because for two hundred metres outside the entrance the roadside leading to Faifoli would be adorned with a row of brightly colored pink, red and white manicured roses.

The people congregated there on the Sunday morning, bringing an abundance of food, wine and joy. A special mass dedicated to the Madonna was conducted at the church at 10am. Then for the remainder of the day and well into the evening, there would be a celebration at the gardens surrounding the abbey church which would be attended by hundreds of families. In addition to the food and wine, games would be played and music would be performed by an assortment of musicians and bands from the region and beyond, on a stage which consisted of a circular carousel in the centre of the gardens.

This festival was considered a prime opportunity for young couples from different families to be introduced to each other. If a young man was interested in a girl, he would approach the family and ask the father for permission to dance with his daughter. If the father approved, he would nod his head in the affirmative, and the couple could then dance. This did not replace the traditional courtship rituals that had applied in Molise for many centuries. It was just an opportunity for a young man to get to know a girl a little better by dancing with her, which would help him decide if he then wanted to take things further by formalizing the courtship. Families would lay their blankets on the lawn surrounding the carousel, which would be lit up brilliantly with multi-coloured lights at night. Many market stalls were also set up, selling fresh produce grown in the region as well as clothing, toys and household items, most of which were hand made by artisans. The main garden area was elevated and surrounded by steps. One set of steps

(326)
The medieval abbey at Faifoli, near Montagano. Pope Celestine V was based here as a monk, in the 13th century.

would lead to a medieval stone cavern in which was placed the sacred statue of the Madonna Santa Maria of Faifoli.

The village which raised the most money for this festival had the honour of carrying the Madonna from the abbey church to the cavern. During the course of the afternoon families filed into the cavern and knelt in front of the Madonna to receive her blessings of good health, fortune and peace for the year ahead. At the end of the festival as the people walked home in the evening, it was customary for each family to pick a rose from the row of roses outside the settlement and take it with them with the blessing of the Madonna.

Celestine was the only pope who originated from the Molise region. Due to constant warfare in and around Faifoli during the late medieval period, the monks had to permanently abandon the abbey and seminary. When I first visited Faifoli in 1986 I was saddened to see that the place had largely been abandoned. All that remained was the abbey church, which to this day is maintained and has been restored to its original condition, by the local municipality. The seminary, palazzo building and gardens are no longer there.

I have wonderful memories of my mother and I walking from Montagano to Faifoli in 2012. It was a bright sunny crisp day as we walked along the road, adorned on either side with colourful wildflowers and lush green trees. We encountered abandoned stone farm houses, olive groves and grape vines as we overlooked the fields from our high vantage point. When we reached Faifoli, the eleventh century abbey church of Santa Maria di Faifoli was the only remaining building of this historical settlement. The severity of the church's architecture suits its connection with Pope Celestine, who became a monk there in 1232. Near the abbey church we visited an ancient well where the tradition was to stand alongside it, and make a wish while touching the stonework encasing.

When my parents were growing up in Montagano, the local baron was Don Giovanni Ianigro. This family and their baronial predecessors controlled extensive holdings of property in the area within and surrounding Montagano and Faifoli from the time the feudal system was introduced into the region by the Norman conquerors in the Middle Ages. They owned the palazzos in the centre of Montagano and at Faifoli, many homes, apartments and large areas of farming land.

The castle and palazzo at Montagano was built at the highest point of the town, for defensive reasons. It was an imposing four level building with a large banquet hall, twelve bedrooms, a lookout tower and extensive underground stables for horses and donkeys, as well as cellars to store the family's annual wine production. On the roof of the palazzo there was a garden which provided a wide variety of fresh fruit and vegetables exclusively for the consumption of the family.

The Ianigro family employed many peasant labourers on their mainly tomato and olive farms, and also operated vineyards producing high quality red and white wines. Don Giovanni had married Theodora, the daughter of a baron who owned estates near the southern Italian city of Foggia. They had two daughters who along with their spouses and children also resided in the palazzo. His son lived in Milan. One of our cousins worked as a cook at the palazzo kitchen whereas another cousin would baby sit the grandchildren of Don Giovanni. His family were by far the biggest employers in the region, exercising much more power than the local municipal governments and very influential with the Molise regional government.

Don Giovanni died in 1954. Upon his death, his son in law Corrardo, married to his eldest daughter, became the new baron, as dictated by Don Giovanni in his will. Don Giovanni did not appoint his own son, because he had scandalized the family by marrying a model from Milan

(327) *The original abbey and adjoining baron's palazzo villa in Faifoli, near Montagano.*

and squandered much of his inheritance on maintaining a luxurious lifestyle which included a large apartment, a red Ferrari, socializing with the Milan elite and constant trips abroad.

The new baron Don Corrardo was best known for expanding the family's winegrowing interests under the label of "Vino Ianigro" and successfully establishing their premium wines in the northern Italian and European markets. As a sixteen-year old, my mother worked part time cleaning wine bottles in the extensive underground cellars of the Ianigro palazzo, along with many other teenagers. She remembers the supervisor Giorgio, as a particularly cruel man who would demand that the girls working there not talk and frowned upon them when they wanted time off for a brief rest or toilet break. He didn't treat the boys this way.

Carmelina also remembers Giorgio demanding that the girls carry heavy wine barrels and scolding them when they stumbled. One day he asked my mother to collect a large clay wine barrel from a nearby home. Although it was empty, it was particularly heavy and difficult to grip. As she was carrying the barrel back to the palazzo, her grip slipped and it fell to the side of the road, shattering into hundreds of pieces. Giorgio reported this incident to baroness Theodora and demanded that Carmelina pay for the damaged barrel from her wages. Agreeing to this, Theodora said, "We need to set an example to our workers. They must accept responsibility for any damage which they cause."

Carmelina did not get paid for the entire eight hours she had worked that day. Rather than sulk, she was determined to work even longer hours to make up for her lost wages. This is a character that I have seen in my mother since the time I was a young child. No matter what hardships she or our family endured, she never complained, instead she always came up with a practical solution and with the fiercest determination and hard work, ensured that her desired outcome was achieved. When Don Corrardo died, his son Michelangelo became the baron.

During his time over the last twenty years, the wealth and power of the Ianigro family has been squandered due to mismanagement of the family property and business interests and mistreatment of their workers. Michelangelo accumulated large debts and had to sell all of the family's property. The palazzo was abandoned because he could not afford to maintain it. As a result, it now lays in ruins, an eyesore and a constant reminder to the people of the demise of the once powerful family. Michelangelo is now unemployed and lives alone in a small apartment.

My mother remembers encountering Michelangelo in Montagano in 2018 during the municipal elections. He had recently been divorced, looking depressed and disheveled. His clothes were shabby and dirty and he hadn't shaved for a number of days. During their brief conversation in the village piazza, my mother Carmelina recounted to him the story of what his mother Theodora and the supervisor Giorgio did to her as a teenager, when her entire day's wages were docked for accidently damaging the clay wine barrel. "My mother should never have employed and listened to Giorgio. He caused so much damage to our family name with the way he treated the local people. That was the beginning of the end for us," Michelangelo responded sadly. During this same visit in 2018, Michelangelo even befriended my father Filippo, wanting his advice on how to grow tomatoes, so that he could supplement his meagre income.

33

MY FATHER
IN AUSTRALIA

⌒

HE FIRST MEMBER OF MY FAMILY TO MIGRATE TO AUSTRALIA WAS MY father's brother, Domenico in 1954, the same year that my father commenced his service in the Italian navy. Domenico was part of a group of migrants who left Montagano for various overseas destinations at the time. Domenico's motivation to migrate was to no longer work the land and live a difficult life but instead to start afresh with new opportunities in a young country where work was plentiful and the Australian government was actively seeking migrants from southern Europe.

There was a catholic priest called " Father (Padre) Nanno" who originated from the Molise town of Ripalimosani and was based at Saint Brigids's Catholic church in North Perth. He actively assisted newly arrived Italian migrants from Molise. Father Nanno would greet the immigrants at the port of Fremantle and arranged to find accommodation for them with a network of Italian families who warmly welcomed these people into their homes until they found a job and were

(328) *Village of Ripalimosani, Molise.*

ready to start their own lives. Being the first to arrive from Montagano, Domenico and the others in the group had no relatives in Perth who could look after them.

Father Nanno performed an invaluable and deeply compassionate role in assisting these migrants, who could not speak a word of English, were unfamiliar with their surroundings including the extreme heat and did not know anybody. His presence was very comforting to them. Once my uncle Domenico was settled in Perth and had saved enough money to put a deposit on his own house, he arranged for his younger brother, my uncle Antonio to join him in Australia. Antonio left from

(329) *Saint Brigid's Church in Perth.*

the port of Naples, but while the ship stopped in Messina Sicily, he was able to spend some time with his brother, my father Filippo, who was stationed there with the Italian navy. While the brothers were together, Antonio convinced Filippo there was a much better life awaiting them in Australia, and that he should also migrate to Perth. At that stage, my father was planning to complete his two years in the navy, return to Molise, marry my mother and remain in Montagano to work the family farm and raise a family. But after his encounter with Antonio in Messina, he changed his plans. In January 1956, after completing his naval service, Domenico and Antonio formally applied for their brother Filippo to migrate to Australia and his application was accepted. On 2nd November 1956, my father boarded the "Neptune" in Naples, to commence his journey to Australia. When he arrived at Fremantle, his two brothers were very excited to see him.

For a number of months, Filippo lived with his brothers in Domenico's small house near the corners of Brisbane and William streets in Perth. By this time, Domenico was married and had a baby daughter, Stella. There was a young newly married couple living in Domenico's residence as well; the husband was Polish and she was German. Antonio was very demanding on this young German lady, expecting her to do his washing and cook his meals, often upsetting her. Finally, Domenico requested that Antonio move out, which he did, moving in with his friend Bernandino. Meanwhile, my father Filippo was carving out a new life for himself. His first job was at a market garden in Osborne Park which included boarding. This did not last long because he wasn't happy with the low wages. He was desperate to earn enough income to put a deposit on a house, just like his brother Domenico had done, so that he could bring his wife Carmelina to Australia and they could start a family.

After leaving the market garden, Filippo worked for a few months at Luisini Wines in the outer Perth suburb of Wanneroo, but again, even though he enjoyed the work, the wages were still too low. His next job was working for an Italian builder. During the mid-1950's the building industry was booming in Perth and there was a shortage of construction labourers. Although the money was better, the work was so gruelling that Filippo often arrived home absolutely spent with exhaustion, collapsing on his bed without having dinner. One day, on a building site, while Filippo was having a brief lunch break, one of the other Italian labourers who understood some English was reading the newspaper. There was a job advertised for a farm labourer to work on a large wheat and sheep farm in Cunderdin, over 150 kilometres north of Perth, not far from the town of Moora. When he told my father about this job, his eyes lit up, this was exactly the kind of job Filippo was looking for. He missed the feeling of freedom when working the land on the family farm in Montagano, surrounded by clean air, nature, animals and fresh produce.

The following day, Filippo took the day off and went to the employment agency in Newcastle street in the central Perth suburb of Northbridge. Using an Italian interpreter, he expressed interest in the Cunderdin job. The agency contacted the Adams family and told them about this young eager Italian migrant who couldn't speak a word of English but wanted the job and could start immediately. Mr Adams said, "Never mind that he can't speak English, that's not important. We want somebody who is loyal and prepared to work hard. Send him up." So an excited Filippo boarded a bus and made his way to Cunderdin a few days later. When he arrived, Mr Adams was waiting for him in his Rolls Royce. It was a very successful farm, one of the largest in the Wheatbelt of Western Australia, with over 10,000 sheep. Filippo remembers feeling an instant rapport with the friendly smiling farm owning patriarch and knew in his heart that this job was going to change his life for the better and lay the foundation for his new life in Australia, as he looked out of the window seeing the harsh Australian bush pass him by. When he arrived, he remembers thinking how massive this farm was, compared to the smaller farms in Molise, so it is not surprising it seemed to him to take an eternity to get from the main gate entrance to the extensive colonial styled homestead.

Although it was primarily a wheat and sheep farm, the family also maintained an extensive fruit and vegetable market garden. Filippo's role was to look after the garden and to also assist the family with various labouring duties as required. He was given basic accommodation in the shearing shed and was provided with food. This was an attractive situation for Filippo because it meant that he could literally save every dollar of the good income he was receiving. Suddenly, he now felt secure enough to start the arrangements for Carmelina to come and join him.

The Adams family colonial residence was newly built. It had many bedrooms, a large dining room and a spacious kitchen. Alongside was a large swimming pool surrounded by a bed of roses and meticulously landscaped lawns, trees and gardens. Part of Filippo's job was to also maintain this outdoor area surrounding the home. The family comprised three sons and a daughter. The two eldest sons were in their teens and were studying and boarding in Perth. The youngest two, seven and five, lived with their parents on the farm.

34

CARMELINA'S JOURNEY TO AUSTRALIA

INALLY, THE TIME HAD COME FOR CARMELINA TO JOIN FILIPPO IN
Australia. Knowing that Filippo had a secure job, she felt very
happy to start a new life in this young country, even though she would
deeply miss her family and friends in Montagano. "Please don't cry
mama, let me be free. We will see each other again soon," she pleaded
to her mother on the day she was going to depart. Carmelina would
not be making the journey to Naples alone. There was a family from
Campobasso who were also departing on the same ship, to join their
father Donato in Perth.

Although they didn't know it at the time, the Pietracatella boys
were to become prominent Italian restauranteurs in Perth, with the
oldest son Agostino starting the popular Uncle Dominic's Italian
restaurant and function centre in the 1970s and his three brothers
Mario, Giovanni and Peppe going on to start successful restaurants of
their own, after the experience they gained working in the kitchen of
Uncle Dominic's. This restaurant holds fond memories for me because

(330) *My mother sailed on the Lloyd Triestino ship,* Australia, *in 1958.*

it was the first place where I worked as a fourteen-year old high school student, making garlic bread with the family patriarch Donato, during my holidays.

When Carmelina arrived at the port of Naples, as a nineteen-year old, on the 10th October 1958 to board the ship "Australia," she only had 5,000 lire in her pocket, the equivalent of fifty dollars; the money that Filippo had sent to her. As she made her way towards the gangplank to board the ship with her heavy suitcase, a porter approached her and carried the suitcase. "Never mind, I will carry this suitcase myself," she said, knowing full well he was expecting a tip. "No, no, no, signora, this is too heavy for you," he replied. When he deposited the suitcase on the ship, he stretched out his hand and said, "1,500 lire, please." Carmelina felt her heart sink. Suddenly, the young man who had boarded behind her said, "Please signora, let me pay this for you, and you can pay me back when you get change on the ship," he insisted. So he did. He told Carmelina that he was born in Molise, in a town not far from Montagano and had already migrated to Melbourne before, but had come back to Italy to find a wife unsuccessfully, so he was now making his way back.

Carmelina instantly felt that this man was attracted to her. After two or three days on the ship, she gave the man back his 1,500 lire. At first he did not accept the money, saying, "Do you know I did not like any of the ladies that my family had arranged for me to meet, but I like you very much, Carmelina." "Oh no, you do not understand, I am already married by proxy and I am going to Australia to start a new life with my husband," she replied. He looked at her with bemusement as my mother gave him the 1,500 lire and wished him a pleasant trip. She now only had 3,500 lire!

Carmelina was in a large cabin below the ocean level, with sixteen other ladies. Like my mother, all of these ladies had been married by proxy and were on their way to meet their husbands and start a new life in Australia. One consolation of being below sea level was no sea sickness. Generally, the higher above sea level one is, the greater the sea sickness. My mother became good friends with all of these ladies during the voyage. They had come from different regions of central and southern Italy, including Molise, Abruzzo, Campania, Calabria and Sicily; and they all had their own unique story to tell. Most nights, the seventeen excited young women would lay awake in their beds until the early hours of the morning, with the lights out, laughing, giggling and crying while sharing their stories with each other, and wondering what the future in this new country of Australia was going to hold for them.

The daily routine on the ship started with breakfast in the dining lounge at 7.30am. After breakfast, Carmelina would attend a daily mass

(331) *The lunch and dinner menu on the* Australia.

at 9am. The rest of the day was spent with her new sixteen girlfriends chatting away, often on the deck in the sunlight as the ocean breeze kept them cool. This was a migrant ship, so it didn't have many of the facilities like swimming pools, bars, restaurants and evening entertainment of cruise ships. It served a functional role of transporting thousands of migrants and so all available space was used to accommodate as many people as possible. But there were some shops on the ship.

Carmelina would often walk past a lady's accessories shop where there was a lovely handbag on display in the window. She loved that handbag! Her mother Assunta had given her a nice dress to wear when she arrived, but she didn't have a handbag. One day, while admiring the handbag in the window, she decided to buy it. The only problem was that it cost 3500 lire, exactly the amount of money my mother had. If she bought the handbag, she would not have any money left for any contingency that might arise for the remainder of the voyage. "What about if I get sick, I won't even have money for medicine. They will throw me overboard!" she thought darkly. But she had to have that handbag. It was going to define her rebirth as a migrant to a new land. So, throwing all caution to the wind, she bought it!

I can remember that handbag being my mother's pride and joy, as a young boy growing up. Every time we went on a family outing, whether it was visiting relatives, going to the Italian outdoor cinema, or weddings and religious festivals, my mother always had it with her. Then one day, she gave the handbag to her niece Stella, when she had her confirmation. To this day, she regrets doing that.

Carmelina was shocked to see the level of poverty when she briefly disembarked the ship at Port Aden in Egypt. After departing Port Aden, they had to wait for nearly two days before the ship could enter the Suez Canal, because of the number of ships and the very narrow passage of the canal. Although she didn't disembark, from the side of the ship, she again noticed people living in poverty at Colombo Sri Lanka and Jakarta Indonesia. "Will Australia have this poverty too? Am I making the right decision to leave Italy?" she can remember thinking to herself. It was the first time that doubt and apprehension about her future in Australia had entered her mind. Finally, four days after leaving Jakarta,

(332) *Perth city in 1958 at the time my mother Carmelina arrived.*

(333) *My parents in Perth 1958.*
(334) *My parents on the sheep and wheat farm.*

the ship arrived at the port of Fremantle Western Australia, at 2am on the 2nd November 1958.

When the ship arrived the Captain announced that whoever had relatives or friends waiting for them could disembark immediately, the others had to wait until 8am. My mother remembers looking over the side of the ship and spotting my father, his brother Antonio and Carlo, a relative who had also recently migrated from our home village of Montagano. From the moment she saw Fremantle, Carmelina could not believe how beautiful it was! This was further reinforced as they drove along Stirling Highway to my Uncle Domenico's house in Northbridge, where my parents stayed for two nights before making their way back to the farm in Cunderdin. "This is nothing like Jakarta and Colombo!" Carmelina thought as an overwhelming feeling of excitement brought on a great sense of optimism in the future that lay ahead.

The following day in Perth, my parents went to a studio in Barrack Street in the centre of the city which was popular with the Italian immigrant community for taking formal photographs. The taking of these photographs was a token gesture which although seen as a symbol of legitimizing their proxy marriage, could never replace the formal wedding ceremony they never had. To this day, Carmelina still regrets that this never happened. On the same day my uncles Domenico and Antonio took my parents for a walk in the city and to nearby Kings Park.

Carmelina recalls Perth at that time being full of lovely green lawns and trees and seeming more like a provincial town rather than the larger city it has become now. As she walked the central streets of Perth she was amazed at how well dressed and friendly everybody was. Those smiling faces made a lasting positive impression on her. There and then she vowed that she was going to make her life in Australia.

That night they all had a lovely traditional Italian dinner of pasta in forno (baked in the oven) with home-made tomato sauce and meatballs at uncle Domenico's home. The next morning, they made their way back to Cunderdin in a Holden Utility car with two fellow farm workers, also called Domenico and Antonio, who were cousins from Calabria. My mother recalls that it was a very tight and uncom-

(335)

My parents Filippo and
Carmelina on the farm
in 1958.

fortable journey with all four of them, shoulder to shoulder sitting on
the front bench seat, feeling every bump shake through her body. They
had brief restroom stops along the way at New Norcia and Moora,
before arriving at the farm. During the journey Carmelina was struck
by the stark contrast between the lush greenery of Perth and the tinder
dry never ending bushland of the Australian countryside, as well as
the intense furnace like November summer heat. The journey never
seemed to end for her. She began to realize just how vast and isolated
Western Australia was compared to the Molise region which was dotted
with villages and towns. "Have we arrived yet?" she would ask regularly.
"No, it's further ahead," my father would reply, wishing that she would
stop asking.

35

SETTLING ON AN AUSTRALIAN FARM

hen they finally arrived, Carmelina was impressed with the size of their living quarters. It was normally used by sheep shearers for two or three months of the year and had ten bedrooms. When the team of shearers arrived, my parents would vacate this residence and stay with the Adams family in one room in their large colonial residence, also on the farm. In spite of the hardships, Carmelina was happy. She would awaken every morning singing jovially. Mrs. Adams gave her house cleaning and cooking duties for four hours every morning, for which she would get paid. To this day my parents have fond nostalgic memories of the time they spent on the farm.

My father Filippo had made friends with a number of young Italian men who either lived in Moora or who were working at nearby farms. My parents, along with the two Calabrian cousins who worked on the same farm, would get together with these other Italians, usually in Moora where they would go to the picture theatre, attend community dances, play cards or have picnics, Italian style with their salami, morta-

(336)

*My parents on the farm in 1959
with my dad's pride and joy,
his Vespa!*

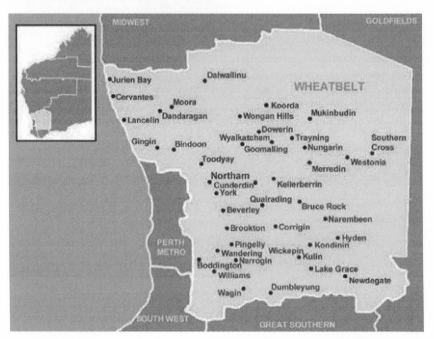

(337 above) *The wheat and sheep
farm near Moora that my parents
worked on was in the Wheatbelt
region of Western Australia.*

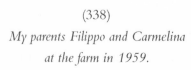

(338)

*My parents Filippo and Carmelina
at the farm in 1959.*

della, dried sausages, a variety of cheeses, crusty bread and home-made wine, while playing popular Italian music on the battery powered record player. Carmelina remembers a group of young Italians often coming to the Cunderdin farm and enjoying the novelty of an Australian barbecue while also jumping into a creek on what clearly were hot summer days. My parents even baptized the first child of one of these Italian couples.

The overriding powerful motivation for Carmelina in this new land was to have a family and make whatever sacrifices she possibly could, through hard work, to ensure that her children were going to live a better life in Australia, compared to her life in Italy. She rarely thought about herself, she was totally magnanimous and selfless in her commitment and devotion to her family. Carmelina has not changed to this current day. This motivation gave her a steely determination and resolve to overcome any hardship or obstacle, always putting the interests of her family ahead of anything else in her life, no matter what distress this may have given her. If she was in distress, she would not show it, her disposition and outlook on life was always positive. Carmelina was always able to ensure that her children did not miss out; that they were always well fed and clothed and that they had the best opportunities with their education.

My parents stayed on the farm for twelve months. When Carmelina was expecting me, they decided to make their way to Perth and establish their future there, arriving when she was eight months pregnant. They had managed to save enough money for a deposit on a semi- detached terraced house in Bulwer Street, not far from the centre of Perth, which they bought. My father Filippo was one of the first Italians in Western Australia to own a Vespa, the iconic Italian motor cycle, which he purchased shortly after my mother arrived in Australia. Carmelina did not want him to buy it, preferring instead that they save every dollar for their home deposit. But Filippo loved it so much that he prevailed!

Whenever I am being stubborn with my mother, she blames the Vespa. During their Vespa trips between the farm and Perth, Carmelina would cling on to my father tightly, but this did not prevent her from falling off at times, while she was pregnant with me. She thinks that's why I am so pig-headed at times, too many falls off the Vespa! Filippo had not taken any lessons and he liked to rev it up and speed. Not only was my poor mother holding on for dear life as a pillion passenger, but often tucked away between her and my father would be cases of fruit and vegetables as well as a suitcase. It was crazy but also exciting and fun, Carmelina recalls.

36

LIVING IN PERTH, AUSTRALIA IN THE 1960S

⌐⌐

T WAS ALWAYS THE INTENTION OF MY PARENTS TO ULTIMATELY LIVE IN Perth. Shortly after Carmelina arrived in Australia, they purchased a house in Bulwer Street Perth, and started making plans to move, while they were working on the farm. On the farm, Carmelina was earning 4 pounds a week and Filippo, 6 pounds. Because all food and accommodation was provided for them, they were able to save most of this money and use it for a deposit on the Bulwer Street property. The house was one semi-detached half of two identical buildings. When my parents bought the home, a Polish couple with a young child were renting and living in it. After purchasing the home, my parents were still working on the farm so they temporarily allowed the young Polish couple to stay in the home and pay the same amount of rent, which was 10 pounds per week; the exact amount my parents were paying to the bank for the mortgage. Their financial situation became very tight though, when they moved into the Perth home in October 1959, one month before I was born. No longer having tenants, they experienced much hardship for the first year in particular, when the mortgage was £10 per week and Filippo was earning around £12 per week, working first in an iron foundry and then in a bottling plant. This only left them with £2 a week for all living costs.

My mother had to find work as well, for the family to survive. When I was six months old, Carmelina started working in a large clothing factory, specializing in manufacturing male pants alongside over fifty other mainly Italian, Greek, Macedonian, Serbian and Polish migrant women. During this time when money was tight, Carmelina would improvise by making my clothes and using fresh vegetables from our backyard garden, for food. My mother and father also secured a night-time office cleaning job, five nights a week, earning extra income for them. Once both of my parents were working and my father was often doing two eight hour shifts at the bottling plant, their financial situation of course improved, but they had to work incredibly hard to make ends meet. Our situation wasn't helped by my father Filippo developing a gambling habit during this time. He would often go with his brother Antonio, to an inner city meeting place where many Italian men secretly gathered to play cards and gamble well into the night. Their first Christmas in Perth in 1959, was an unhappy one for Carmelina because Filippo gambled and lost all of the money they had put aside for food and presents. After a lot of pressure from Carmelina, including numerous occasions when she would turn up to the gambling place late at night unannounced, with me in a pram, calling for my father; the guilt got the better of him and he soon gave up this habit. After two years of incredible family dedication, hard work and sacrifices, my parents had earnt enough money to completely pay off their house mortgage. They were very proud of this accomplishment because debt was not something they were ever comfortable with; to this day. They now owned their own home! This symbolized for them, the strong foundation they had now laid in Australia and the commitment they had to their future in this country.

One of the more distressing recollections Carmelina has during this time were the many occasions she would walk into the city, with me as a baby in a pram, and see all of the lovely baby clothes, toys, furniture and other household products in the shops, none of which she could afford. Carmelina loved the location of her first home, which was opposite a large recreational park, on a busy road, close to a primary school and only a pleasant fifteen-minute walk into the city centre. Also at the time, the area was full of other mainly Italian, Greek, Macedonian and Polish newly arrived immigrants. Apparently I was a very compliant baby and young child. My mother would often leave me alone in the house sitting in my baby-chair, or fast asleep, knowing full well that when she returned, I would be in exactly the same tranquil state in which she left me.

Soon after my parents and I settled into the Perth home, my other relatives started to arrive from Italy. The first of which was my mother's brother Nicola, who arrived in 1960 and moved in with us. A promising soccer player, some of my earliest happy memories are of my uncle Nicola taking me to the recreation park across the road and teaching me how to kick a soccer ball. Another fond early memory I have is of

(339) *Highgate Primary School, Perth.* (340 inset) *MLC Building, Perth.*

my parents taking me on a train trip every Sunday to visit my mother's relatives, Domenico and his family, who lived on a fruit and vegetable farm in an area called Cannington south of Perth. We would get there at around 11am and there would be a big traditional Molise lunch in their outdoor garden area, with Italian music from singers such as Mario Lanza and Dean Martin, playing in the background. With his family and other relatives who would attend, there were over twenty of us, on these joyous family occasions. We would then return home in the evening. Domenico's youngest son Paolo, was born on the same day I was. We became good friends as young children.

In 1963, my father was able to gain employment as a cleaner at the MLC building in the centre of Perth, at the time the tallest building. This was a major turning point for the financial security of my family, because it was a long term job, and the income he earnt was higher than his previous jobs. As a child of ten, eleven and twelve, I have wonderful memories of helping my father clean the building during my school holidays. I remember the building had a weather beacon on its roof which could be seen from a distance, and twelve floors, one of which

(341 and 342) *My parents with Antonio and I; My mother with Antonio and I.*

was entirely occupied by the international accountancy firm, "Arthur Andersen," at that time, the most prestigious accountancy firm in the world, but which has since collapsed as a result of the "Enron" financial scandal. As a child, I would take home many of the firm's magazines and promotional material and this is where I first developed my interest in the business world in general, and accounting in particular. Fast forward to the end of my high school years, when I decided to study accountancy at Curtin University and then went on to have my first career as a chartered accountant from 1980 to 2007; firstly, working for the international accounting firm, "Coopers & Lybrand" and then from 1989 in my own professional practice until 2007, when I went back to university to study history and education and undertook my second career journey as a high school history teacher, which I enjoy immensely to this day.

In those early years, my mother would leave me with a lovely Italian couple, relatives on my father's side, Rina and Annibale who lived nearby. Rina would look after me while Carmelina was at work. One of my earliest recollections was sitting at the front of Rina's house watching the children on their way to the primary school nearby. During this time, terror struck my family. I had vanished. Apparently, one evening at age two and a half years, while my parents were in the kitchen chatting with my uncle Nicola, I walked out of the front door and disappeared into the night. My parents, Nicola, Rina and Annibale were searching for me frantically, but I was nowhere to be seen. My father then suggested they search the grounds of the nearby primary school. Sure enough, there I was sitting on a bench near the playground with my father's shaving bag as my little school case, insisting to my parents that I wanted to be like the other kids, and go to school. I was happily sitting there on my own, waiting for the school to open! I can only imagine how overjoyed and relieved my parents were. I always loved going to school, hardly missing a day in my entire twelve years of education. My mother tells me, although I didn't start walking until I was eighteen months old, I was talking fluently by age one, and I haven't shut-up since! At age eighteen months to two years, I would sit outside on the front veranda and shout out to my father: "Papa, Papa, come quickly, there is another pretty girl walking past our house!"

On another occasion again, while my mother was doing the ironing one day, she could hear the continuous "beep beep" of car horns. Wondering what the commotion was, she ventured outside only to be horrified when she saw me crawling on my hands and knees on the busy road, with cars stopped and beeping their horns! At barely twelve months old, I had managed to push the unlocked front flywire metal door open, crawl down the six steps, onto the footpath and then the road. Luckily, by the time my little hands and legs managed to propel me onto the road, the cars had stopped.

The next big milestone in our family was the birth of my brother Antonio, in July 1962. I adored my brother, always looking after him, playing with him, putting his dummy in his mouth whenever he was crying and rocking him to sleep in his little cot. Carmelina says there was no brotherly jealously between us. She knew she could rely on me to help her look after him, and I didn't let her down. Whereas I would eat everything my mother presented to me, Antonio instead was a very fussy eater, and he has been ever since. It was a huge ordeal for Carmelina, whenever she fed Antonio. It was after the birth of Antonio when Carmelina first started showing signs of her later nervous breakdown. Many times, my brother would vomit his food back to my mother, after spoon feeding him. He was very defiant about his food. He was also very attached to my mother at a young age; following her everywhere, constantly tugging at her dress and crying out for her when she wasn't around. If anybody asked my brother to go with them, his reply would be: "Is mama coming too?" Apparently I was more independent than Antonio, happily going along with anybody and every situation as it presented itself to me. Then, less than eighteen months after the birth of Antonio, came my brother Francesco in November 1963, ten days before the JFK assassination. Not long after the birth of Francesco, it became apparent to my parents that Antonio was intensely jealous of the attention my mother was giving to his newly arrived younger brother. She recounts stories of Antonio pulling Francesco's hair or pinching and biting him whenever Carmelina was feeding Francesco. He would constantly compete with his brother for my mother's attention and for her to hold him in her arms. Also in 1963, my fathers' parents and my grandparents, Giuseppe and Teresa, arrived from Italy. This was going to be a great help for Carmelina, because her mother-in-law helped in looking after myself and my brothers.

Nevertheless, this was becoming all too much for Carmelina. At age thirty-four, she was an immigrant, working hard to raise a family of three young children, as well as feeding and washing clothes for her husband and brother. It was after the birth of Francesco when my mother had her first nervous breakdown; especially when in May 1964, we moved from our first home, which only had two bedrooms to a three-bedroom house not too far away at 96 Chelmsford Road (not where they are now, at 142). Although it was a bigger house, it was located on a quiet street where there was little traffic and few people passing by, unlike at Bulwer Street. Now, many people would prefer this quieter seclusion, but my mother wasn't used to this situation, so this further aggravated her nervous condition. Carmelina regrets not buying the other half of the Bulwer Street adjoining house when my godfather Mario put it up for sale in 1964. They then could have stayed at that location, which she loved, and converted the twin dwellings into a larger single home, with four bedrooms. Her health was deteriorating rapidly during this highly stressful time in her life. She wasn't eating regularly. She was working incredibly hard. Her mental state wasn't good. She had three very active young kids. She also was developing a stomach ulcer. The pain was so acute that she often had to lay on her stomach to alleviate it. This all culminated in Carmelina being admitted into Royal Perth Hospital for three weeks in January 1965. While she was in hospital, my grand-mother Teresa looked after us.

The doctors wanted Carmelina to stay in hospital and rest for longer than the three weeks, but she refused. She demanded to be sent home, believing in her mind that her responsibility to look after her family must outweigh her own state of health. She realizes now, it was wrong of her to sacrifice her health. In any event, over a period of time, with medication to calm her nerves, and by better taking care of herself, Carmelina was able to cope and come to terms with her demanding selfless life. During the time of my mother's sickness, an interesting side-story was developing within our extended family. My father's brother and sister-in-law, Antonio and Carmela, developed a fondness for my brother Francesco. Whilst Carmelina was in hospital, my uncle Antonio and auntie Carmela looked after Francesco in order to take the pressure off my grandmother. During this time, Carmela developed a deep connection and fondness for the young Francesco, particularly since she could not have children of her own. Also, during this time, Francesco would call out "papa" and "mama" to my uncle and auntie. When my mother came out of hospital auntie Carmela formally asked my parents whether she could adopt Francesco. Carmelina refused point-blank. This created a rift between the two sisters-in-law which hasn't healed to this day.

My godfather Mario, was the owner of the adjoining Bulwer Street property and the owner of my parents' home before they bought it. It is from this connection that he and his wife Aldalgisa, became good friends with my parents. So much so, that my parents asked the couple to baptize me. At the time, Mario had an Italian continental delicatessen, also in Bulwer Street, in which a young girl Maria was employed. She became my uncle Nicola's girlfriend. He was so serious about her that he met her parents and there was a definite intention they were going to get engaged and then married. Also working at the delicatessen was Mario's wife, my godmother Aldalgisa. She would only work until lunchtime. In the afternoon, Mario and Maria would remain alone. Soon they developed a clandestine relationship. He was fifteen years older than the seventeen year-old Maria. At first, my uncle new nothing about the affair Maria was having with my godfather, but soon, people within the closely knit Perth Italian community started talking about how close they appeared to be. Also, Mario and his wife were good friends with Maria's parents and would often visit when my uncle Nicola was also there. My uncle couldn't help but notice the prolonged eye contact and affectionate gestures between Mario and Maria on these occasions. Eventually, my uncle confronted his girlfriend, and in tears, she admitted she was seeing Mario.

My devastated uncle left her. Soon after, my godfather Mario and the young Maria ran away to Sydney. Not long after that, Maria's father and brother travelled to Sydney, tracked the couple down, assaulted Mario and brought Maria back to Perth. They didn't remain apart for long though. Mario came back to Perth, started secretly seeing Maria again and then they eloped and left Australia for Italy, where they settled in Salerno for the remainder of their lives, and ended up having four sons; two sets of twins. About ten years later, Mario and Maria came to Perth on holidays. Being my godfather, my mother invited Mario for dinner at our place. She also invited his ex-wife, my godmother Aldalgisa. She didn't turn up, but he did. Tragically Mario died of cancer, but Maria is still in Salerno. Many years later, word got back to my uncle from mutual friends that Nicola was Maria's first love and she regretted hurting him so deeply and not marrying him.

I have mentioned that Carmelina arrived in Australia in 1958. After her, the next immediate relative on her side to arrive was my uncle Nicola in 1960, her brother Antonio in 1965, followed by my mother's parents Raffaele and Assunta along with my mother's youngest brother Mario, in 1967. Tragically, my grandmother Assunta was to die of a sudden heart attack in 1975 at age 62, particularly traumatizing my mother who last spoke to her at Royal Perth Hospital two hours before she died. Returning to the hospital in the evening she caught a brief glimpse of her laying on a gurney down the corridor as the sliding doors opened and then closed again, minutes before she died. On my father's side, the first to arrive was his brother Domenico in 1954, brother Antonio in 1955, my father in 1956, his sister Maria in 1960 and then finally my father's parents Giuseppe and Teresa in 1962. My father's brother Roberto, also wanted to come at the same time as his parents, but was prevented by the Australian immigration authorities because he was a member of the Communist Party of Italy. At that time, in the height of the Cold War and "Reds under the beds" communist paranoid propaganda, this was a major obstacle. After my father and uncles in Australia arranged for an advocate to write a letter to the Immigration Department in Canberra, explaining Roberto was not a practising communist and was no threat to this country, he was ultimately allowed entry into Australia, arriving in 1970. I am proud of the fact that my father led this family lobbying effort to get his brother admitted into Australia. Roberto then arranged for his wife Maria and two young daughters to also migrate under the Prime Minister Whitlam-led Assisted Passage Scheme whereby the government would sponsor their immigration as long as the family stayed for three years. Arriving in 1972, Maria was immediately homesick, hated the hot dry climate, incessant bushflies, alien language and what she described as the hostile attitude Australians had towards Italians at the time, and wanted to go back to Italy. The family were forced to stay for three years. During this time, my auntie Maria suffered from depression and was literally counting down the days to go back to Molise, Italy; which Roberto and Maria did, in 1975. Their eldest daughter, my first cousin Teresa, had met a Calabrian man Domenico, on the ocean voyage to Australia in 1972. They continued with and developed their relationship after disembarking in Australia, to the point that they were married in late 1972 and had a daughter Fiona in 1973, but then also returned to Italy in 1975.

My father Filippo loves playing cards. To this day he still gets together with his friends at the Italian Club of Perth and passes many hours playing the traditional Italian card games of briscola and scopa. As a young child I remember visits to my grandparents or relatives' homes and sure enough the women, including Carmelina, would sit around the kitchen table and just chat and chat and chat, while sipping espresso coffee and eating Italian shortbread biscuits. Meanwhile the men, including Filippo would congregate in the lounge room, set up a folding table and start their all-night marathon of playing cards, while enjoying home-made red wine with dry Italian sausages cut into pieces.

My brothers, Antonio, Francesco and I learnt to play the piano-ac-cordion, so we would often bring these instruments with us and during an interval of card-playing and chatting, we put on a performance which always delighted my parents and relatives. When I was a little older, say ten, eleven and twelve, I would particularly enjoy our visits to my grandparents Raffaele and Assunta's place because my uncle Antonio, who was living with them at that time, had a record-player, so my brothers and I could pass the time playing my uncle Antonio's collection of Italian 45rpm vinyl singles, including artists such as Little

(343, 344 and 345)
Perth Italian Club.
Little Tony (right).
Gianni Morandi (left).

Tony, Gianni Morandi and Al Bano. It was at this time when my love of Italian popular music developed.

Italian weddings within the Perth Italian community were a particularly big deal in the 1960s and 1970s, and as a child I can remember having so much fun when my family was invited to one. These weddings were a golden opportunity for Italian migrants to showcase their "coming of age" in Australia and were a wonderful celebration of the family. It was not uncommon during this time for the Italians who were less well-off to approach their accommodating bank managers, at a time when these managers had real authority, and borrow money to fund their children's weddings. Community halls were the popular venues at the time and there were a number of excellent Italian caterers who looked after all of the food, drink and entertainment. Children were always invited to weddings then. We would all get together with other kids and literally ran "amok" sliding up and down the floorboarded halls, throwing sugar-coated almonds, confetti and streamers everywhere, creating chaos and havoc. Nobody would reprimand us because children running wild was a central fabric of the traditional Italian wedding. So, we knew we could let-loose at these weddings, and boy-oh-boy we did! Two family weddings that stand out in my mind in the 1960s and early 70s are my uncle Nicola's marriage to auntie Minella at the Perth Town Hall, and my uncle Mario's marriage to

(346) *My Uncle Mario and Auntie Isabella's wedding in 1971.*

auntie Isabella at the La Villa Reception Centre in the Perth suburb of Osborne Park. Both marriages were at Saint Brigid's Church, adjoining the primary school where I completed my first year of school.

In the 1960s, my uncles were all able to secure long-term employment relatively easily, shortly after they arrived in Perth. On my mother's side, my uncles Mario and Antonio worked for many years at the Peters Ice Cream factory which at the time was located in the inner Perth suburb of Northbridge. They secured Christmas school vacation work for me at the factory, of which I have very fond memories. My mother also worked full-time at Peters Ice Cream for a year in 1968, but she eventually left suddenly, walking out on the job one day, because of the appalling way she was treated by her Greek supervisor "Helena," who was particularly cruel and demanding not only of my mother, but many of the other migrant women who worked there as well. My uncle Nicola worked for many years at one of the largest importers and wholesalers of Italian food products at the time, Pisconeri. On my father's side, my uncle Antonio was a gardener at the iconic Kings Park, for many years and my uncle Domenico was a cleaner at Australia Post until he tragically died suddenly of a heart attack while working, at a relatively young age, in 1977.

(347)
Peters Ice Cream factory.

(348)
*Pisconeri Food and
Wine Wholesalers.*

Within our family, there is the hilarious "on-again and off-again"
migration story of my mother's cousin Carlo, who first arrived in
Australia in 1958 as a single man. When my mother and father visited
him in the Perth suburb of Cannington shortly after he arrived, he asked
my mother: "Carmelina, are there any beautiful girls left in Montagano?
Because I want to marry one." My mother replied: "Yes. There's one
particularly beautiful girl who lives in the nearby village of San Angelo.
Her name is Anna." Literally within weeks of having this conversation,
the twenty-three years old Carlo hurriedly returned to Italy! He told
the family he was going to complete his compulsory twelve-month
military service, just as my father had done, to make a "man" of himself.
Upon arriving in Italy, he took my mother's advice and started courting
the young and eligible Anna. Carlo already had a reputation for being a
serial dater and pursuer of young women, so Anna and her parents were

understandably hesitant about how serious he was about her. In later years, Carlo recounted the story to my parents about his train trip to northern Italy to start his military service, shortly after he had met and courted Anna in Molise. While on the train, he encountered a Sicilian family with a beautiful young daughter. Strategically seating himself in the same compartment, Carlo started waxing lyrical to the father about how gorgeous his daughter was and that he was an eligible and financially secure single man looking for a bride! Before disembarking the train, Carlo managed to convince the father he was serious and obtained her home address. After exchanging a few letters with her though, nothing further came of it. This was typical of the modus operandi of Carlo. He even tells the story of trying to befriend an attractive young nun, to the great annoyance of the mother-superior, when he encountered a group of nuns in meditation while visiting a medieval church and convent in northern Italy during his year of military service! He managed to correspond with this young nun as well. Anyhow after all this, he did end up marrying Anna shortly after completing his military service. Now well into his eighties, Carlo is still happily married to Anna and runs one of the most successful farms in Montagano, producing a variety of vegetables, cheeses and wine; and herding sheep and goats in the Molise traditional fashion. Before marrying Anna, he promised her they would migrate to Australia. Even when my parents visit him in Molise, he still expresses intentions to move to Australia, reminiscing of his fond memories during the short time he was there. Many times over the years, in the 1960s and 1970s, his brother Domenico in Australia would arrange to complete the necessary immigration paperwork in vain, only to find that Carlo always changed his mind, often the day before he was due to travel to Naples to board the ocean liner.

Whenever Carmelina is in Montagano she particularly loves to spend time with her cousin Giuseppina, fondly known as "Pina." Pina has a severe hearing impairment from a childhood accident, but nevertheless studied Italian literature, Latin, Greek and ancient Roman history at the University of Naples. Suffering from acute anxiety though, she did not complete her final examinations, so never received her Arts degree. Still living in Montagano and never marrying, Pina is not perturbed by not having any formal qualifications, instead she has written a number of acclaimed books about life in Montagano as well as original poetry and prose. My mother enjoys sitting with Pina and listening to her endless stories about Italian history, including her love of ancient Rome and local Molise legends. A number of times while visiting Molise, I have accompanied Carmelina on these very inspiring visits to Pina. She does all her writing in longhand, filling up many notebooks with her musings, reflections and observations of life in Molise. She has no interest in commercializing any of her books; instead she has a genuine love of writing and literature. The local Montagano "commune" or local government, finance the publication of her books, support her writing efforts and handle all sales and distribution on her behalf. Pina's captivating storytelling and the uniqueness of her books, has been one of my inspirations for writing this book. She is highly respected within the close knit community of Montagano; a real "treasure" intent on preserving our unique culture and identity.

As I have mentioned previously, polio was the scourge of southern Italy in the nineteenth and first half of the twentieth century. One of the most kind-hearted and loyal souls in Montagano is my mother's cousin, Nicola. His grandfather Paolo and my mother's grandfather Luciano, were brothers. Whenever Carmelina travelled back to Montagano, Nicola's mother Maria, who lived next door to our family home, and in the home of my mother's birth, always treated my mother like a daughter. Unfortunately, Maria died in 2019 at age 92. It was her son Nicola, who lived with her and looked after her. Nicola was stricken by polio from a young age. As a result, he developed brain damage resulting in an intellectual disability. Now in his late sixties, he has the intellect of a twelve-year old. He has had little schooling, so cannot read and write; but his love and devotion for his mother Maria, was unconditional. He looked after her as her health began to deteriorate; cleaning the house, running errands, doing her grocery shopping, giving her medication, doing repairs and maintaining the garden; he did everything he could for his mother. Nicola is very fond of my parents, beaming with happiness whenever they return to Montagano. He loves native Australian animals so every time my parents go back, they give him a stuffed animal. He has a kangaroo, emu and koala bear amongst his collection, as well as a variety of "Australiana" tee-shirts which he loves wearing.

Maria had four sons. Nicola is the eldest. Next is Paolo, who is the municipal inspector for the town of Montagano and a history buff; always spending a lot of time with me, taking me all over Molise whenever I visit. After Paolo is Silvano, an accomplished artist who never sells any of his works. He has his own studio in Montagano which he built himself and also works for the local government looking after the village cemetery. The youngest son Enzo, is a successful lawyer with two practices in Campobasso and Rome. A few years ago, after separating from his wife, he developed a relationship with a popular television journalist and newsreader Cinzia, based in Rome. They are still together.

In the 1960s and 70s, one of the most popular pastimes for the local Italian community in Perth was to watch films at the "Premier" outdoor cinema. It was located close to where we first lived in Bulwer Street. I can remember my family regularly going to this cinema on Saturday nights, particularly in the summer months when we casually walked there. We packed a picnic basket full of my mother's delicious food. Once at the cinema, it was fun times for my brothers and I, because we would catch up with dozens of other Italian kids around our age who we saw only at the Premier. The front half of the cinema contained a series of long continuous canvas seating. All of the children would sit in the front rows right under the large white screen, and the adults seated towards the rear. I also remember an excellent shop that sold the most delicious home-made pastries and ice cream.

Many of the popular Italian movies of the 1960s and 70s were screened at the Premier. A famous Italian comedian at the time was "Toto." I remember seeing his classic movies, "Whatever Happened to Baby Toto" (1964), "The Hawks and Sparrows" (1966) and "The Witches" (1967). Then there was the comedic duo of "Franco and Ciccio" who were the Italian equivalent of Laurel and Hardy or Abbot and Costello. Together, they appeared in 116 films between 1960 and 1984. My brothers and I really enjoyed their slapstick humour, laughing at their antics until we had stomach cramps. The funniest movie of theirs was "Franco and Ciccio Superstars" made in 1974. Another unforgettable movie was "I Girasoli" ("Sunflower") released in 1971; a romantic story about an Italian bride (Sophia Loren) who finds her long-lost, assumed dead, soldier husband (Marcello Mastroianni) living in Moscow suffering from amnesia and starting a new life marrying a Russian woman and having a daughter with her.

It was magical being at the Premier on those balmy summer moon-lit nights, with the haunting silhouette of the tall pine trees on either side of the screen, adding to the festive atmosphere and excitement of so many Italians laughing and chatting before and after the movies and during the intermission, happy to see each other. It was a major social gathering within the local Italian community. Carmelina remembers how wonderful it was to see the latest Italian movies on a big screen and hear the Italian language so eloquently spoken at a time when she was a recently arrived immigrant and her connection with the Italian culture and language remained strong. In addition to contemporary movies the Premier regularly screened Italian classic movies from the 1940s and 50s, including those featuring two of my mother's all-time favourite Italian actors, Claudio Villa and Giacomo Rondinella.

Another fond memory I have as a young child were the religious festivals we attended as a family in Fremantle, the sea port near Perth, and of course, where my parents first arrived after their long voyage to Australia from Italy. Known world-wide as the location where Australia

(349) *Italian comedian, Toto* (below left).
(350) *Franco & Ciccio* (comedians).
(351) *I Girasoli* (film poster).

won the America's Cup yachting event in 1983, Fremantle was literally built by the convicts who arrived there from Britain in the early-mid nineteenth century; but after the Second World War, the town became a haven for southern European immigrants; not only Italians, but predominately Croatians and Greeks as well. The attraction was the seaport. The main industry these migrants pioneered was fishing. To this day, Fremantle is very different to the nearby city of Perth. It definitely has a southern European ambience to it, with its fishing boat harbour, many Italian cafes and trattorias selling authentic coffee, pastries, pizza and pasta, and its historical heritage protected buildings. I loved going to Fremantle as a child; especially when there was an Italian religious festival to celebrate.

The most prominent festival is the "Blessing of the Fleet," an annual procession which makes its way from St. Patrick's Catholic Basilica in the centre of town to the Fremantle Fishing Boat harbour and culminating in a spectacular evening fireworks display. The Blessing of the Fleet is a tradition that began centuries ago in Mediterranean fishing villages to ensure a safe and bountiful fishing season. It was first celebrated in Fremantle by an Italian migrant fisherman in 1948, and has been held annually since. I remember so many Italians from Fremantle and Perth attending this annual event. There would be traditional music, food, entertainment, amusement rides and displays showcasing Fremantle and its fishing industry. The highlight at sunset, was the arrival of the statue of Our Lady Madonna of the Martyrs, after being paraded in the procession through the streets of Fremantle, and then taken out to sea and accompanied by a flotilla of fishing boats beautifully decorated with multi-coloured ribbons and roses, while traditional Italian music was performed by a brass band. It was an eerie mystical sight to then see the Madonna and the procession of boats, all brilliantly lit up, come back to the harbour at sunset. After the arrival of the flotilla, the spectacular fireworks would begin. I can remember being mesmerized by the fireworks, because I had never seen such a dazzling and thundering display before.

Two other prominent religious festival in the calendar of the Italian community in the 1960s and 70s, of which I have very fond memories,

(352) *The Blessing of the Fleet Festival in Fremantle, Western Australia.*

were the Saint Nicola and Saint Giuseppe festivals, celebrated opposite Saint Brigid's church and school, nearby where we lived. Saint Nicola is the patron saint of young women wanting to be married and also of children; and Saint Giuseppe for the prevention of disease and famine. Again, it would be a procession of the statues through the streets of Northbridge in central Perth, followed by lots of food, live performances featuring local Italian talent and culminating in fireworks. These festivals were very important in the local Italian community at the time for two main reasons. Firstly of course, they preserved cultural and religious heritage which helped maintain the connection of these migrants to their homeland, even though the vast majority were equally keen to integrate into the Australian culture at the same time. Secondly, they were fantastic social gatherings which gave the Italians in Perth an excellent opportunity to catch up with friends, make new friends and often also, to set up daughters with sons in the hope of future matrimony.

The Italian Club of Perth and its sister venue in Fremantle, also performed these vital social roles for the Italian community, at a time when there just weren't many other opportunities for these migrants to meet their fellow compatriots. I first met my ex-wife at a Saturday night dance at the Italian Club of Perth in 1979, for example. Before she agreed to dance with me, her mother and aunt sitting either side of her, had to give their nod of approval, which they did.

(353)

My family in 1972, when I was 13.

(354)

My first holy Communion in 1965.

The memories of those days before Carmelina left for her voyage to Australia when a spell had been cast upon her all came flooding back with a disturbing episode which occurred when my brother Luciano was around six-months old. One morning in 1969 my mother awoke to find Luciano very distressed, not wanting to eat anything and looking "zombie-like," devoid of his usual bright-eyed cheerful smile. It looked like all of the life had been sucked out of him as he sat in his pram, motionless. Carmelina was so concerned that she immediately took him to the local doctor, who after examining him, came to the conclusion there was nothing wrong with baby Luciano. Carmelina wasn't satisfied with this diagnosis, she instinctively knew something was seriously wrong, so she took him to Princess Margaret Children's Hospital. After being admitted into the hospital and kept there for observation for a week, they too came to the conclusion nothing was wrong with Luciano. Bringing him home, Carmelina was exasperated because my baby brother was still not eating, lay motionless, expressionless, sullen and silent, all day.

My mother was beside herself with concern, wondering what had happened to her baby son. One day, while visiting her parents-in-law, my grandmother Teresa took Luciano in her arms and after seeing how lifeless he was, said to my mother: "Carmelina, I don't think he is going to recover, I think my grandchild has been cast with a spell. Do you know of anybody who can remove this spell?" Carmelina remembered many local Italians talking about an elderly man, "Pungini," who lived nearby and apparently was able to remove spells cast by witches. When my mother told my father about this man, he said she was crazy to believe in witches in Australia! Even Carmelina found it hard to believe the possibility of witches spells in this new southern land; thinking she had left all of that behind her in Molise. Nevertheless, along with my grandmother Teresa, they took Luciano to see the wise old man, Pungini. As soon as Carmelina explained to him what happened and he saw the lifeless Luciano for himself, he removed the small blue blanket covering my brother in the cot, folded it into an elongated shape and ran his hands up and down the blanket, with his eyes closed. Then he said: "This child has been ruined, a spell has been cast over him. Did a stranger touch this child?"

Pungini took an old book from a chest of draws, opened a particular page and while reading a passage in Italian and constantly repeating my brother's name, he took Luciano in his arms. Incredibly, while Pungini was performing this ritual, all of a sudden baby Luciano came back to life, alert, smiling, making happy giggling sounds and rapidly moving his arms and legs. My mother and grandmother were dumbstruck! Before they left and thanked Pungini, he said: "You must remember who it was that cast this spell on your child." After a few days and much thought, Carmelina suddenly remembered the day before Luciano fell "ill," she was taking him to the medical clinic, and while walking with her baby son in the pram, an elderly, haggard woman approached, dressed in black, hair unkempt, walking with a cane and accompanied by a black dog. She stopped and said: "What a beautiful baby," while touching him on the forehead a number of times. The old lady walked with my mother all the way to the medical clinic. Eerily, when my mother and brother left the clinic, after around thirty minutes, the old lady was still waiting outside and accompanied them for the fifteen-minute walk home.

Realizing what happened, Carmelina returned to tell Pungini. "You must keep away from her if you ever see her again", he said. "She cast a spell that could have killed your son. If you had left him the way he was for just one more day, he would have died." Ever since that day, Luciano never experienced those "zombie-like" symptoms again. "Thanks to Pungini, we have our Luciano", my grandfather Giuseppe would joyfully say when he regularly came to our home to take the young Luciano for walks in the nearby Hyde Park. He adored my brother. Carmelina never imagined this could have happened in Australia, thinking back on what happened to her and previously convinced that witches and spells had been left behind in Molise. She now knew better.

There are three particularly fond memories that have stuck in my mind, as a young teenager growing up in the early 1970s in Perth. Firstly, the traditional Italian family lunches we used to have every Sunday. They would end up being gatherings of over twenty people, including myself, my brothers, parents, grandparents, uncles and aunties. Carmelina would do all the preparation and cooking, getting up at 5am on the Sunday mornings; refusing assistance from us or other members of my extended family. She would hand-make all the sheets of pasta for her specialty traditional lasagna, gnocchi or veal ravioli dishes. The first course would be antipasto, including a variety of cold meats such as salamis, hams, mortadellas, cheeses, olives, anchovies and rockmelon. The second dish would either be her homemade lasagna, ravioli, gnocchi or pasta-in-forno, covered in our own homemade tomato sauce. The third course would be her specialty veal and chicken crumbed cutlets or roast chicken, served with steamed broccoli, salad, tomatoes, peas and baked potatoes. Then we would finish up with Italian cannoli pastries filled with custard and ricotta. These were wonderful get-togethers! There would be much laughter, traditional music playing in the background, everybody talking at the same time, as Italians tend to do, yet we all understood and respected each other's points of view.

The second great memory I have was the annual making of our traditional homemade tomato sauce. This was based on a recipe which has been in my mother's family for at least three hundred years. My father Filippo and my uncle Antonio would personally pick the tomatoes from the same farm which they would visit each year, operated by a Croatian family. My brothers and I would go along with them and have much fun while picking the tomatoes. Then over a weekend, the extended family would get together and actually make the tomato sauce in the traditional way, including boiling the tomatoes in a large stainless steel pot, adding various spices and other ingredients to the sauce and then hand-pouring the steaming hot tomatoe sauce into thoroughly cleaned dark beer bottles. We would make over three hundred bottles each year; using them for ourselves and giving bottles to relatives and family friends.

The third nostalgic memory I have from my early teenage years was attending my very first high school "hop-social" in the school gymnasium, at the end of my first term of high school in April 1972, one month before my parents and youngest brother Luciano departed for their ocean voyage to Italy. Originally called "sock-hops" because teenagers would take their shoes off; they were held as early as 1944 in America to raise money for the war effort. But they became very popular in high schools throughout America particularly in the 1950s and 60s. The hop became strongly associated with rock and roll when Danny and the Juniors released a big hit song in 1957 titled "At the Hop." Our hop-socials were held on the Friday night of the last day of each school term. I remember it as if it was yesterday. All of the girls would sit together, side by side on a very long wooden bench at one end of the gymnasium. The boys would sit opposite them, at the other end of the gymnasium. There would be a disc-jockey with a traditional vinyl record-playing turnstile, large speakers and a collection of 45rpm singles, playing continuous rock and roll music hits from the 1950s, 60s and early 70s; including artists like Elvis, Little Richard, Dion and the Belmonts, Jerry Lee Lewis, Fats Domino, Chubby Checker, Beach Boys, Marc Bolan and T-Rex, The Who, Beatles, Rolling Stones, The Sweet, Slade, Status Quo and David Bowie. The gymnasium was decorated with multi-coloured streamers and lights. Before the start of the first song, there was a long-standing ritual where each boy, one at a time, would walk across the gymnasium and ask a girl of his choice to dance, by standing in front of her and holding out his outstretched hand, for her to clasp. The girl he chose could not refuse the dance! This is how I got to dance with Rosemary, the girl in my class whom I had a crush on! No alcohol was allowed. There would be a large fruit-punch bowl and a variety of food snacks. These dance hop-socials were heavily supervised by teachers, but there would never be any fights, arguments or other trouble. The boys were always able to sort out between themselves before the hop night, who would dance with which particular girl. Today of course, teenagers go to such extraordinarily expensive lengths to attend school socials and formals at elegant ballrooms in hotels; the girls wearing lavish gowns and the boys in tuxedos. Our hop-socials were very informal, with the girls wearing their favourite colourful dresses and the boys typically in jeans and tee-shirts. In those days, it was pure and innocent fun!

Carmelina had come to Australia with literally nothing. Her first possessions when she left the Moora farm were two forks and the steam clothing iron farm matriarch Mrs Adams had given to her as a present on the day my parents left to come down to Perth to start their family lives in Australia; she still has the forks and iron, to this day. By that Sunday morning in May 1972, when she and my father and youngest brother Luciano were about to embark on their journey back to the motherland of Molise, Carmelina had every reason to be proud of the family she had raised with my father; and the secure future she had created for my family. As sick as she was, with her nervous condition, I am certain she felt the hard work, commitment, sacrifices and devotion to family, had paid off. These are the thoughts I can remember circulating in my mind, as I lay in bed on that Sunday morning, listening to my mother Carmelina, harmonizing to the voice of Tom Jones, as he sang "Delilah."

(355) *Carmelina.*

(356) *Filippo.*

BIBLIOGRAPHY

Abbey of Montecassino. "1943: The Removal of Treasures," (2019).

Abiuso, A. "Dialect Sayings from Gambatesa," Valente and Di Renzo Family History, (2013).

Abulafia, D. "Ferrante of Naples, the Statecraft of a Renaissance Prince," History Today, (2010).

Acocella, J. "The Forbidden World. Did a sixteenth century heretic grasp the nature of the cosmos?" Books, (2008).

Albert, J. "Facts About the Legendary Robert De Niro," Editor Choice, (2019).

Alighieri, D. "Inferno," Modern Library, (2003).

Alighieri, D. "The Divine Comedy," Everyman's Library, (1995).

All History. "An Introduction to the Pre-Roman Samnites of Molise", (2019).

Ancos, A. "Life in Italy During the 19th Century," History, Life in Italy, (2018).

Angelo, R.W. "The Canadian Army's Capture of Gambatesa, 7-8 October 1943," Valente and Di Renzo Family History, (2007).

Armstrong, E. "Pasquale Villari: 3 October 1827 – 8 December 1917," The English Historical Review, (1918).

Bailey, M.D. "Magic and Superstition in Europe: A Concise history from Antiquity to the Present," Rowman & Littlefield, (2006).

Baldwin, B. "Suetonius: Biographer of the Caesars," A.M. Hakkert, (1983).

Barstow, A.L. "Witch Craze: A New History of the European Witch Hunts," Pandora, (1994).

Beard, M. "SPQR: A History of Ancient Rome," Profile Books, (2015).

Bensalhia, J. "Discover the Secret Region of Italy, Molise," ITALY Magazine, (2016).

Biocca, D. and Canali, M. "L'informatore: Silone, i comunisti e la Polizia," Reviewed by John Foot in New Left Review 3, (2000).

Boccaccio, G. "The Decameron," Wordsworth Editions, Limited, (1996).

Blumenthal, R. "50 Years Later, Lanza Booms Forth; The Mystique of a Tenor Better known in Movies Than in Opera," The New York Times, (1998).

Bosworth, P. "The Shadow King," From The Magazine, (2014).

Brooks, X. "Don De Lillo on Trump's America: 'I'm not sure the country is recoverable'," The Guardian, (2018).

Brown, G.S. "The Norman Conquest of Southern Italy and Sicily," McFarland & Co., (2003).

Browne, P. "Seven reasons Molise (yes, Molise) is Italy's best kept secret," (2016).

Bruell, C. "Aristotle as Teacher," St. Augustine's Press, (2014).

Canali, M. "Ignazio Silone and the Fascist political police," Journal of Modern Italian Studies, (2000).

Cantalamessa, R. "Words of Light: Inspiration from the Letters of Padre Pio," Paraclete Press, (2009).

Carroll, R. "Darling of Italy's left spied for Mussolini," The Guardian, (2000).

Cataldo, N. "Tribes of Italy: The Samnites," America Veritas, (2017).

Catto, B.A. "Venus and Natura in Lucretius: De Rerum Natura," The Classical Journal, (1988).

Cesari, A. "Mario Lanza: An American Tragedy," Baskerville, (2004).

Churchill, W.J. "The Career of Robert Guiscard according to the Annales Lupi Protospatharii," The Society for Medieval Military History, (1979).

Churchill, W.S. "The Second World War," Bloomsbury Revelations, (2013).

Collins-Elliott, S.A. "Social Memory and Identity in the Central Apennines Under Augustus," Historia, (2014).

Croce, B. "Storia del Regno di Napoli," (English translation), Laterza, Bari, (1966).

Cuoco, V. "A Historical Essay on the Neapolitan Revolution of 1799," University of Toronto Press, (2014 edition).

D'Annunzio, G. "The Triumph of Death," Good Press, (2020).

Darlington, S. "Italy to Robert De Niro: You're family," Los Angeles Times, (2004).

Davis, J.A. "The Napoleonic Era in Southern Italy: An Ambiguous Legacy?" Proceedings of the British Academy, (1993).

Decurtis, A. "Q&A: Don De Lillo Exploring 'Libra' and the Assassination of John F. Kennedy," Rolling Stone, (1988).

DeLillo, D. "Americana, "Actes Sud, (1993 edition).

DeLillo, D. "Mao II," Penguin Books, (1992 edition).

DeLillo, D. "Libra," Penguin Books, (1991 edition).

DeLillo, D. "Cosmopolis," Picador, (2003 edition).

DeLillo, D. "White Noise," Penguin Classics, (2016 edition).

Di Giovine, M.A. "Re-Presenting a Contemporary Saint: Padre Pio of Pietrelcina," Critical Inquiry, (2009).

Dwyer, P. "Citizen Emperor: Napoleon in Power 1799-1805," Bloomsbury Publishing, (2013).

Ebner, M.R. "This Is the Violence of Which I Approve. A short history of the political violence that helped Mussolini attain power," (2017).

Edwards, P. "Battle of Monte Cassino," (2011).

Eye Witness to History. "The Black Death, 1348," (2001).

Eye Witness to History. "Life in a Christian Monastery, ca. 585," (2004).

Fante, J. "Ask the Dust," Ecco Publishing, (2006 edition).

Ferrone, Carmelina "Recordings of Interviews conducted by Giuseppe Ferrone in July 2019."

Field, C. "Rites of Passage in Italy," Gastronomica, (2010).

Forlano, L. "Migrant who helped build Australia," The Sydney Morning Herald, (2012).

Galassi, F.L. and Cohen, J.S. "The Economics of Tenancy in Early Twentieth-Century Southern Italy," The Economic History Review, (1994).

Gentile, E. "Fascism as Political Religion," Journal of Contemporary History, (1990).

Gilkes, O. "Abruzzo & Molise: Oliver Gilkes goes in search of the Samnites," World Archaeology, (2016).

Giovannitti, A. "Arrows in the Gale & Other Poems," Quale Press, (2014 edition).

Greene, N. "Biography of Giordano Bruno, Scientist and Philosopher," Thought Co., (2019).

Hamilton, L.I. "Memory, Symbol, and Arson: Was Rome 'Sacked' in 1084?" Speculum, (2003).

Heath, C. "The Narrative Worlds of Paul the Deacon: Between Empires and Identities in Lombard Italy," Amsterdam University Press, (2017).

Heritage History. "Samnite Wars", (2019).

History.Com. "Italian Campaign," (2009).

Holmes, R. "World War Two: The Battle of Monte Cassino," (2011).

Hughes, T. "Rome's Early Rivals: Who Were the Samnites?" History Hit, (2018).

Italy Heritage. "The Year of the Plague 1657," (2000).

Kardong, T. "Saint Benedict and the Twelfth-Century Reformation," Cistercian Studies Quarterly, (2001).

Kellogg, C. "Q&A: A rare interview with Don De Lillo, one of the titans of American fiction," (2016).

Klein, D. English translation of Giordano Bruno's, "Cantus Circaeus: The Incantations of Circe together with the Judiciary Being the Art of Memory," Ouroboros Press, (2009).

Komnene, A. "The Alexiad," Penguin Classics, (2009).

Kramer, H. and Sprenger, J. "The Malleus Maleficarum," Cosimo Classics, (2007).

Levy, S. "De Niro: A Life," Random House, (2015).

Lord, V.M. "Saint or Sinner? Pope Celestine V," The Ultimate History Project, (2019).

Loud, G.A. "Monarchy and Monastery in the Mezzogiorno: The Abbey of St. Sophia, Benevento and the Staufen," British School at Rome, (1991).

Luce, T.J. "Livy: The Rise of Rome. Books 1-5," Oxford University Press, (1998).

Machiavelli, N. "The Prince," Dante University of America Press, (2003 edition).

Manfredi, J. "Lecture on History of Naples and Southern Italy – Given in Sorrento – 2000," Naples Life, Death & Miracles, (2000).

Markus, R.A. "Gregory the Great and His World," Cambridge University Press, (1997).

Martin, D. "Memories Are Made of This: Dean Martin Through His Daughter's Eyes," Crown Archetype, (2010).

Matthews, J. "The Duchy of Salerno: Sichelgaita – Warrior Princess and then some!" Naples Life, Death & Miracles, (2012).

Matthews, S. "22 Dean Martin Quotes That Are A Kick in the Head," Women. Com, (2019).

McCrum, R. "Don De Lillo: I'm not trying to manipulate reality – this is what I see and hear," The Guardian, (2010).

McDonald, J.S. "Some Socio-Economic Emigration Differentials in Rural Italy, 1902-1913," Economic Development and Cultural Change, (1958)

McNeill, R. "Horace," Oxford University Press, (2010).

McQueen, W.B. "Relations Between the Normans and Byzantium 1071-1112," Byzantion, (1986).

Mellor, R. "Tacitus' Annuls," Oxford University Press, (2010).

Montagna, P. "La Pestilenza: The Black Death in Italy," (2015).

Montesano, M. "Classical Culture and Witchcraft in Medieval and Renaissance Italy," Palgrave Macmillan, (2008).

Mosley, N. "Julian Grenfell: His Life and the Times of his Death," Weidenfeld and Nicolson, (1976).

Moss and Cappannari. "Estate and Class in Southern Italy," American Anthropologist, (1962).

Mossman, J. "Medea: Introduction, Translation and Commentary," Aris & Phillips, (2011).

Padre Pio Devotions. "Padre Pio: A Short Biography," (2020).

Pappas, D. "Joachim Murat and the Kingdom of Naples: 1808-1815," The Napoleon Series, (2008).

Passaro, V. "Dangerous Don De Lillo," The New York Times, (1991).

Patin Jr, J.F. "Robert Guiscard of hauteville, duke of Apulia & Calabria," Geni Profile, (2019).

Pelino, E. "The Freedom Trail," (2002).

Pesaresi, C. "The Democratic Drop in the Molise Region from 1861 to 2011, With A Look to the Future," Bollettino Della Societa Geografica Italiana Roma, (2014).

Potter, D. "The Origin of Empire: Rome From The Republic To Hadrian 264 BC – AD 138," Profile Books, (2019).

Pugliese, S.G. "Bitter Spring – Prologue: The Landscape of My Soul," The New York Times, (2009).

Pugliese, S.G. "Bitter Spring: A Life of Ignazio Silone," Reviewed by Michael Scammell in an article titled: Saint and Sinner, (2010).

Purcell, N. "Strabo," The Oxford Companion to Classical Civilization, Oxford University Press, (2014)

Pryce-Jones, D. "The exemplar: Ignazio Silone," The New Criterion, (2001).

Raucci, R. "Archaeological sites in Italy: Altilia in Molise", Molise Turismo, (2019).

Regione Molise, internet website.

Rich, N. "Misunderstood Southern Italy," Los Angeles Times, (2005).

Rickard, J. "Battle of the Biferno, 1-7 October 1943," History of War, (2018).

Riesenberger, N. "King of the Renaissance: Art and Politics at the Neapolitan Court of Ferrante 1, 1458-1494," (2016).

Rizi, F.F. "Benedetto Croce and Italian Fascism," University of Toronto Press, (2003).

Rodgers, N. "Roman Empire," Metro Books, (2008).

Rossella, L. "Medieval Hermit Pope Not Murdered, as Believed," Discovery News, (2014).

Rowland, I. "Giordano Bruno: Philosopher/Heretic," University of Chicago Press, (2009).

Russo, M. "Oh-Oh, Ay-Ay! Riding to an Italian Rhythm on the Transumanza," The New York Times, (2019).

Sakalis, A. "The Italian Region That Doesn't Exist," BBC Travel, (2019).

Salmon, E.T. "Samnium and the Samnites," Cambridge University Press, (1967).

Santilli, R.M. "Il Grande Grido: Ethical Probe on Einstein's Followers in the U.S.A. – An Insider's View," Alpha Publishing, (1984).

Shuster, A. "Communism Italian Style," The New York Times, (1976).

Silone, I. "Fontamara," Kiepenheuer & Witsch, (1997 edition).

Silone, I. "Bread and Wine," Signet, (2005 edition).

Silone, I. "The Seed Beneath the Snow," Atheneum Publishers, (1965 edition).

Silone, I. "A Handful of Blackberries," Harper, (1953).

Smith, D.M. "Modern Italy – A Political History," Yale University Press, (1997).

Spizzica, M. "Why Australia must apologise to Italians interned during World War II," The Conversation, (2011).

Sullivan, R.T. "Runaway Pope: The Saint Dante Condemned to Hell's Antechamber," (2017).

Swan, P.M. "The Augustan Succession. An Historical Commentary on Cassius Dio's Roman History Books 55-56 (9BC – AD14)," Oxford University Press, (2004).

Tranter, R. "Don De Lillo on researching Libra," (2015).

Travaglini, N. "Roccascalegna: History and Legend," Italy Heritage, (2000).

Trevor-Roper, H. "The European Witch-Craze of the Sixteenth and Seventeen Centuries and Other Essays," Harper & Row, (1969).

Tucci, R. & Messori, L. "A Primitive Bagpipe from Molise, Italy," The Galpin Society Journal, (1985).

Von Kleist, H. and Scheuer, L.R. "Robert Guiscard, Duke of the Normans. Fragments of a Tragedy," The Tulane Drama Review, (1962).

Wasson, D.L. "Horace," Ancient History Encyclopedia, (2017).

Willan, P. "Moro's ghost haunts political life," The Guardian, (2003).

Winters, A. "Erasmus' Doctrine of Free Will," Union University Press, (2005).

World Archaeology. "Searching for Samnites in the Region of Little Cities," (2017).

Xochitl, P. "Dean Martin: King of Cool," The Desert Sun, (2015).

IMAGE CREDITS

All of the images in this book not referenced below have been sourced from Wikimedia Commons on the internet.

2. Castle Classics
3. NASA
4. Rena Correia
5. Twist 'n' Scoot
6. Freerola
8. Carolyn Mariano
12. Red Carpet Magazine
13. Molise Network
15. Wiley Online Library
17. Heritage History
18. Weapons & Warfare
19. Britannica
21. Mary Evans Picture Library
22. IL Regno
23. Romano Impero
26. British Museum London
28. Molise Turismo
29. National Geographic
31. Larry Vienneau Artworks
35. Anton von Werner
37. Manner of Thing
40. National Trust Norfolk
41. Biography.com
45. Heritage History
46. Heritage History
47. Heritage History
48. Laurentian Library
56. Liberation Route Europe
57. Trek Earth
58. The Orthodox Life
61. Spinello Aretino
62. Ancient History Encyclopedia
63. Sophialns Press
65. College of St. Scholastica
69. Museo Nacional del Prado
79. House of Names
81. Papal Artifacts

82. Ancient Pages
83. War History Online
85. Scientific Women
86. History Extra
87. Naples, Life, Death & Miracles
113. Booktopia
115. Booktopia
120. Military Wikia
123. Visit Citta Sant Angelo
126. Medievalists
131. History Channel
132. Cultural Larino
134. Britannica
136. Greek Gods and Goddesses
137. Educational Clearinghouse
144. Free Information Society
149. Britannica
157. Lapham's Quarterly
158. Biography.com
160. Britannica
167. Atina Italy
178. Britannica
181. Britannica
185. Forces War Records
190. Canadian Soldiers.com
191. Canadian Soldiers.com
207. Catholic News Agency
209. Italia.It
210. Padre Pio. Ie
211. Vatican News
214. Saint Brigid CCD Program
218. Delicious Italy
220. Immobiliare Casero
222. Film Art Gallery
225. Film Art Gallery
226. Hollywood Reporter
227. Film Art Gallery

228. Film Art Gallery
229. Alt Film Gallery
230. Film Art Gallery
339. Education Western Australia
231. Picuku.com
232. Film Art Gallery
233. Ranker
234. Ranker
235. Film Art Gallery
236. The Wrap
247. Biography.com
240. Informa Molise
251. Opera Club de Paris
260. Aernet.com
262. Chicago Pixel Presents
263. Discogs
266. Fan Share
269. Discogs
274. Carmelina Ferrone
275. Carmelina Ferrone
276. Trivago
278. Carmelina Ferrone
279. Carmelina Ferrone
284. Carmelina Ferrone
285. Carmelina Ferrone
292. Carmelina Ferrone
293. Carmelina Ferrone
298. Discogs
299. Mario Lanza Tenor.com
305. Carmelina Ferrone
308. Carmelina Ferrone

309. Carmelina Ferrone
319. Carmelina Ferrone
320. SS Maritime.com
321. Carmelina Ferrone
322. Carmelina Ferrone
323. Carmelina Ferrone
326. Carmelina Ferrone
327. Carmelina Ferrone
330. Museums Victoria
332. Perth Electric Tramway Society
333. Carmelina Ferrone
334. Carmelina Ferrone
335. Carmelina Ferrone
336. Carmelina Ferrone
338. Carmelina Ferrone
341. Carmelina Ferrone
342. Carmelina Ferrone
343. WA Italian Club
344. A Million Steps – Velasca
345. Sunny Place Records
346. Carmelina Ferrone
347. State Library of Western Australia
348. Psconeri Wholesalers
349. Italy on this Day
352. Museum of Western Australia
353. Carmelina Ferrone
354. Carmelina Ferrone
355. Carmelina Ferrone
356. Carmelina Ferrone

Made in United States
Troutdale, OR
07/10/2024

21139650R00241